STUDIES IN EUROPEAN
COASTAL MANAGEMENT

Sponsors

EUCC

Countryside Council for Wales

University of Glamorgan

Studies in European
Coastal Management

Edited by

P.S. Jones

M.G. Healy

and

A.T. Williams

Samara Publishing Limited

In association with the EUCC

EUCC
European Union for
Coastal Conservation

Published by:	Samara Publishing Limited, Samara House, Cardigan SA43 2JG, UK

Copyright:	1996. EUCC

Citation:	Jones, P.S., Healy, M.G. and Williams, A.T. (eds). 1996. *Studies in European Coastal Management*. Samara Publishing Limited, Tresaith, Cardigan SA43 2JG, UK. xii + 292 pp.
ISBN:	1 873692 07 2

Disclaimer:	While every effort has been made to ensure the accuracy of the information contained in this publication, neither EUCC, its members, nor participating organisations will assume liability for any use made thereof. The designations of geographical entities in this book, and the presentation of the material, do not imply the expression of any opinion whatsoever on the part of the participating organisations concerning the legal status of any country, territory, or area, or of its authorities, or concerning the delimitation of its frontiers or boundaries. The opinions expressed in this book do not necessarily reflect those of the editors nor the participating organisations

Printed by:	Smith Settle, Otley, West Yorkshire LS21 3JP
Cover photographs:	Front: Liassic limestone cliff face and shore platform near Nash Point on the Glamorgan coast of South Wales, UK (see A.T. Williams, this volume). Photo: P.S. Jones
	Back: Sand dune blowout and recently formed wet slack at Kenfig National Nature Reserve on the coast of South Wales, UK (see P.S. Jones, this volume). Photo: P.S. Jones

Editors:

P.S. Jones, Bridgend County Borough Council

M.G. Healy, University of Limerick

A.T. Williams, University of Glamorgan

Table of Contents

Shoreline Management

Management and Conservation of Coastal Habitats

Coastal Management Studies in South Wales, UK

Acknowledgements

The editors wish to thank the following for their help in the production of this volume.

Production

Mrs Susan Hughes, Dr Bob Hughes, Dr Jan Martin, Mrs Eveline Forrest and Mr R.A. Cave of Samara Publishing Limited

Terry Powell, Department of Property & Development Studies, University of Glamorgan

Editorial Assistance

Dr Rhoda Ballinger	University of Wales, Cardiff
Dr Pat Doody	Joint Nature Conservation Committee
Dr Nick Davidson	Joint Nature Conservation Committee
Mr Paul Rooney	Sefton Coast Life Project
Dr Susan Howard	Countryside Council for Wales
Miss Gill Barter	Countryside Council for Wales

General Support

Dr Pat Doody	European Union for Coastal Conservation, UK Branch
Mr Gordon Hall	Mid Glamorgan County Council
Mr Martin Hooker	Bridgend County Borough Council
Miss Sonya Palasiuk	Joint Nature Conservation Committee
Mrs Linda Bridge	European Union for Coastal Conservation, UK Branch
Miss Sharon Thomas	Kenfig National Nature Reserve
Mr Robert Davies	Kenfig National Nature Reserve
Mr Nigel Ajax-Lewis	Glamorgan Wildlife Trust
Dr Peter Rhind	Countryside Council for Wales

Mid Glamorgan County Council
Bridgend County Borough Council
Joint Nature Conservation Committee
Manchester Metropolitan University
University of Limerick
University of Glamorgan

Financial Support

The editors particularly wish to thank the following organisations for sponsoring the production of this volume:

European Union for Coastal Conservation - United Kingdom Branch
Countryside Council for Wales
University of Glamorgan

Without their generous financial support, publication would not have been possible.

Finally, the editors wish to thank the many authors who submitted their work for publication in this volume.

Prologue

Coastlines '95: The 5th Conference of the European Union for Coastal Conservation (EUCC)

On setting out to organise the biennial conference of the European Union for Coastal Conservation (EUCC) for 1995, the UK Organising Committee decided that a determined effort should be made to encourage and facilitate the participation of colleagues from less economically favoured parts of Europe. The conference was extremely successful in encouraging attendance by colleagues from a variety of countries, including a significant number of delegates from the Baltic states. Many informative oral and written papers on diverse aspects of coastal management around Europe were contributed to the *Coastlines '95* conference. These are reflected in the content of this volume. Several papers, notably the contribution from Bruno Julien of the European Commission, make a new and important contribution to signposting the way forward for integrated coastal management from a political perspective. In addition to promoting Europe-wide participation in *Coastlines '95*, the organisers aimed to involve those who use or exploit the coast in any way in conference debates. Those involved in enterprises such as fishing, tourism and the extractive industries (oil, gas and aggregates) were not represented at Swansea. This was partly because the organisers did not have appropriate contacts within those sectors. It may also be that we still have a long way to go in establishing meaningful contacts with those groups, but it is essential that such contacts develop. Ultimately all the fine words about sustainability of human use of the coastline and maintenance of biodiversity will come to nothing if those who currently use or enjoy the coastal environment are not convinced of our case. Future conferences and the work of the EUCC should be directed more conspicuously towards involving all coastal user groups as partners in the development of integrated coastal management. We have learned much in terms of science and conservation experience. We now need to apply this knowledge in practice to further effective husbandry of the European coastal resource.

Dr Pat Doody

Chairman, Organising Committee for *Coastlines '95*
25th March, 1996

About the Editors

Peter S. Jones

Peter Jones graduated with a 1st Class Honours Degree in Plant Science from the University of Wales in 1985. In 1993 he was awarded the degree of Doctor of Philosophy by the University of Wales for his research on the vegetation and hydrology of dune slack ecosystems in South Wales, UK. As well as serving as the current deputy Council Member and Treasurer for the UK branch of the EUCC, he also serves on the editorial board of the EUCC's *Journal of Coastal Conservation*. Until recently he was employed by Bridgend County Borough Council (formerly Mid Glamorgan County Council) as the Project Officer for Kenfig National Nature Reserve. He is now Head of the Vascular Plants Section in the Department of Botany at the National Museum and Gallery of Wales, Cardiff.

Michael G. Healy

Michael Healy is a University College Cork graduate with an Honours Degree in Geography. In reading for his Master of Arts Degree (1986) he studied the lateglacial and postglacial vegetation history of selected sites in southwest Ireland. He was awarded the degree of Doctor of Philosophy by the National University of Ireland in 1993 for his research on the coastal evolution and sea-level history of west Cornwall, UK. Since 1987 he has been involved in CEC's Framework Programmes on the Environment (Climatology and Natural Hazards 1987-1990; European Programme on Climatic Hazards 1991-1993; IMPACTS) through his association with the Coastal Resources Centre, University College Cork (CRC-UCC). He acted as chief editor in producing *Directions in European Coastal Management* in 1995. Between 1991 and 1996 he lectured in Physical Geography and Environmental Management at the Manchester Metropolitan University. He currently lectures in Physical Geography at Mary Immaculate College, University of Limerick, Republic of Ireland.

Allan T. Williams

Allan Williams is a Chartered Engineer and has degrees in Geography and Geology. He was awarded the degree of Doctor of Philosophy by the University of Hong Kong in 1974 for his research on coastal geomorphology. He is currently Professor of Environmental Sciences at the University of Glamorgan and has published over 130 scientific papers, many of which relate to the coastal environment. He is a founder member of the International Secretariat of Medcoast; foreign scientist advisor to the DISEPLA Research Group, Instituto Hidrografico, Lisbon, Portugal; and scientific advisor to the Coastal Environment Research Centre, San Benedetto del Trento, Italy.

Foreword

The European coast and its attendant resources has been the focus of human interest and activity for several thousands of years. However, only in the relatively recent past has there been explicit recognition that intensive exploitation of the coastal resource places considerable strain on the fragile coastal environment. The degree to which such recognition has lead to appropriate conservation and regulation varies considerably across Europe. Many countries consider themselves to be 'advanced' and 'proactive' in coastal policy-making, planning and management. Few nations would admit to carelessness in this regard. The reality, however, is that wholly appropriate coastal management at local, national and European levels remains a 'Holy Grail'. A set of ideal solutions, encompassing all aspects of over-exploitation of resources and associated degradation of the coast, is not perceived as an achievable goal. To date, the response to coastal problems has been mainly at local/regional level, with emphasis on identification and alleviation of actual or potential environmental hazards. The European Union Habitats Directive (European Council Directive 92/43/EEC on the conservation of natural habitats and of wild fauna and flora) may represent a significant step forward in this regard, offering an opportunity for a more integrated and comprehensive approach to the management of Europe's coastal lowlands.

Studies in European Coastal Management presents a range of papers which report on a variety of European coastal management themes. The material presented in this volume reflects the nature of many of the most pressing issues currently exercising those with responsibilities in coastal policy formulation, planning and site-based management. Contributions from diverse locations and perspectives come together to provide fresh insights into European coastal management at both regulatory and management practice levels. The spread of ideas, approaches and philosophies reported makes it clear that individual European countries are at significantly different stages in terms of defining, adopting and implementing appropriate coastal management.

Since its establishment in 1989, the European Union for Coastal Conservation (EUCC) has promoted the wise use of the coast, emphasising the importance of exchanging information and ideas on coastal management across Europe. The most recent EUCC international conference was held in Swansea, UK in July 1995. Arising from this, a complementary volume of papers based on the themes of the conference was produced (*Directions in European Coastal Management*. Eds: Healy, M.G. & Doody, J.P. 1995. Samara Publishing, Cardigan, UK). *Studies in European Coastal Management* builds on the work already published. It includes further papers on the themes of the Swansea conference ('linking science, nature conservation and human activity on European coasts'), as well as including additional papers on further aspects of concern in coastal management. The primary objective of this volume is to offer an opportunity to those currently involved in any aspect of European coastal management to publish their ideas, voice their concerns and provide details of their work for the benefit of the European audience.

Material contained in individual papers published in this book (including ideas, information, source data and research findings) is the sole responsibility of individual authors. Contributions have been stylistically and structurally standardised by the editors, but this does not constitute a peer review process.

Unless otherwise stated, plant species nomenclature in this volume is in accordance with the following sources: Stace (1991) for vascular plants; Smith (1980) for mosses; Smith (1990) for liverworts; Canon *et al.* (1985) for lichens. Bird nomenclature follows K.H. Voous's *List of Recent Holarctic Bird Species* (1977), as subsequently modified in the reports of the British Ornithologist's Union Records Committee published in the journal *Ibis*, as used in BOURC's *Checklist of Birds of Britain and Ireland* (1992). The latter authority has also been used for the English names of birds. Other vertebrates have been named in accordance with Wilson & Reeder (1993) for mammals and Smith (1951) for British amphibians and reptiles. Nomenclature for mainland European amphibians and reptiles and all other vertebrate groups follows that used in the Habitats and Species Directive (Directive 92/43/EEC, Council of the European Communities, 1992). Invertebrate nomenclature follows Fowles (1994).

The editors wish to thank all of those who contributed in any way to the process of producing this volume and all individuals and organisations are acknowledged elsewhere in this volume. However, a special mention of thanks is due to Sue and Bob Hughes, Jan Martin and Eveline Forrest at Samara Publishing for their advice, patience and support over many months and to Terry Powell of the Department of Property and Development Studies at the University of Glamorgan who patiently, expertly and voluntarily redrew many of the figures found in this volume. The editors also wish to acknowledge the considerable support provided by their respective institutions, in particular Mid Glamorgan County Council. Special thanks are also due to Pat Doody, Chairman of the EUCC UK Branch for his support, advice and encouragement throughout the production of this volume. Miss Sonya Palasiuk of the JNCC Coastal Conservation Branch also provided invaluable help during the production of this volume. It is hoped that the final product will be seen to justify the efforts made by all concerned and contribute in some measure to advancing worthwhile developments in European coastal management.

Peter S. Jones, Cardiff
Michael G. Healy, Limerick
Allan T. Williams, Pontypridd
17th June, 1996

Canon, P.F., Hawksworth, D.L. & Sherwood-Pike, M.A. 1985. *The British Ascomycotina. An annotated checklist.* Commonwealth Mycological Institute, Slough, UK.

Council of the European Communities. 1992. Council Directive 92/43/EEC of 21 May 1992 on the conservation of natural habitats and of wild fauna and flora. *Official Journal of the European Communities* No. L 206: 7-36.

Fowles, A.P. 1994. *Invertebrates of Wales: a review of important sites and species.* Joint Nature Conservation Committee, Peterborough, UK. 157 pp.

Smith, A.J.E. 1980. *The Moss Flora of Britain and Ireland.* Cambridge University Press, Cambridge, UK. 706 pp.

Smith, A.J.E. 1990. *The Liverworts of Britain and Ireland.* Cambridge University Press, Cambridge, UK. 362 pp.

Smith, M. 1951. *The British Amphibians and Reptiles.* Collins New Naturalist Series No. 20. Collins, London, UK. 318 pp.

Stace, C.A. 1991. *New Flora of the British Isles.* Cambridge University Press, Cambridge, UK. 1226 pp.

Wilson, D.E. & Reeder, D.M. (Eds). 1993. *Mammal species of the World: A Taxonomic and Geographic Reference.* Smithsonian Institution Press, Washington DC, USA. 1206 pp.

Studies in European Coastal Management. Jones, Healy and Williams (eds)
1996, Samara Publishing Limited, Cardigan. ISBN 1 873692 07 2

PRESIDENTIAL ADDRESS

Present and Future Directions for EUCC - The European Union for Coastal Conservation

P. Fabbri - President of the EUCC

Office of the President, University of Bologna, Italy

Introduction

Along with the emergence, evolution and development of a European Union of Member States, there has been an ongoing re-evaluation of notions of nationalism, regionalism and local identity within late 20th century Europe. Allied to this there has been a growing appreciation and support for conservation as an ideology and as a line of political action at the European level. The range and scope of conservation applications within such a paradigm is large, spanning many aspects of politics, economics and social maturation.

The importance of coastal conservation in Europe is best examined within this context. The critical traditional roles of the coast as political frontiers, physical buffers and national borders have served to elevate the perceived importance of the coast. The central place of the coast in the development of the tourism and leisure industries has been evident since the Age of Romanticism and particularly conspicuous in the past fifty years. Parallel pressures have been brought to bear on the coast by industrial and commercial landuse, as well as the tendency for the growth of coastal urban settlements. These in combination have generated a largely unplanned and unregulated demand for space and facilities within European coastal environments. The result, often referred to as 'coastal development', has a major impact on the inherent environmental value of the coastal zone as the interface between the marine and terrestrial environments.

The authentic and tangible problems which stem from these realities justify vigorous commitment to coastal conservation. A collective effort among individuals and groups from local to supra-national level is required if basic principles and objectives of conservation are to be supported.

EUCC - The European Union for Coastal Conservation

The EUCC aims to assist in any way possible with the objective of linking science, human activity and nature conservation on European coasts through its network of national branches and regional offices. This is an ambitious and strenuous task and full success cannot be claimed so far. Further progress may require that EUCC joins forces with other similar agencies and organisations. At present there are several associations which are wholly dedicated to coastal issues while others focus much of their activity on coastal matters. It is questionable whether this plurality of effort is beneficial. Indeed, it can be argued that this situation produces confusion. The existence of many organisations with similar, if not identical, interests may lead to reciprocal damage. The common objectives of these many organisations ought to provide sufficient reason to transcend superficial co-op-eration in favour of merging into one single and strong organisation, not necessarily EUCC. Within such an organisation differences in approach and motivation of individuals or groups and special fields of interest could survive and develop in a truly free and democratic context, as they do now within separate organisations. While personal and emotional feelings may mitigate against a willingness among existing organisations to merge with one another, it is unlikely that anything less will allow a proper and efficient approach to the scientific and political tasks which lie ahead in the coastal conservation field.

The most recent (fifth) conference of the EUCC held at Swansea in South Wales provided an opportunity to discuss this and many other issues relating to the conservation of the coastal environment. The 250 speakers and delegates included scientists, representatives of government and government agencies, decision mak-ers, managers and members of the public. Through this broad representative base the conference successfully achieved a prime ongoing aim of the EUCC, namely to provide a forum for discussion by all those involved with coastal matters.

Conclusion

The EUCC prioritises its role as a discussion forum for all those concerned with the coast. It tries to bridge the gaps which result from the inevitable conflicts of interest in such a fragile and critical area as the coastal zone. We, the EUCC members, do not know enough about coasts in the present day or about what is likely to happen to the coastline in the future, but we do know much about the past. Those involved in coastal conservation face formidable tasks which continu-ally become more difficult and time consuming. We must continue to increase our commitment and our knowledge to advance our common purpose. Above all, we need unity.

Integrated Coastal Zone Management and Planning

Studies in European Coastal Management. Jones, Healy and Williams (eds)
1996, Samara Publishing Limited, Cardigan. ISBN 1 873692 07 2

Integrated Management of the European Coastal Zone

B. Julien

Head of Nature Protection, Coastal Zones and Tourism Unit, DGXI, European
Commission, Brussels, Belgium

Abstract: The economic importance of the coastal zone for a wide range of human activities
places its natural resources under severe pressure from development and pollution. The result
is that environmental degradation is widespread through the European Union. The implementation of the Habitats Directive, although not specifically orientated to the coast, will
have a major impact on the conservation of the natural European coastal resource. Under
the Directive the designation of Special Areas of Conservation will ultimately create a
pan-European network of key nature conservation sites on the coast. However, if the Habitats
Directive, in concert with other related measures such as the Birds Directive and LIFE funding
programme, is to be fully effective then better integration between different sectors at local,
regional, national and European level is urgently required. Action at European level is now
necessary in order to make faster progress towards the sustainable development of coastal
zones. To this end a demonstration programme on the integrated management of coastal
zones is planned with the aim of showing how to apply in practice the principles of integration
and subsidiarity in order to increase the effectiveness of existing instruments. One key factor
to be addressed by the programme will be the need for better co-ordination between sectors
of activity and the various levels of territorial authority. The demonstration programme will
be used to test co-operation instruments and mechanisms. The lessons learnt and the
response to the programme will enable possible complementary measures to be identified
and implemented at the European and other levels of decision-making.

Introduction

The need to conserve the coastal zone as an element of the European Community's
natural and cultural heritage and as an essential basis for economic and social
development has long been recognised (Council of Europe, 1973; European Commission, 1973, 1978; Organisation for Economic Cooperation and Development,
1976). To this end there are numerous legal, financial and planning instruments
available, both at Union and Member State level, which are directly or indirectly
applicable to coastal zones. Despite this, the quality of the environment is continuing
to deteriorate in many European coastal regions. This situation is largely due to the
absence of mechanisms allowing the complex relationships between human activities
and the environment to be taken into account in the decision–making processes.

The deterioration of the European coastal environment is leading to the loss and
degradation of biodiversity. Although not primarily orientated towards the coastal
zone, the Habitats Directive (Council Directive 92/43/EEC on the conservation
of natural habitats and of wild fauna and flora) will have an enormous positive
impact on the conservation of the coasts natural resources. Nevertheless, a more
integrated approach to coastal management is essential for the maintenance of

biodiversity and the formulation of policies for the sustainable use of the coastal zone. This paper will examine progress to-date with the implementation of the Habitats Directive and the earlier Birds Directive (Directive 79/409/EEC for the conservation of wild birds) and will go on to consider why action at the level of the European Union (EU) is necessary in order to make faster progress towards the sustainable development of coastal zones. The final part of the paper discusses how this may be achieved and is based on the recent Commission communication to the European Council and Parliament on the integrated management of coastal zones (adopted 31 October 1995). This describes a demonstration programme on the integrated management of the coastal zone which aims to show how the principles of integration and subsidiarity can be applied in order to increase the effectiveness of existing instruments.

Definition of the coastal zone

For the purposes of this paper, the coastal zone is defined as a strip of land and sea territory which varies in width, depending on the nature of the environment and management needs. It seldom corresponds with existing administrative or planning units. With regard to fisheries, it is common to limit the coastal zone to territorial waters as defined in the 1982 Montego Bay Convention on the Law of the Sea, although this limit does not correspond to any distinct biological or management unit. Natural coastal systems and the areas in which human activities involve the use of coastal resources may therefore extend well beyond the limit of territorial waters, as well as several kilometres inland (Figure 1).

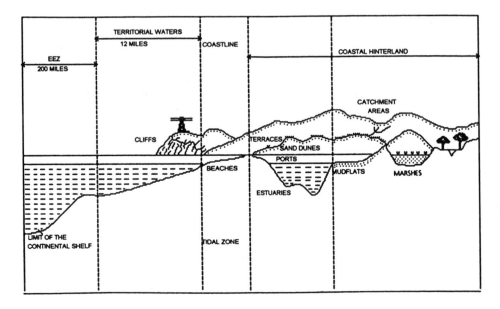

Figure 1   **Definition of the coastal zone for the purposes of integrated management (the abbreviation 'EEZ' refers to Economic Exclusion Zone)**

The Habitats Directive

The Habitats Directive has expanded the nature conservation remit of the European Union well beyond that of the previously established Birds Directive. Together with its accompanying financial instrument, the LIFE programme, the Habitats Directive has become a cornerstone of the Community's environment policy. One of the principal ways in which nature conservation objectives will be achieved through the Habitats Directive is by the creation of the Natura 2000 ecological network. This will focus on the protection of sites of Community-wide interest. Particular attention is given to the protection of priority habitats and species identified as being at greatest risk of loss, consequently the EU has responsibility at a global level for their conservation.

More than 40 exclusively coastal habitats are listed in Annex I of the Directive. Some priority coastal habitats are identified in Table 1.

The conservation of each of these habitats presents a particular challenge which will need to be addressed in order to fulfil the Directive's objective of assuring their favourable conservation status. One example of such a challenge concerns the conservation of *Posidonia* beds (CORINE type 11.34), a highly productive habitat of the continental shelf which is very sensitive to drag net fishing, pollution and the effects of yacht anchorages.

In order to select the most appropriate sites for inclusion in Natura 2000 the preparation of national inventories of these and other habitat types is being financially supported under the LIFE programme in Greece, Ireland, Italy, Portugal and Spain.

Annex II of the Directive lists a wide range of animal and plant species which are dependent on the coastal zone for part or all of their life cycle. These species therefore require habitat conservation measures under Natura 2000. Conservation actions for some priority vertebrate species have already been financially supported under the Union's LIFE programme (or its predecessors ACNAT and ACE) and a selection of these are listed in Table 2. Projects include a conservation programme for the monk seal (*Monachus monachus*) and loggerhead turtle (*Caretta caretta*) in the Ionian Sea region, protection of the monk seal and its habitat in Madeira, recovery programmes for the hierro giant lizard (*Gallotia simonyi*) and European sturgeon (*Acipenser sturio*) and an action programme for the conservation of two wetlands and the creation of a reserve network for the samaruc (*Valencia hispanica*).

The Birds Directive

The protection of birds at a European level is covered separately under the Birds Directive. One of the principal objectives of the Directive is the conservation of bird habitats, particularly through the designation of Special Protection Areas (SPAs). To date over 1,100 SPAs, covering approximately 7 million ha, have been designated and many of these occur in coastal locations. However, only Belgium and Denmark have largely completed this designation process and many internationally important bird areas still await protection. This task needs to be completed with urgency.

Table 1   Priority habitat types of the European coastal zone

Habitat category	Priority habitat type	Geographical distribution
Open sea and tidal areas	*Posidonia* beds	Only present in the Mediterranean
	Lagoons	Coasts throughout the EU, especially in the Mediterranean
Atlantic and continental saltmarshes and salt meadows	Continental salt meadows (*Puccinellietalia distantis*)	Germany, France and United Kingdom
Sea dunes of the Atlantic, North Sea and Baltic coasts	Fixed dunes with Herbaceous vegetation (grey dunes) - seven types listed	Atlantic coasts (plus the English Channel), shores of the North Sea, Baltic and the Mediterranean
	Decalcified fixed dunes with *Empetrum nigrum*	Germany, Denmark, The Netherlands and United Kingdom
	Machairs (priority type for Ireland only)	Ireland and United Kingdom
Sea dunes of the Mediterranean coast	Dune juniper thickets (*Juniperus* spp.)	Mediterranean coasts, Iberian Peninsula, Denmark and United Kingdom
	Wooded dunes with *Pinus pinea* and/or *Pinus pinaster*	Greece, southern and western Iberian Peninsula, southern France and Italy
Temperate heath and scrub	Dry coastal heaths with *Erica vagans* and *Ulex maritimus*	United Kingdom and France
Sub-Mediterranean and temperate sclerophyllous forests	*Cistus palhinhae* formations on wet maritime heaths (*Junipero-Cistetum palhinhae*)	South-west Portugal
Mediterranean sclerophyllous forests	Palm groves of *Phoenix*	Crete and the Canary Islands

Table 2 **Some priority vertebrate species listed under the EU Habitats Directive that depend on coastal zones for all or part of their life cycle**

Species name	Geographical distribution
Monachus monachus (Monk Seal)	Greece, Portugal (Madeira), Italy (Sardinia) and Spain (Chafarinas)
Caretta caretta (Loggerhead Turtle)	Greece and Italy
Gallotia simonyi (El Hierro Giant Lizard)	Endemic to the Canary Islands (Spain) where it is now restricted to one coastal cliff site
Acipenser naccarii	Italy
Acipenser sturio (European Sturgeon)	Germany, Spain, France, Greece, Italy, Portugal and United Kingdom
Valencia hispanica (Samaruc)	Endemic to Valencia, Spain
Coregonus oxyrhynchus	Denmark, United Kingdom, Ireland, Finland and Sweden

Table 3 **Some threatened bird species listed under Annex I of the Birds Directive that depend on coastal zones throughout their annual cycle**

Bird species	Principal EU Member States concerned
Pterodroma madeira (Zino's Petrel)	Portugal (Madeira)
Pterodoma feae (Fea's Petrel)	Portugal (Desertas Islands of Madeira)
Phalacrocorax pygmaeus (Pygmy Comorant)	Greece
Pelecanus crispus (Dalmation Pelican)	Greece
Larus audouinii (Audouin's Gull)	France, Greece, Italy and Spain
Sterna dougallii (Roseate Tern)	France, Ireland, Portugal and United Kingdom

The most threatened bird species in the EU are listed in Annex I of the Birds Directive. This includes species, especially seabirds and waterfowl, which are dependent on coastal zones at some stage during their annual cycle and some notable examples are listed in Table 3. With the exception of the roseate tern (*Sterna dougallii*), all of these species are globally threatened and funding for their conservation is considered a priority under the LIFE programme. This programme has already supported the preparation of action plans for all globally threatened bird species in Europe and the EU has also supported conservation measures targeted at coastal bird species and their habitats. Examples of such projects include urgent actions to conserve the breeding grounds of roseate terns and the development and management of dalmation pelican (*Pelecanus crispus*) habitats in northern Greece.

The Birds Directive is not restricted to protecting the habitats of the most threatened species, its protective provisions extend to all migratory species and their habitats. The need for this is acute and is embodied in the Odessa protocol which calls for "international co-operation on migratory flyway research and conservation" (Wader Study Group, 1992). Coastal zones play a key role in this respect as many migration flyways occur along the coastline of Europe. Coastal wetlands are especially important for migratory wildfowl, and conservation actions at key sites are now being supported. For example, the EU has supported the preparation by Denmark, Germany and The Netherlands of a common co-ordinated management plan for the Wadden Sea area. More generally, the Commission has recently adopted a communication to the Council and Parliament on the wise use and conservation of wetlands (European Commission, 1995a). However, it is important to note that wetlands are not the only important coastal habitats for migratory birds.

The creation of Natura 2000

The creation of an effective Natura 2000 network is the top nature conservation priority for the European Commission in the coming years. Figure 2 illustrates the phases involved in the creation of the network as laid out in Article 4 of the Habitats Directive.

The first phase entails the submission of national lists of sites to the Commission and was scheduled for completion by June 1995. Unfortunately, despite very significant progress by several member states, none has yet fully complied with this obligation. Several member states are at present engaged in a public consultation process prior to submitting their lists, and this work is expected to be nearing completion by the end of 1995.

During the second phase the Commission will evaluate the national lists and, with the member states, establish the final list of sites to be included within Natura 2000. Each member state will then have a further six years in which to designate all these sites as Special Areas of Conservation (SACs).

The designation of sites as SACs is not an end in itself. Member states will also need to implement, where appropriate, management measures to ensure that those Annex I habitat types and Annex II species which are present on a site are

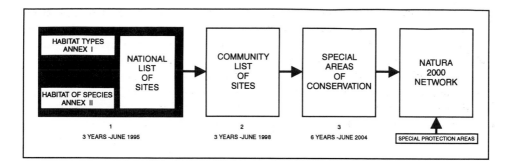

Figure 2   Steps towards the realisation of the Natura 2000 network

maintained or restored to a favourable conservation status. This will necessitate, among other things, the adoption of sound agricultural practices, the control of public access and strict control on infrastructure within or affecting a site. Such measures should benefit many of those coastal areas which are destined for inclusion in Natura 2000.

The protection regime for SACs is defined in Article 6 of the Habitats Directive. This establishes procedures to deal with any plan, project or measures which may affect a site including the following: an appropriate environmental assessment, examination of alternatives, agreement to such measures once it has been established that they will not affect site integrity, public involvement and compensatory measures to ensure the coherence of Natura 2000. In cases where a site hosts priority habitats and/or species, then a higher level of protection is offered.

Since the entry into legal effect of the Habitats Directive (June 1994), all SPAs under the Birds Directive have also been included in the Natura 2000 network. The protection regime defined in the Habitats Directive (Article 6, paragraphs 2,3 and 4) also applies to SPAs.

The need for improved co-ordination between levels of management in the coastal zone

Unfortunately these measures alone will not be sufficient to prevent the continuing degradation of the European coastal zone. The European Union for Coastal Conservation (EUCC), among others, has played an important role in highlighting the continuing decline in coastal environmental quality. Problems continue despite political recognition and knowledge that the coast is one of Europe's richest and most varied natural environments.

Awareness of the need to strengthen protection of the coast and political commitments to this end have led, since the beginning of the 1970s, to numerous measures resulting in some countries in specific legislation and national strategies, and, more generally, to a wide range of regional management schemes, studies, inventories and research.

At the wider level of the European Community, few measures have been introduced which specifically concern the coastal environment, most being directed at the territory as a whole. Nevertheless, a considerable body of legislation and instruments are available which, if applied, should contribute to protecting the coastal environment. These measures have not been fully effective because of the lack of co-ordination between the numerous actors influencing the development of the coast.

This issue not only concerns the need for horizontal relations between sectors of activity (summarised in Table 4), but also the integration of policies and actions carried out at various levels of territorial authority. Over-zealous application of the subsidiarity principle all too often leads to a parcelling out of responsibilities, which are simply distributed between the levels of competence, with no scope for taking account of the numerous interactions between them. Owing to this lack of co-ordination, the complex relations between human activities and the coastal environment are neglected and the isolated measures fail to achieve their goal or may even be mutually contradictory.

Table 4   Sectoral planning in the coastal zone

Sectors that often have a specific coastal dimension	Sectors not specific to the coastal zone, but which may have a significant impact
Defence	Agriculture
Port and harbour developments	Forestry
Shipping and navigation	Nature management
Tourism and recreation	Parks and recreation
Fisheries	Education
Aquaculture	Public health
	Housing
	Water supply
	Control of water pollution
	Transport
	Control of natural risks
	Development of mining resources
	Industrial development
	Energy generation
	Research

Demonstration programme on the integrated management of coastal zones for sustainable development

'Solutions to these problems can only be pursued at a European level and have been requested by political bodies such as the European Parliament, European Council and the Council of Europe. The fifth Community programme of policy and action in relation to the environment and sustainable development (European Commission, 1993a) provides for an initiative in response to the Council's request for an overall Community strategy for the integrated management of coastal zones (European Council, 1992). More recently work on the European aspects of spatial planning, in particular the Commission Communication *Europe 2000+* (European Commission, 1994) and the preparation of a European Spatial Development Perspective (German Presidency, 1994), has confirmed the need to devote particular attention to the fragile environment of coastal zones, which require an integrated approach. .

There are three reasons for the European Union's interest in the fate of coastal zones:

a) the existence of problems of a European dimension which cannot be solved by the countries separately (common natural and cultural heritage, transfer of pollutants and sediments, tourist flows, maritime safety);

b) the influence of the policies and actions of the EU on the development of coastal zones (regional, transport, fisheries, environment, agriculture, energy and industrial policy); and

c) the need for an exchange of experience and knowledge in a field where successes are still rare and where there is substantial public and political demand for the conservation of coastal zones and their sustainable development.

While it is clear that the EU has a role to play, the question arises as to the advisability of a particular course of action, complementing the many existing generic or specific measures. The Commission considered this question in the context of its communication COM (86) 571 final (European Commission, 1986), prepared following the adoption of the European Coastal Charter (Anon, 1981) and in response to the request of the European Parliament (1982) and the European Council (European Commission, 1986). The Commission stated that it would continue to apply existing or planned measures rigorously, taking particular account of coastal aspects. Measures specific to coastal zones were therefore not envisaged. However, since the 1986 Communication, progress on the protection and integrated management of the coast has been inadequate. This is due to two factors: firstly, a new approach takes time to implement and, secondly, conditions were less ripe then politically and in terms of the available instruments than is the case today. The Commission had already noted in 1986 that preventative measures provided the key to the success of an integrated approach, concerning in particular:

a) an internal Commission procedure to take account of the environment dimension in the operation of the Structural Funds;

b) the obligation to carry out environmental impact assessments of plans and programmes;

13

c) a reference framework to take account of the spatial consequences of Community policies; and

d) economic instruments that integrate environmental and natural resources aspects.

Since 1986, substantial progress has been made in these four areas including:

a) an internal procedure for integrating the environment in European policies has been adopted and applied (European Commission, 1993b). The Regulation on the Structural Funds contains environmental compatibility clauses (Regulation [EEC] No. 2081/93; Articles 8.9.11a);

b) a draft Directive on the strategic environmental assessment of plans and programmes should be submitted to the Council and Parliament in 1996;

c) work on European spatial planning is progressing (German Presidency, 1994); and

d) research on environmental economics is proceeding according to plan (Anon., 1991, 1994).

Accelerating the implementation of sustainable development

In recent years, two major policy lines have assumed concrete form:

a) the systematic integration of environmental objectives into economic development through the participation of all the actors; and

b) the taking into account at European level of territorial and spatial planning aspects, in a spirit of subsidiarity and co-operation.

The necessary conditions are therefore in place, both as regards the fundamental approach and the instruments, for the implementation of sustainable development in coastal zones. However, experience with the application of the fifth environment action programme and spatial planning, both at European level and in the member states, has clearly shown that actual progress in this area is too slow in light of the gravity and complexity of the problems which affect coastal zones.

Joint action by the Union and the member states is therefore required in order to accelerate implementation at all levels by improving the effectiveness of legislation and of the existing financial and planning tools.

Given that a) there is not a tried and tested model available to achieve this objective easily, and b) the natural and socio-economic conditions within the EU vary considerably, the Commission proposes that a demonstration programme should be carried out in order to make best use of the available experience in a broad, joint learning process. Such a collaborative, pragmatic approach is also a necessary preliminary to any decision on possible subsequent action, making appropriate use of the various instruments available.

Objective of the demonstration programme

The practice of sustainable development requires the full and systematic application of the principles of integration and subsidiarity. This can be achieved only with the active participation of all the players (political authorities, administrators, economic actors, scientists and the general public). Moreover, changes of approach are often necessary. Sectoral attitudes have to give way to co-operation and appropriate instruments, including co-ordination and information machinery, need to be refined.

The objective of the demonstration programme will therefore be to show the practical conditions that must be met if sustainable development is to be achieved for European coastal zones in all their diversity. It will have a dual function:

a) to test co-operation models for the integrated management of coastal zones; and

b) as it progresses, to provide the technical results necessary to foster dialogue between the European institutions and all the players with a stake in the development of coastal zones.

The lessons to be drawn from the programme and the accompanying debate will serve as a basis for elaborating possible additional measures to be carried out in concert at the European and other levels. They should also provide input for various Community initiatives on the environment and spatial planning, in particular:

a) the development of detailed criteria and mechanisms for the integration of the environment in the operation of the Structural Funds;

b) the launch of the draft directive on strategic environmental impact assessment;

c) initiatives pertaining to other types of area posing similar problems, such as urban or mountain areas.

Finally, they will also constitute a response to the commitments entered into by the European Union in respect of Agenda 21, namely that "Coastal states commit themselves to integrated management and sustainable development of coastal zones and the marine environment under their national jurisdiction." (Chapter 17, sections 17.3 & 17.5; United Nations Conference on Environment and Development, 1992).

Demonstration programme partners

The partners in the programme should be representative of the levels involved in the management of coastal zones (Table 5). Moreover, the cases chosen to participate in the demonstration programme should cover the full range of possible European coastal scenarios (urban/industrial; intensive tourism; nature/rural/fisheries). A limited number of cases involving a high level of knowledge and experience would be preferable to a large number of cases of moderate interest. To succeed, the programme will have to rely as far as possible on existing information and concertation mechanisms. The preferred partners will be those who have already carried out many of the tasks listed in Table 6 and who have the will to share and compare their experience in the interests of sustainable development.

Table 5   Levels and products of co-operation in the coastal zone

Level	Product
European/Transnational	Vision/Perspective
National	Strategy
Interregional	Perspective/Strategy
Regional/Local	Programme/Scheme/Plan

Table 6   Principal tasks of the European Commission's demonstration programme on the integrated management of coastal zones

Description	State of the environment and of the environmental management infrastructures - Fauna, flora, habitats - Landscapes - Landuse - Water quality - Air quality - Pollutant emissions and waste production - Coastal dynamics - Environmental management infrastructures Inventories of the measures * - for environmental protection (quantified and located) - for development (plans, programmes, sectoral development measures: transport, industry, fishing, energy, etc.) - for planning (infrastructures, equipment)
Analysis	- Origin of the current environmental problems - Effect of the environment measures in force and planned - Strategic evaluation of the development measures decided or planned - Effects of socio-economic development and of the natural environment (major trends) - Analysis of consistency between the measures taken or under consideration in the various sectors and at the various levels - Evaluation of management options, including economic evaluations - Syntheses of information produced, to permit concertation
Concertation	- Adjustment where necessary of the concertation structures to involve all relevant actors - Evaluation of information and of the options - Formulation or adaptation of plans/programmes/strategies/visions
Lessons	Dissemination of know-how * - on plans/programmes/strategies/visions of sustainable development of the coast in the territories of the partners in the demonstration programme - on the conditions of sustainable development according to the levels or to the types of areas - on the operation of horizontal and vertical co-ordination

*   Identification of additional measures to be carried out in co-operation at European national, regional and local levels

The Commission will have to ensure that the partners have access to all the information available at European level on the coastal environment and activities (European Environment Agency, Eurostat, RTD programme), and on the relevant Community policies and measures. It will structure and organise the analysis and evaluation of the results as the programme progresses, with a view to drawing conclusions for follow-up action at the Community and other levels, paying particular attention to the evaluation procedure.

Demonstration programme content

The hypotheses underlying the demonstration programme are as follows:

a) improved concertation between the actors is the basis for sustainable development. It helps identify synergies or contradictions between actions resulting from the various policies and facilitates the acceptance of arbitration. In short, it develops the actors' awareness;

b) such concertation can develop only from full, comprehensible information on the state of the environment, the origin of the changes affecting it, the implications of the policies and measures at the various levels and the options; and

c) concertation has to be organised and maintained. There is a need for mechanisms and working methods to ensure dialogue between the actors in the various sectors of activity and at the various levels of territorial authority, and an ongoing exchange of information, from the local level towards the Community level and *vice versa*.

Each partner in the programme should therefore carry out the same work for the territory concerning it, as shown schematically in Figure 3. Starting from an inventory of the situation (description of the environment and of the socio-economic measures envisaged), the causes of the current problems should be analysed and the consequences of the prospective developments assessed. These data should be processed in order to provide the players with comprehensible information enabling them to assess the situation and confer on the management options. A non-exhaustive list of the tasks to be performed by the various programme partners is provided in Table 7.

The adoption and monitoring of the demonstration programme and the analysis, dissemination and discussion of the results will constitute an essential part of work.

Resources for implementation of demonstration programme

Implementation of the programme will involve tasks and therefore costs for each partner. However, these should not necessarily result in additional expenditure in the Community budget. There are various instruments and programmes available or in preparation, the general objectives and criteria of which are directly relevant to coastal zones. Without any changes in the rules governing these instruments, partners could submit proposals for parts of the demonstration programme, in particular:

a) the new Community initiative for transnational co-operation on regional planning in Europe (INTERREG IIC, in preparation);

b) the second action programme under Article 10 of the ERDF Regulation, in particular action in the field of spatial planning;

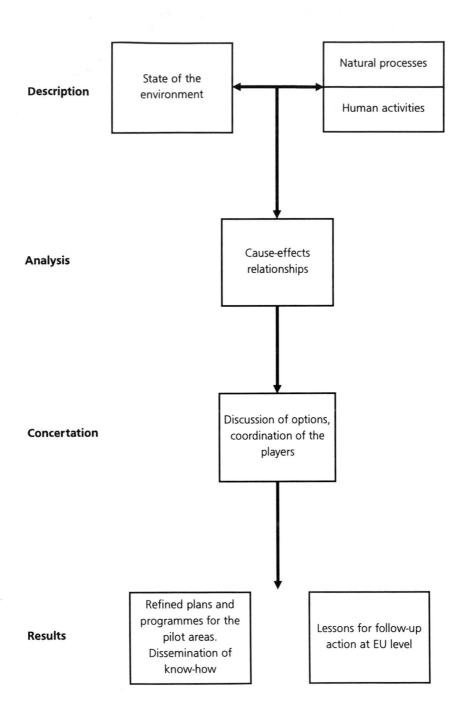

Figure 3   **Schematic content of the European Commission's demonstration programme on the integrated management of coastal zones**

Table 7   Illustration (non-exhaustive) of the tasks of the partners at various levels of the European Commission's demonstration programme on the integrated management of coastal zones

	Local/Regional	National	European Transnational/ Interregional
Description	- Detailed state of the environment - Indicators - Environmental measures - Development measures	- Synthetic environment indicators National plans	- Definition of synthetic indicators (European Environment Agency, Eurostat) - Databases on the state of the European coast (EEA, Eurostat) - Inventory of the Community policies and programmes relevant to the coast
Analysis	- Impact of the local and other measures on the coast - Impact of the general, natural and socio-economic trends - Mutual consistency of the sectoral measures and with policies at other levels - Evaluation of management options	- Strategic environmental assessment of the national plans and sectoral programmes from the point of view of their impact on the coast	- Strategic environmental assessment of the impact of Community policies on the coast - Evaluation of consistency of policies
Concertation	- Use of existing mechanisms and procedures, supplemented and adjusted as required, for intersectoral concertation between territorial units	- Interdepartmental coordination existing or to be adjusted	- Inter-DG group - Co-ordination with international organisations - Concertation with the countries and regions
Results	- Plan/concerted schemes for integrated management of the coast, consistent with the other levels	- State of the coastal environment - Coastal strategies	- Information on the state of the European coast - Information on the environmental and spatial effects of the Community policies - Criteria and methods for the implementation of sustainable development in the Structural Funds - Means of improving co-operation for sustainable development

c) LIFE, for which the new draft Regulation (European Commission, 1995b) specifically mentions the coastal environment;

d) European Environment Agency (European Thematic Centre on Coastal Zones);

e) PHARE, multi-country programme, according to the interest of the countries;

f) environment research programme, e.g. for the organisation of evaluation seminars; and

g) operational means for the conduct of the programme and the analysis of the results (studies, meetings, etc.).

The concerted use of various financing sources to support an objective common to several Community policies is also in conformity with the Commission's desire to ensure optimum consistency of the financial instruments. It would also demonstrate that, in the short term, progress towards sustainable development depends to a large extent on better use of existing means at all levels.

Timetable for demonstration programme

The following phases are planned over a total period of approximately 3 years:

a) launch of the programme;

b) dissemination of the Communication to the actors who influence coastal development (European institutions, countries, associations of regions and local authorities, Non-Governmental Organisations):

c) gathering of reactions (Council Resolution, Parliament opinion), discussions, identification of potential partners, project selection, development of work specifications - 6 months;

d) implementation of the programme - 2 years; and

e) analysis of the lessons learnt and identification of follow-up actions - 6 months.

Conclusions

A wide range of mechanisms is available to aid the conservation of the European coastal resource. Nevertheless, the effectiveness of such measures is highly dependent on the further integration of different sectors at local, regional, national and European level with responsibility for management of the coast. This present lack of integration is one of the main reasons why the European Commission has decided not to start its action with a legislative proposal on integrated coastal management. Instead a demonstration programme will show how good integration between sectors (horizontal) and levels of responsibility (vertical) can be used to build co-operation models for the integrated management of coastal zones. This programme will play a key role in identifying the practical conditions that must be met if sustainable development is to be achieved in the coastal zone of Europe and should enable the identification of further actions which may be required at the European and other levels. Lessons to be learnt from the programme are not restricted to the coastal zone and should also benefit other EU actions, in particular the directive in preparation on Strategic Environmental Assessment and activities for urban and mountain areas.

References

Anon. 1981. Plenary session of the Conference of Peripheral Maritime Regions of the European Community, 1981.

Anon. 1991 & 1994. RTD programmes in the field of the environment (1990-94): *Official Journal of the European Communities*. L 192: 16.7.1991 and (1994-1998): *Official Journal of the European Communities*. L 361: 31.12.1994 - Human dimensions of environmental change.

Council of Europe. 1973. Resolution (73) 29 of the Committee of Ministers of the Council of Europe on the protection of the coast.

European Commission. 1973. European Community Environment Programme (1973-1977). *Official Journal of the European Communities*. C 112: 1973.

European Commission. 1978. Integrated coastal management in the European Community. EUR 6105. 1978.

European Commission. 1986. Communication from the Commission to the Council. Integrated planning of coastal areas: its role in Community environment policy. COM (86) 571 final.

European Commission. 1992. Council Directive 92/43/EEC of 21.5.1992 on the conservation of wild habitats and of wild fauna and flora. *Official Journal of the European Communities*: No. L 206: 22.7.1992.

European Commission. 1993a. *Official Journal of the European Communities*. C 138: 17.5.1993.

European Commission. 1993b. Internal measures designed to promote the objective of integration, adopted on 2.6.92

European Commission. 1994. Commission Communication "Europe 2000+". Co-operation for European Territorial Development. COM/94/354. ISBN 92-826-9100-4.

European Commission. 1995a. Wise use and conservation of wetlands. Commission Communication to the Council and European Parliament. COM(95) 189 final.

European Commission. 1995b. Proposal for a Council Regulation amending Regulation (EEC) No. 1973/92 COM(95) 135 final.

European Council. 1992. Resolution of 25/2/92. *Official Journal of the European Communities*. C 59: 6.3.92.

European Parliament. 1982. Resolution of 18.6.92, EP 73424.

German Presidency. 1994. Conclusions of the German Presidency following the informal Council meeting of the Ministers responsible for regional planning at Leipzig on 21-22/9/94.

Organisation for Economic Cooperation and Development. 1976. Recommendation of the OECD Council on the principles of coastal management. C(76)161, adopted on 12.10.1976.

United Nations Conference on Environment and Development (UNCED). 1992. *Agenda 21: Programme of Action for Sustainable Development*. United Nations Department of Public Information, New York, USA.

Wader Study Group. 1992. The Odessa Protocol on international co-operation on migratory flyway research and conservation. *Water Study Group Bulletin*, 65.

Appendix I

Contacts with organisations involved in the integrated management of the European coast

For the purposes of preparing the Communication on the integrated management of coastal zones (on which this paper is partly based) information and views were exchanged in 1995 with the following organisations:

- European Union for Coastal Conservation
- Conference of the Maritime Peripheral Regions of the European Community (Commissions of the Islands, of the North Sea, Atlantic Arc, the Mediterranean and the Eurisles Network)
- European Environment Agency and contractors: Laboratorio Nacional de Engenharia Civil (Lisboa), Centro de Estudios y Experimentacion de Obras Publicas (Madrid) and National Institute for Coastal and Marine Management (Den Haag)
- Délégation l'Aménagement du Territoire et Mission Interministérielle de la Mer (Paris)
- Co-ordinated Action for Seaside Towns (Coast Network)
- The National Trust (UK)
- Coastwatch Europe
- Birdlife International
- Council of European Municipalities
- Blue Plan (Action Plan for the Mediterranean).

Studies in European Coastal Management. Jones, Healy and Williams (eds)
1996, Samara Publishing Limited, Cardigan. ISBN 1 873692 07 2

The Council of Europe Action for a Sustainable Integrated Management of Coastlines

F. Albanese

Director of Environment and Local Authorities, Council of Europe

Abstract: The Council of Europe was one of the first organisations to recognise environmental problems in coastal areas. Vested interests bring pressure to bear on coasts which has led to serious biological degradation and aesthetic disfigurement. The best safeguard for European coasts is integrated policy at European level, along with an international convention with the authority to implement the various instruments of territorial planning, historical heritage protection and nature conservation. The convention would set up an international monitoring committee to oversee the implementation of basic coastal conservation principles. Such a model would ensure appropriate and effective protection for European coasts.

Introduction

European coasts are particularly sensitive biotopes as well as being important heritage areas. Correspondingly, these coasts are important in the context of trade, industrial and commercial location, human habitation, mass tourism and other human activities (Healy, 1995). Diverse vested interests bring several pressures to bear on coastal resources; this in turn has led to serious biological degradation and aesthetic disfigurement linked to indiscriminate development.

The work of the Council of Europe

The Council of Europe (CoE) was one of the first organisations concerned with environmental problems in coastal areas. The problems recognised by the CoE Committee of Ministers when adopting Resolution (73) 29 (1973) on the protection of coastal areas led to recommendations for the adoption of sixteen measures for coastal protection. These included maintenance of the ecological and biological balance; preservation of landscape; conservation of natural resources; promotion of appropriate economic and tourism development; and protection of coastal hinterlands.

While the Parliamentary Assembly and the Standing Conference of Local and Regional Authorities of Europe subsequently adopted various other texts, the only one to receive approval at governmental level since 1973 is the 1985 Recommendation of the Committee of Ministers concerning planning policies in maritime regions. The 1973 resolution therefore remains as a key element in the overall strategy of mechanisms for the protection of the European coastline.

Resolution (73) 29 (1973) sets out six main categories of recommended measures:

1. The division of the coast into homogenous zones with rational landuse planning for the coastal environment and adjacent areas.
2. The regulation of development in coastal areas through development bans and conditional development permits.
3. The adoption of measures to protect and conserve flora and fauna and specific coastal habitats.
4. The creation of nature reserves to conserve historic, scenic and archaeological sites as well as coastal ecosystems, particularly inter-tidal wetlands and marshes, such as proposed in Project MAR.
5. The adoption of special measures (such as stabilising sand dunes, regulating sand quarrying and prohibiting damage to vegetation) to combat coastal erosion.
6. The generation of public awareness campaigns designed to safeguard the coast, particularly through creating and managing protected areas.

In accordance with these recommendations, the CoE has concentrated its activities on the adoption of appropriate planning strategies, the protection of coastal flora and fauna, the creation of coastal protected areas and public awareness campaigning for coastal protection.

Appropriate planning strategies

CoE planning policies (general principles, objectives and regional/spatial policy) are objectively defined by Recommendation No. (85) 18 (1985) concerning Planning Policies in Maritime Regions. Approved policies direct that coastal areas should benefit from balanced development which incorporates terrestrial and nearshore marine spheres. Planning strategies set limits for urbanisation, industrialisation and infrastructural growth, as well as controlling the impact of tourism on the environment. While the policy principles are generally accepted, effective application is rarely practised in CoE member states.

Protection of flora and fauna

The CoE's 1979 Convention on the Conservation of European Wildlife and Natural Habitats (The Bern Convention) is a general instrument which is also applicable to coastal areas. The Convention is aimed at ensuring that the conservation of wildlife and natural habitats is taken into account in general national planning and development policies and in pollution control. As a veritable European biodiversity convention, it is open to a wide range of non-European parts of the Mediterranean since it particularly endeavours to promote co-operation in the conservation of migratory species. The Convention currently has twenty-nine European Contracting Parties and two African states (Burkina Faso and Senegal). New nations are regularly invited to register under the Convention, with Albania, Russia, Morocco and Tunisia as recent examples. Other states are to be approached in the near future. A Standing Committee of representatives from Contracting Parties examines violations of the Convention and makes recommendations for eliminating such violations or, more generally, for improving conditions for particular species of flora and fauna, including those in coastal environments.

The Bern Committee's activity programme has included a number of projects based in the Mediterranean basin. For example, a seminar held in Senegal in 1993 to promote co-operation with north and northwest African states, dealt particularly with the management of the Mediterranean fauna and the conservation of wetland, coastal and marine habitats. Two other activities have focused on Mediterranean wetland habitats through seminars held in conjunction with the Ramsar Convention at Ria Formosa (Portugal) in 1989 and Donana (Spain) in 1992.

The Convention's activity programme in the Mediterranean has also included research and expert studies on two particularly endangered species, the monk seal (*Monachus monachus*) and loggerhead turtle (*Caretta caretta*). Several recommendations arising from these studies have been adopted by member states, although this does not necessarily mean that obligations are met. For example, the Standing Committee recently concluded that Greece had not fulfilled its obligations under the Convention regarding the conservation of loggerhead turtles at Laganas Bay (Zakythos).

The conservation of species groups has also been addressed by the Convention; examples include the adoption of recommendations concerning the conservation of threatened amphibians and reptiles in the Gulf of Orosei (Sardinia), and the preparation of a draft agreement on the conservation of small cetaceans in the Mediterranean and Black Seas and their contiguous waters. More general measures to aid the conservation of marine fauna include the prohibition of all indiscriminate means of capture and killing under Article 8 of the Bern Convention. This article enabled the Latium Administrative Court to declare drift nets illegal, a declaration which has led to the reform of Community legislation in this field.

Creation of protected areas

The CoE selects sites in need of urgent protection due to their biological, scientific, cultural or educational value. By adopting Resolution (76) 30 (1976), the CoE has made an enormous contribution to identifying and clarifying factors to be taken into account in creating protected areas. In another resolution, adopted in 1976, the CoE set up a European Network of Biogenetic Reserves for the protection of representative natural European habitats. Over the past fifteen years, 161 reserves in 12 countries have joined the network, including 23 coastal sites. In order to encourage a high standard of work in the protected areas, the CoE awards a European Diploma to the most prestigious natural sites. To be eligible, areas must comply with a set of strict criteria and as an indication of quality 10 of the 32 diplomas so far awarded have been to coastal sites. Although this indicates that the general situation is positive, more still needs to be done to establish a concentrated network of protected areas throughout Europe and to facilitate wildlife conservation and the protection of habitats.

Public awareness

Another CoE activity benefiting coastal areas, but concentrating on the Mediterranean, is the ongoing Campaign on the Mediterranean Coast. The starting point for this programme was the Blue Plan for the Mediterranean which highlighted many of the threats to the region, especially urban, industrial and tourist developments, and prompted the Council to implement the requisite large scale conservation operation. Aspects of this operation included using the position and status of the CoE to influence local officials and territorial authorities with responsibilities in the field of regional development. Public awareness has also been stimulated by organising colloquies in vulnerable areas of the Mediterranean to consider various themes in the field of coastal conservation. The Messina (Italy) colloquy held in November 1988 concentrated on land purchase as a means of protection and presented the experiences in this field of the French Conservatoire du Littoral and British National Trust as possible models. The 1989 Limassol colloquy (Cyprus) adopted an innovatory approach to the issue of tourism and its effects on the environment. It was stressed that the development of tourism beyond a certain threshold is liable to destroy the assets (nature and historic heritage) which attract visitors so that the economic cost of restoring environments could exceed the additional income generated by such development.

A third colloquy, held in 1989 at Ismir (Turkey), reinforced this view and also showed that the behaviour of north European tourists is changing as they become more sensitive to environmental conditions at holiday destinations (see also Hawkins, this volume). Such concerns clearly show the importance of regional/spatial planning instruments as a means of protecting coastal environments.

Colloquies held at Escola (Spain) in 1990 and Bastia (France) in 1991 focused on the use of protected areas and marine parks as instruments for coastal protection. The Bastia colloquy also affirmed the fundamental unity of the Mediterranean as an ecosystem and laid emphasis on the need to include the Black Sea, as a source of many pollutants, in any attempt to protect the Mediterranean. Such concepts, although obvious to conservation practitioners, have by no means gained general acceptance.

The first colloquy to be held in Albania took place at Tirana in October 1994. Its purpose was to encourage the Albanian authorities to resist pressures for the indiscriminate development of the coastline through the formulation of policies for rational use and balanced development. A more widespread proposal concerning the protection of coasts across the whole of Europe was also launched during the Tirana colloquy. The proposal concerned the establishment of an international framework convention to lay down a series of basic principles for implementation by national legislators in the fields of territorial planning, historical heritage protection and nature conservation. The convention would also set up an international monitoring committee to review progress. There are indications that this innovative proposal may be implemented in the near future as the Steering Committee on Nature Conservation has agreed to begin an in-depth review of coastal protection with a view to setting up a working group.

Other initiatives launched in 1995 included the provision of finance for a range of specific conservation projects and the organisation of colloquies to investigate the integrated management of multi-use marine areas and the protection of watercourses flowing into the Mediterranean.

Through its organisation of these colloquies, the Council of Europe has contributed to a growing awareness of the importance of the Mediterranean region as a natural resource.

The conservation of wildlife outside protected areas is also of key interest to the CoE. This was adopted as a campaign theme through the CoE's designation of 1995 as European Nature Conservation Year.

Conclusion

The only real possibility for safeguarding European coasts is an integrated policy at European level. While some countries already have effective national legislation in place, the majority do not. Furthermore, in the majority of cases monitoring measures at an appropriate level of authority do not exist. These problems would be overcome by establishing an international framework convention with the authority to employ appropriately the various instruments offered by territorial planning, historical heritage protection and nature conservation. A central objective of such a convention would be to set up an international monitoring committee to oversee the implementation of basic coastal conservation principles. Such a model would ensure an appropriate and effective level of protection for the coast of Europe.

References

Hawkins, R. 1996. Green Globe: a new approach to environmentally responsible tourism. This volume.

Healy, M.G. 1995. European coastal management: an introduction. In: *Directions in European Coastal Management*. Eds: Healy, M.G. & Doody, J.P. Samara Publishing Limited, Cardigan, UK. pp. 1-6.

Studies in European Coastal Management. Jones, Healy and Williams (eds)
1996, Samara Publishing Limited, Cardigan. ISBN 1 873692 07 2

Coastal Zone Management in England: The Policy Context

D. Holgate-Pollard

Coastal Policy Branch, Department of the Environment, England

Abstract: In recent years there has been increased debate on coastal issues. Responding to this, in 1994 the UK Government announced new policy initiatives in England to enhance effective co-ordination of policies for the coast. These include a broad-based Coastal Forum, proposed policy guidelines for the coast, work to compile a best practice guide on coastal management and a wide-ranging review of byelaw-making powers for the coast.

Introduction

Various UK Government Departments have policy and executive responsibilities for the coast: for example in England, the Ministry of Agriculture, Fisheries and Food (MAFF) leads on fisheries issues, coastal defence and on regulating the deposit of substances or articles at sea; the Department of Transport has responsibility for ports, navigation and the safety of shipping; the Department of Trade and Industry administers licensing procedures for oil and gas exploration and production; and the Department of the Environment (DoE) has a range of policy interests, including the conservation of habitats, water quality issues and, on the landward margin, responsibility for the development control system.

To help relate these different aspects of coastal use and management a small coastal policy branch has been created within the DoE. This acts as a general liaison point on coastal issues and provides the Secretariat of a standing body - the Inter-Departmental Group on Coastal Policy. All UK Government Departments with interests in the coast are represented on this Group, which helps link relevant policy developments by the respective Departments.

As pressures on the coast have grown, so there has been increased interest in coastal zone management both in the UK and elsewhere. Other factors have also drawn attention to the complex interactions of the coastal zone, e.g. concern with respect to climate change and sealevel rise, as well as marine pollution. Awareness of coastal problems is not new, but now there is new recognition that coastal issues must be looked at in the round. Improved liaison and co-ordination between all interested parties are essential to the successful development of policies.

Report by the House of Commons Environment Committee

In Parliament, the issue of coastal zone management was taken up by the House of Commons Environment Committee, which reported in 1992 following its own extensive inquiry into coastal zone protection and planning. The Committee considered detailed evidence from a large number of bodies and organisations. Its final report was wide-ranging, covering a variety of individual topics, but central to the Committee's vision was the need for a comprehensive and integrated approach to coastal issues – taking in offshore and inshore waters, inter-tidal areas and the landward coast. To achieve this the Committee saw scope for improved links between respective authorities and agencies and was critical of what it saw as overlaps in policies and procedures.

The UK Government's response

In its response the Government welcomed the Committee's report as a valuable contribution to the wider debate (DoE, 1992). The response confirmed Ministers' commitment to the effective protection and planning of the coast and described a substantial programme of work already in hand. This included action to reduce coastal pollutants; a new guidance note on coastal planning (Planning Policy Guidance Note No. 20 – *Coastal Planning;* DoE & Welsh Office, 1992); the enactment of environmental duties for ports, sea fisheries and other bodies; and the development of statutory water quality objectives for coasts and estuaries. The response also pointed to the new Inter-Departmental Group on Coastal Policy as providing a valuable means for discussion of broad policy issues.

The response also recognised the importance of a broad management framework for helping resolve different demands on the coast. Where appropriate, it also considered that the preparation of non–statutory management plans by local authorities and others could play a valuable part.

Department of the Environment discussion papers

The debate was taken a stage further in autumn 1993 when DoE published two linked discussion papers (DoE & Welsh Office, 1993a,b) which were widely distributed. The first, *Development Below Low Water Mark*, assessed the current sectoral systems for regulating development in inshore waters; the second, *Managing the Coast*, looked at the scope, form and potential role of management plans for key coastal areas.

These two papers prompted a high degree of interest. Comments on them were extensive but three main themes emerged. First, a need was seen for improved co-ordination of administrative arrangements, but giving full recognition to the different uses of the coastal zone. Second, there was widespread acknowledgement of the unique ecology and amenity value of the coast, and the need to ensure that environmental issues should be fully integrated into the decision-making process. Last, of crucial importance, it was stressed that any measures of regulation must be practical – and strike a fair balance with the broad range of uses which the coastal zone must serve.

Other recent initiatives

In parallel with the above, Government Departments have been taking policy action on a number of fronts, some of which are summarised below.

1. In Autumn 1993, MAFF and the Welsh Office published the *Strategy for Flood and Coastal Defence in England and Wales* (MAFF & Welsh Office, 1993). This was widely welcomed and paid special attention to the need for a full consideration of natural coastal processes in coast defence or flood protection strategies.

2. In 1994 DoE and the Welsh Office issued a consultation paper on proposed new arrangements for controlling the dredging of marine aggregates, (DoE & Welsh Office, 1994). (A statement announcing the outcome of the review was made in November 1995.)

3. In 1994, regulations were approved by Parliament to implement the EC Habitats and Species Directive (HMSO, 1994) thereby making provision for the protection of Special Areas of Conservation, including certain internationally important marine areas, as part of a Community-wide network (Natura 2000). Lists of the proposed areas for designation were published in March 1995. (Following consultation two lists of candidate sites have been sent to the European Commission - including a first tranche of ten marine sites.)

4. Provision was included in the Environment Bill giving new environmental powers to sea fisheries regulators, (MAFF & Welsh Office, 1994). (These were approved by Parliament and came into force in September 1995.)

5. In June 1995, MAFF issued new guidance to coast defence groups concerning the preparation of shoreline management plans (MAFF *et al.*, 1995). This guidance is aimed at helping to ensure a strategic approach and the development of close partnerships between key parties.

Coastal policy statement

Comments received on the DoE coastal management papers (DoE & Welsh Office, 1993a,b) have also led to new initiatives. These were announced by the Minister for the Environment and Countryside in July 1994 (DoE, 1994) in a statement which gave recognition to the heightened importance attached to effective coastal management and to ensuring a balance between commercial, environmental, leisure and other demands, reflecting the principles of sustainable development.

The statement announced four new policy measures in England as follows:

1. The Coastal Forum

The Coastal Forum has a wide brief aimed at promoting discussion and the exchange of views on coastal issues. The new body was launched in December 1994 in London and a second meeting took place in May at Southampton. (A third meeting was held in Liverpool in November and a fourth is scheduled for Chichester in June 1996.)

To help fulfil its role the Coastal Forum has a broad-based membership and brings together the main national representative bodies with interests in the coastal zone. Organisations of all kinds are represented, from commerce and industry to environmental and leisure organisations. The Forum also has representatives from central and local Government and relevant professional groups. It is chaired and serviced by the DoE.

The Coastal Forum therefore offers a vital channel of communication, complementing the work of other bodies. Delegates on all sides have welcomed the initiative and debate at meetings has been lively and constructive. To bring the work of the Forum to a wider audience a regular newsletter – *Wavelength* – is published which contains full Forum reports and news and updates on other coastal initiatives. Copies are available from the DoE.

As part of the Forum process, topic groups will be established to discuss specific issues in more detail. The first of these is concerned with the management of coastal habitats (this group reported in November 1995, and a formal consultation paper was issued early in 1996).

2. Policy guidelines

Also announced were new policy guidelines setting out objectives for the coast, (the guidelines were published in November 1995: available on request from DoE). Consultation showed the demand for a clear and comprehensive statement covering guidance on a wide range of topics. The new guidance would not replace existing sources (e.g. Planning Policy Guidance Notes) but highlight key aims, advice and procedures in a concise digest, helping underscore common themes and principles.

Following publication, public and private bodies, agencies and other organisations have been asked to have close regard to the guidelines in pursuing effective management of the coastal resource.

3. Best practice guide

The third initiative relates to the rapid growth in the role and coverage of coastal zone management plans prepared by local authorities and others. The aim is to highlight best practice in a keynote guide, drawing on the wide experience gained in this area in the past few years. As part of its task, the guide will define the role of the key players; give examples of best practice in helping resolve competing pressures on the coast; and help clarify how different elements of management interact.

In May 1995, following a competitive tendering process, the DoE appointed consultants to compile the guide. An Advisory Group has also been established with representatives of user interests and practitioners. After a series of regional workshops and a national seminar the consultants will complete their work early in 1996. The target date for publication of the guide is Spring 1996.

4. Review of byelaw-making powers

The last of the four initiatives looks at byelaw powers and how best to achieve effective solutions at local level. To help fulfil their functions, regulatory authorities can exercise various byelaw powers relating to the coast. Many of these powers continue to see good service; others are less widely used, or in some key respects have not kept pace with modern trends.

Against this background an Inter-Departmental Working Party, chaired and serviced by the DoE, is currently reviewing the scope and use of available powers and the extent to which they succeed in meeting their objectives. The review is placing special emphasis on the means by which increased demands on the coast for leisure and recreation can be managed. In this context it is also looking at voluntary approaches to management.

Discussions with a broad range of regulatory and user bodies have taken place and these are currently preparing comments for detailed consideration by the review team. In due course the Working Party will make recommendations to Ministers.

Conclusion

These four initiatives in England complement policy action for the coast by lead Departments and their agencies. The package aims to help reconcile competing pressures on the coastal zone and good progress has been made in taking the initiatives forward in close consultation with practitioners and the main interest groups.

References

Department of the Environment. 1992. *The Government's Response to the Second Report from the House of Commons Select Committee on the Environment - Coastal Zone Protection and Planning*. HMSO, London.

Department of the Environment. 1994. News Release 413. *Environment Minister Announces New Initiatives for the Coast*.

Department of the Environment. *Wavelength* - Newsletter of the Coastal Forum (available from Department of the Environment [Room 913], Tollgate House, Houlton Street, Bristol BS2 9DJ, UK).

Department of the Environment. 1995. *Policy Guidelines for the Coast*. HMSO, London. 65 pp.

Department of the Environment & Welsh Office. 1992. *Planning Policy Guidance: Coastal Planning*. PPG 20, HMSO, London.

Department of the Environment & Welsh Office. 1993a. *Development Below Low Water Mark: A Review of Regulation in England and Wales*. HMSO, London.

Department of the Environment & Welsh Office. 1993b. *Managing the Coast: A Review of Coastal Management Plans in England and Wales and the Powers Supporting Them*. HMSO, London.

Department of the Environment & Welsh Office. 1994. Consultation Paper *Review of Licensing Arrangements for Minerals Dredging in England and Wales*.

House of Commons Environment Committee, Second Report. 1992. *Coastal Zone Protection and Planning*. HMSO, London.

HMSO. 1994. *The Conservation (Natural Habitats, & c.) Regulations 1994*: Statutory Instrument No 2716. HMSO, London.

Ministry of Agriculture, Fisheries and Food & Welsh Office. 1993. *Strategy for Flood and Coastal Defence in England and Wales*. MAFF Publications, PB 1471.

Ministry of Agriculture, Fisheries and Food & Welsh Office. 1994. News Release 427/94. *Fisheries Management and the Marine Environment*.

Ministry of Agriculture, Fisheries and Food, the Welsh Office, Association of District Councils, English Nature & the National Rivers Authority. 1995. *Shoreline Management Plans: A Guide for Coastal Defence Authorities*.

Studies in European Coastal Management. Jones, Healy and Williams (eds)
1996, Samara Publishing Limited, Cardigan. ISBN 1 873692 07 2

Towards a More Integrated Management Approach for the Welsh Coastal Zone

R.C. Ballinger, M. Havard, S. Pettit & H.D. Smith
University of Wales, Cardiff, PO Box 907, Cardiff, UK

Abstract: Despite the recent upsurge of interest in coastal and estuarine management and, in particular, the wide variety of environments found along the Welsh coast, surprisingly little research has been undertaken to evaluate the effectiveness and scope of coastal planning and management in Wales. This paper presents the results of such a study, recently commissioned by the Countryside Council for Wales. It reviews the approach to coastal management in Wales, focusing on three contrasting coastal areas: the Menai Strait, the Mid Wales coastal zone of north Ceredigion and the Dyfi estuary, and the industrialised embayment of Swansea Bay. Discussion highlights the complexity and inadequacy of the current organisational framework for integrated coastal management. Attention is focused on the ways in which the present system could be improved. In addition, the importance of effective networking and the future role of agencies and local government is explored.

Introduction: background to the study

Over the last few years, there has been a substantial rise in interest in coastal management within the UK: there has been a proliferation of non-statutory coastal management plans as well as rapid growth in the establishment of informal regional coastal fora. Integration between bodies is a central concern, particularly between organisations with offshore and onshore remits, as this helps to ensure consistency between policies and actions, and between planning and implementation (Chua, 1993). This paper attempts to assess the types and degree of integration within coastal management in Wales. An introduction and background to the study is provided, and the paper analyses the organisational framework for coastal management before addressing possible future directions in Welsh coastal management.

Background to coastal management in Wales

As well as being a resource of high conservation value, the Welsh coast is essential to the well-being of many coast based activities, including the tourist industry, a vital component of the Welsh economy (Owen, 1994). Over the last five years, a number of national events and publications have focused attention on the management and planning of the coastal resource, including the Irish Sea Conference of 1990 (Irish Sea Study Group, 1990), the House of Commons Environment Committee report on *Coastal Zone Protection and Planning* (HMSO, 1992), Planning Policy Guidance Note No. 20 - *Coastal Planning* (Department of the Environment & Welsh Office, 1992), a supplementary topic paper on Coastal Wales (Coastal Strategy Working Party, 1992) to the consultation draft of the *Strategic*

Planning Guidance in Wales (Assembly of Welsh Counties, 1992) and, more recently, the consultation document *A Policy Framework for the Coastal and Marine Zone of Wales* produced by the Countryside Council for Wales (CCW), (CCW, 1994). The latter, although recognising that 70% of the Welsh coast is covered by landuse sympathetic to its surroundings, has advocated the formulation of an holistic approach to coastal management (*ibid.*). To provide data to complement the information forthcoming from consultations on this document, CCW commissioned a review of the maritime (coastal) management for the Welsh coastal zone, including both land and coastal waters out to the median line (the approximate mid-point between the Welsh coast and the coasts of England and Ireland, see Figure 1). This paper presents the results of part of this survey.

Methodology

The study focused on what were considered to be the main influences on and components of coastal management in each of the three study areas. This included analysis of the effectiveness of the organisational and policy frameworks influencing coastal management in Wales, along with a review of the management programmes, plans and technical management measures being implemented at a local level in the three areas. Over 200 individuals and organisations with coastal responsibilities from the Welsh Office, district and county councils through to private industries and non-government organisations, were consulted.

Characteristics of study areas

Three contrasting areas, the Menai Strait, Swansea Bay and the Mid Wales coast including the Dyfi Estuary were chosen for detailed analysis. Apart from the obvious geographical spread of these areas (Figure 1) and their contrasting physical and biological features, they represent coastal zones at different levels of development. The north Ceredigion coast, including the Dyfi estuary, is essentially rural, whereas the Menai Strait, although superficially rural, lies on the fringe of the northeast Wales urban region and with improvements to the A55 Euro-route it is coming under increasing pressure for development. However, it is Swansea Bay which displays the true characteristics of a developed, urban coastal zone, lying within the most densely populated and intensely industrialised region of Wales. Despite these differences, all three coasts contain considerable stretches of both nature and landscape conservation interest, including a proposed Marine Nature Reserve along the Menai Strait and the first Area of Outstanding Natural Beauty (AONB) to be designated in England and Wales on the Gower Peninsula, to the west of Swansea Bay (Mullard, 1995).

The organisational framework

Introduction

The many organisations involved in coastal matters, including the public, private and voluntary sectors, is the dominant feature of coastal management in Wales. A review of the specific statutory and non-statutory functions of these bodies is not provided here: instead, the main links between different interest groups in the

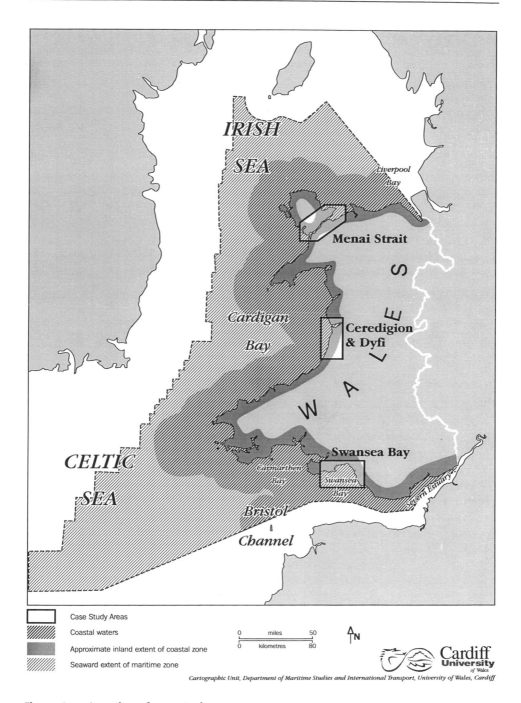

Figure 1   Location of case study areas

Welsh coastal zone are displayed in Figure 2. Reference should be made to the recent publication by the Department of the Environment (DoE) *Coastal Planning and Management; a review* (DoE, 1993) for a detailed consideration of the role of such organisations.

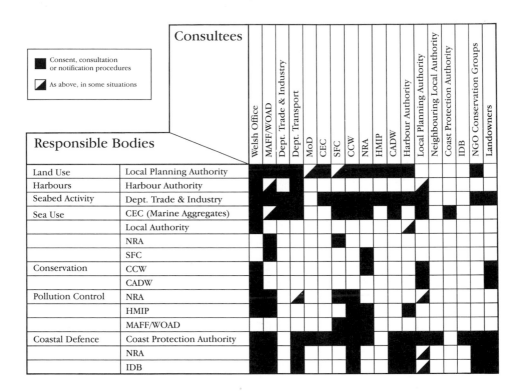

Figure 2   Summary of the links between different interest groups in the Welsh coastal zone

Key to abbreviations/names of organisations:

CADW	Crown Agency for Welsh Historic Monuments
CEC	Crown Estate Commissioners
CCW	Countryside Council for Wales
HMIP	Her Majesty's Inspectorate of Pollution
IDB	Internal Drainage Board
MAFF	Ministry of Agriculture, Fisheries and Food
MoD	Ministry of Defence
NGO	Non-government Organisations
NRA	National Rivers Authority
SFC	Sea Fisheries Committee
WOAD	Welsh Office Agricultural Department

Integration at national level

At a national level, there are a number of government agencies and bodies responsible for the management and regulation of the many different activities which occur in the Welsh coastal zone. This framework, which has evolved over decades in response to piecemeal national legislation, cannot be readily amended and makes for a fragmented structure and difficulties with co-operation and co-ordination between statutory bodies. From consultations for this study, there appeared to be relatively poor liaison between many of the agencies involved at the policy forming levels in Wales, even between bodies within the 'environmental management' sector. Within the Welsh Office a large number of departments share a range of 'coastal' responsibilities, with no one department responsible for coastal management. Consequently, within the Welsh coastal zone, the situation is even more complicated than in England, already singled out as unsatisfactory by the House of Commons Environment Committee (HMSO, 1992). Out to the limit of Territorial Waters, organisations with coastal responsibilities include those which are entirely Welsh based and those, such as the National Rivers Authority (NRA), which have their headquarters outside Wales. The situation is complicated further where Welsh and 'English' organisations come together, such as in the Dee and Severn Estuaries.

Integration at a local level within the case study areas

Coastal management was generally seen to be the province of the planning departments, particularly countryside services, within most of the local authorities interviewed. However, in a number of district and borough councils, particularly in the Swansea Bay area where there has been a severe loss of beach material over the last few years (Cooper & Dun, 1995), coastal management has also caught the attention of engineers within technical services departments. Although both these departments are involved in various aspects of coastal management, the level of liaison between these two departments is often less than satisfactory, dependent on personalities involved and the presence of inter-departmental environmental working groups. This can result in an 'information gap' and the formulation of sub-optimal management solutions to coastal problems.

In addition to planning and technical services departments, a range of other local government departments have coastal interests and responsibilities. However, different organisational arrangements often exist between neighbouring authorities, particularly for non-statutory functions. Outdoor leisure and recreation functions, perceived as non-economic earners, often lie in different departments to tourism, which frequently falls within the economic development section. Consequently, these activities are frequently given different priorities, even in neighbouring districts. This, and the very variable level of interaction between neighbouring local authorities, results in difficulties in providing an integrated recreation and tourism strategy for the coast. When it comes to formulating more integrated coastal strategies between neighbouring district councils, there are no formal mechanisms or guidelines to assist: most of the links are confined to individual sectors, such as the coastal groups of engineers, the safety liaison fora and environmental health groups.

Generally at a local level there appears to be a good working relationship between the other main statutory bodies involved in coastal management, with little overlap between agencies. In particular, the relationship between the NRA and Sea Fisheries Committees, both of which have responsibilities for inshore fisheries, seems to work well. Links between statutory bodies and the private sector are variable, although improving, once again often dependent on personalities. In general though, the link between the privatised utility Dŵr Cymru /Welsh Water (DC/WW) and the NRA is exemplary in its discussions over the planned improvements in sewage treatment and disposal (Lowe, 1995). However, some-times insufficient liaison can occur between bodies as occurred when the South Wales Sea Fisheries Committee neglected to liaise with the Countryside Council for Wales over the impacts of hydraulic shellfish dredging at a particular site. In addition, links with the National Trust (NT), a major landowner along many stretches of the high cliffed Welsh coastline, including much of the Gower Peninsula, have not always been as effective as they could have been. Until recently there has been a tendency for the NT to undertake coastal management in relative isolation, relying on in-house expertise and information. However, liaison and information exchange is now increasing through local fora such as the Gower Countryside Forum (Mullard, 1995).

Integration between 'onshore' and 'offshore' organisations

Particular problems occur in coastal management in Wales where organisations involved in land and sea-based management come together. Central government or other nationally based organisations are often involved offshore, whereas onshore, local authorities and other more locally based bodies are the principal managers. On either side of the shoreline, organisations can have widely different objectives and finance available, and may also vary in terms of their active involvement and local knowledge of the coast. In addition to these differences, offshore public organisations frequently work within longer timescales and are less accountable than the land-based local authorities. The amount of consultation, co-operation and understanding between these two levels may then sometimes be inadequate: for example, there was a lack of consultation between the Ministry of Agriculture Fisheries and Food (MAFF) and CCW over spoil dumping in the vicinity of a Site of Special Scientific Interest in the Mid Wales coast study area.

Coastal groups and fora

The previous sections have illustrated some of the weaknesses of the current framework for coastal management. However, over the last decade there has been a steady increase in the formation of non-statutory coastal groups and fora across England and Wales to help improve liaison between organisations with coastal interests. A considerable number of these occur on the coast of Wales, ranging from multi-sectoral fora covering large sea areas, to smaller scale environmentally focused groups addressing the needs of single estuaries and stretches of coast (Figure 3). It is interesting to note that the greatest concentration of such groups occurs along the most confined and urbanised coasts where pressures of develop-ment, offshore and onshore, are at their most intense.

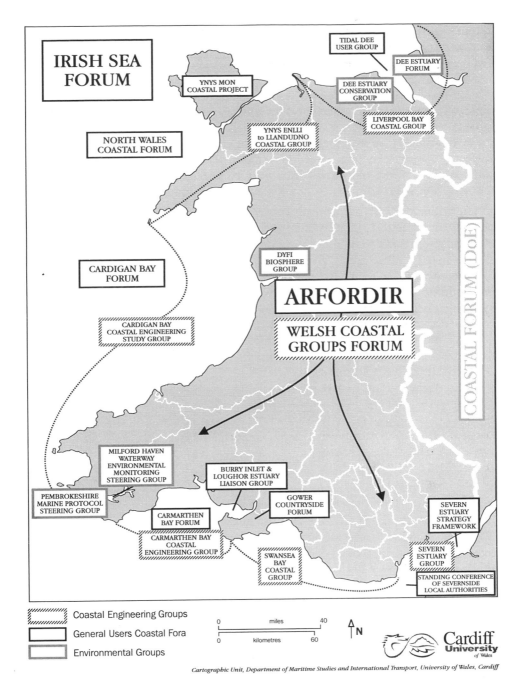

IRISH SEA FORUM

YNYS MON COASTAL PROJECT

TIDAL DEE USER GROUP

DEE ESTUARY FORUM

DEE ESTUARY CONSERVATION GROUP

LIVERPOOL BAY COASTAL GROUP

YNYS ENLLI to LLANDUDNO COASTAL GROUP

NORTH WALES COASTAL FORUM

CARDIGAN BAY FORUM

DYFI BIOSPHERE GROUP

ARFORDIR

WELSH COASTAL GROUPS FORUM

COASTAL FORUM (DoE)

CARDIGAN BAY COASTAL ENGINEERING STUDY GROUP

MILFORD HAVEN WATERWAY ENVIRONMENTAL MONITORING STEERING GROUP

BURRY INLET & LOUGHOR ESTUARY LIAISON GROUP

GOWER COUNTRYSIDE FORUM

SEVERN ESTUARY STRATEGY FRAMEWORK

PEMBROKESHIRE MARINE PROTOCOL STEERING GROUP

CARMARTHEN BAY FORUM

CARMARTHEN BAY COASTAL ENGINEERING GROUP

SWANSEA BAY COASTAL GROUP

SEVERN ESTUARY GROUP

STANDING CONFERENCE OF SEVERNSIDE LOCAL AUTHORITIES

Coastal Engineering Groups

General Users Coastal Fora

Environmental Groups

miles
0   40

kilometres
0   60

N

Cardiff University of Wales

Cartographic Unit, Department of Maritime Studies and International Transport, University of Wales, Cardiff

Figure 3   Regional coastal groups and fora in Wales

41

There is almost complete coverage of the Welsh coast by the engineering-based coastal groups and a Welsh Coastal Groups Forum, co-ordinated by the Welsh Office, which forms a liaison focus between these groups. It should be noted that these are the only 'organisations' whose geographical extent is directly related to the natural boundaries of coastal cells.[1] However, these groups are not without their problems: their membership is somewhat variable and is usually dominated by local authority engineers. Critics argue that these groups should take a more multi-disciplinary approach and widen their membership: however, this is easier said than done as there have been difficulties persuading certain sectors, notably some sections of the industrial community, to join these groups unless they have a direct interest.

Other coastal fora have grown up according to local needs and tend to vary in both their objectives, membership and impact on coastal management. Some, including representatives from the Welsh Office, argue that these non-statutory groups may be more appropriate than statutory prescriptions, but others would like these fora to develop into bodies with more formal powers. Some, particularly the multi-sectoral ones, are local authority led, whereas others, particularly those focusing on conservation, are co-ordinated by non-government organisations. These fora facilitate information exchange and provide a 'voice' for the local population in discussions about offshore development. They have also helped to place the offshore environment much higher up the political agenda in some areas of Wales, notably Cardigan Bay.

Another forum, Arfordir (Welsh for 'coast'), was established two years ago to provide a forum to discuss, evaluate and encourage 'best practice' in environmental management throughout the coastal zone of Wales. This group replaces the Heritage Coast Forum in Wales and as a means of networking it appears to be working well, raising the profile of 'good coastal management', particularly along Heritage Coast/AONB coasts. However, due to its limited resources, both staff and financial, its success in promoting the extension of the Heritage Coast concept to urban fringe coasts, where conservation is a low priority, has been, as yet, rather limited. At a national level, many of those interviewed for the project, particularly those representing conservation bodies, expressed dismay at the lack of Welsh involvement in the Coastal Forum recently established by the DoE (see Holgate-Pollard, this volume). At present, this forum involves organisations representing the main coastal interests within England. Some of those interviewed referred to it as another 'talking shop', but the fact that Wales is not represented could lead to further peripheralisation of Welsh coastal management. However, the Inter-Departmental Group (IDG) of central government departments may, hopefully, ensure that this does not occur.

---

1   Radley (1995) defines geomorphological process cells as "sections of coastline which operate as relatively self-contained units in terms of the interchange of relatively coarse sediment".

Future organisational changes

Major restructuring and redefinition of the roles of many key organisations with coastal responsibilities is ongoing. One of the largest upheavals is the reorganisation of local government in Wales, which is taking place in advance of England: one tier of local government, the Unitary Authority, is to replace the current two-tier system of counties and district councils by April 1996. This change will have profound long-term administrative and financial implications, although these will vary according to local circumstances. There is also great concern over the lack of a strategic view for the coast with the loss of the county level of government, and further worry over future funding of the non-statutory functions of local authorities, particularly coastal management initiatives, countryside services and the successful Heritage Coast programme. However, it is generally recognised that the single tier system should provide a more unified and simpler system for coastal management, cutting down on a few of the many organisations with coastal responsibilities.

A new Environment Agency is to be formed which will combine the functions of the NRA and Her Majesty's Inspectorate of Pollution (HMIP) as well as taking over some of the waste management responsibilities from the local authorities. It is too early to determine the effects of this on coastal management, although there is much concern that this particular organisational restructuring is having a destabilising effect in the short-term. There are also fears that coastal management, once again because of its low status, may become neglected and that the powerful new agency could lead to less accountability and democratic control of some 'coastal management' decision-making.

Conclusion: the future of coastal management in Wales

This discussion has highlighted the present inadequacies of the organisational framework for addressing the needs of integrated coastal management in Wales. However, there are some promising developments, particularly the development of the non-statutory regional coastal groups and fora. A further impetus for the development of more appropriate organisational arrangements has been the UK commitment to a number of international and supranational instruments and agreements, including Agenda 21, Chapter 17 (United Nations Conference on Environment and Development, 1992). However, the long-awaited European Union (EU) coastal strategy, requested by the Council of the European Community (EC) in its *Resolution on the future Community policy concerning the European coastal zone* (1992), has yet to appear, although various targets and instruments for coastal management have been suggested within the EC 5th Environmental Action Programme (see Julien, this volume). Many of those interviewed for this study expressed concern that an EU Directive on Coastal Zone Management could be difficult to implement given the legislative framework and the current government's position on coastal management. Tyler, of the All Party Coastal Working Group of Members of Parliament, has questioned the commitment of the government to coastal management, noting that the last debate on the coast in the House of Commons took place in 1992. In the short-term in Wales then, it may be a range of local non-statutory initiatives and a number of key official publications, such as CCWs draft policy document (CCW, 1994), which raise the profile and understanding of coastal management so that management practice can improve in spite of the present organisational framework.

Acknowledgements

Thanks to the Countryside Council for Wales for funding this study and to Alun Rogers of the Department of Maritime Studies and International Transport (University of Wales, Cardiff) who designed and produced the figures for this paper.

References

Assembly of Welsh Counties. 1992. *Strategic Planning Guidance in Wales*. Consultation Report.

Chua, T-E. 1993. Essential elements of integrated coastal zone management. *Ocean and Coastal Management*, 21,(1-3),81-108.

Coastal Strategy Working Party. 1992. *Coastal Wales*. Topic report no. 4, Strategic Planning Guidance in Wales.

Cooper, B. & Dun, R. 1995. Swansea Bay coastline response study. In: *Directions in European Coastal Management*. Eds: Healy, M.G. & Doody, J.P. Samara Publishing Limited, Cardigan, Wales, UK. pp. 489-495.

Countryside Council for Wales. 1994. *A Policy Framework for the Coastal and Marine Zone of Wales - Consultation Document*. Countryside Council for Wales, Bangor, UK. 12 pp.

Department of the Environment & Welsh Office. 1992. *Planning Policy Guidance: Coastal Planning*. PPG 20, HMSO, London.

Department of the Environment. 1993. *Coastal Planning and Management; A Review*. Lee, M. HMSO, London, UK. 178 pp.

House of Commons Environment Committee, Second Report. 1992. *Coastal Zone Protection and Planning*. HMSO, London.

Irish Sea Study Group. 1990. *The Irish Sea: an environmental review; introduction and overview*. Liverpool University Press, Liverpool, UK.

Lowe, N. 1995. Welsh Water (Dŵr Cymru) environmental improvement programme and the benefits it will bring to our coast. In: *Directions in European Coastal Management*. Eds: Healy, M.G. & Doody, J.P. Samara Publishing Limited, Cardigan, Wales, UK. pp. 425-428.

Mullard, J. 1995. Gower: A case study in integrated coastal management initiatives in the UK. In: *Directions in European Coastal Management*. Eds: Healy, M.G. & Doody, J.P. Samara Publishing Limited, Cardigan, Wales, UK. pp. 471-476.

Owen, E. 1994. Coastal management - a tourism perspective, *The Coastline Conference: public participation in coastal management*. pp. 40-43.

Radley, G.P. 1995. English Nature's campaign for a living coast. In: *Coastal Management and Habitat Conservation*, Volume 1. Eds: Salman, A.H.P.M., Berends, H. & Bonazountas, M. EUCC, Leiden, The Netherlands. pp. 289-297.

United Nations Conference on Environment and Development (UNCED). 1992. *Agenda 21: Programme of Action for Sustainable Development*. United Nations Department of Public Information, New York, USA.

Studies in European Coastal Management. Jones, Healy and Williams (eds)
1996, Samara Publishing Limited, Cardigan. ISBN 1 873692 07 2

A Comparative Analysis of Coastal Zone Management Plans in England and The Netherlands

S. Jones

School of Geography and Earth Resources, The University of Hull, UK

Abstract: The coastal zone is of crucial economic and ecological significance. Integrated planning and environmental management systems provide an important means of conflict resolution between these two, often competing, interests. Integrated Coastal Zone Management Plans have recently been developed for two ecologically and economically important areas, the Wash Estuary (UK) and the Voordelta (The Netherlands). The two plans have developed independently and whilst the Voordelta Plan is a government led initiative, the Wash Estuary Plan is driven primarily by local authorities with national agency involvement. A comparison of the two plans reveals national differences in the administration of coastal management issues. This analysis also reveals fundamental similarities between the two plans and demonstrates the importance of multiagency and public involvement in plan formulation and implementation.

Introduction

Traditional sectoral approaches to managing resources and activities in coastal areas are inadequate. The coastal zone is the shared responsibility of numerous agencies, but the sole responsibility of none. Many separate laws and regulations concern coastal activities, but explicit policies for coastal resources are generally absent at a national level. Integration of planning and management is considered one way of minimising conflicts of interest and ensuring sustainable development in the coastal zone. Indeed, the adoption of nationally integrated planning and management has been promoted by numerous international organisations (e.g. Intergovernmental Panel on Climatic Change (IPCC), 1992; Council of the European Communities, 1992; United Nations Conference on Environment and Development, 1992; Organisation for Economic Co-operation and Development (1993).

Many national governments are currently discussing the potential role of Integrated Coastal Zone Management (CZM) within their prevailing legal and organisational frameworks. The process of developing a national CZM strategy, however, is not simply top-down control or bottom-up decision-making. Rather, it is a mixture of consensus on broad policy goals, and competition over specific means to achieve them (Godschalk, 1992). The formulation of specific goals, ensuring the sustainable use of coastal resources, may provide a framework within which CZM can be achieved.

Policy integration is not a quixotic quest, but a model suggesting appropriate methods to reduce potential conflicts (Cicin-Sain, 1993). Any planning model can be traceable to varying assumptions and propositions from political thought, which in turn arises from different political practices (Low, 1991). Therefore each CZM Plan reflects the planning and policy culture of the national system.

This paper examines how the coastal zone in the UK and The Netherlands is currently being planned through two management plans: The Wash Estuary Management Plan and Integraal Beleidsplan Voordelta. The two areas are similar in that development depends on coastal defences against flooding and erosion, no national CZM policies exist, they are estuarine in nature and the socio-economic and ecological issues are complimentary. By comparing their policy development and (proposed) implementation, it is possible to identify how each plan seeks to achieve its aims. This also provides insight into comparative national CZM planning strategies and regional initiatives.

Coastal zone management in The Netherlands

Protection against erosion and flooding is a national imperative for the Dutch coast. Without protection, approximately 50% of the land, in which 65% of the gross national product (GNP) is earned, would be liable to flooding (IPCC, 1992). Coastal engineering and water management were, until recently, based solely on technical knowledge, without having to assess implications from non-engineering viewpoints. However, the overall decline of natural and ecological resources in the coastal zone has raised public interest and concern for the conservation of those remaining natural resources. Consequently, a balance is now sought between socio-economic and environmental factors in coastal areas.

Dutch administrative structures strongly reflect the protective functions of coastal planning and water management. A complex system has evolved based on Waterschappen (water boards) which have certain legal powers regarding water management within their jurisdiction. The Waterschappen are supervised by a provincial government's advisory technical agency (Provinciale Waterstaat) and through regional plans defining flood defence and safety standards. Each province is supervised at a national level by the Ministry of Transport and Water Management (Verkeer en Waterstaat) through an executive agency, the Rijkswaterstaat. This agency is responsible for dike safety standards, research, and the design, construction and maintenance of major dikes and flood protection schemes. The national water management policy framework ensures an integrated water management system.

Landuse planning has also evolved into a sophisticated system. Economic planning and water management are functions of national government but physical planning is conducted within local authorities. The main legal instrument is the municipalities' legally binding landuse plan (Bestemingsplan). This plans is approved by provincial government, having been checked against the regional physical plan (Streekplan) and other policy documents. National government acts as a final supervisory level. The physical planning system is highly regulatory and decentralised, and municipalities have the main legal planning powers.

Provincial governments are concerned with stimulating economic development and, until recently, focused on planning the developed coast (Mitchell, 1982). The water management system (through the Rijkswaterstaat) took priority along the 'undeveloped' coast. However, following a fundamental reassessment of coastal defence policy in 1990, the Dutch coastline may now be managed in a more holistic fashion. The national government pursues a policy of 'dynamic preservation', with artificial beach nourishment being used as the main technique to combat erosion (De Ruig, 1995). Policy implementation is the provinces' responsibility (van Gelder, 1995) and co-operation between the State (Rijkswaterstaat), provincial authorities and water boards is essential. Co-operation is effected through statutory provincial consultative bodies (POKs), which can also include representatives from coastal municipalities and nature conservation organisations.

'Preserving' the coastline might increase development pressure. For example, dune areas as natural defence structures have historically been protected by water boards. With their defence importance now lessened by the 1990 policy, their potential for tourism and recreation might now be exploited, possibly compromising their important nature conservation function as well as the planning function of local planning authorities. This future planning and management of coastal zones will therefore require increased co-operation and policy integration from all organisations (Table 1).

The Voordelta Plan (Beleidsplan Voordelta)

The Netherlands has no national CZM system. The integrated policy plan for the Voordelta (Integraal Beleidsplan Voordelta) is a recent example of CZM that deals with multiple issues. It is noteworthy in its policy and instrumental ambition to preserve ecological processes, guarantee coastal safety and safeguard activities such as fishing, tourism, recreation, sand extraction and navigation (van Alphen, 1995).

The Voordelta is the area seaward of the delta coastline (Figure 1). The Delta Project, initiated after the 1953 floods, shortened the estuarine coastline from approximately 900 to 100 km, replacing traditional defences with an engineered solution. As a result of estuary closure, there were rapid large scale morphological adaptations to the new hydrodynamics, and inter-tidal shore-parallel shoals formed, behind which a lagoon-like environment developed.

Despite the loss of estuarine area, the Voordelta remains an internationally important area for juvenile fish, breeding and migratory birds and seals. The transport infrastructure resulting from the Delta Project made the Zeeland coast more accessible to The Netherlands, Belgium and Germany, thus favouring economic development. Consequently, in the past twenty years, tourism and recreation have become a more important source of income than traditional fisheries (van Alphen, 1995).

New opportunities and conflicts have occurred in the Voordelta due to the increasing concentration of human activities in environmentally sensitive areas. The decision was therefore taken in 1988 to prepare an integrated policy plan aimed at preserving natural processes and indicating how (and where) recreation and fisheries could be continued and further developed. Significantly, this decision was taken by national government rather than by local authorities, and acted upon by the Rijkswaterstaat (North Sea Directorate). The major part of the plan's area is situated beyond provincial and municipal jurisdiction, making the government the competent authority. Furthermore, major conflicts between nature, recreation and fisheries were expected to extend beyond the local level. Local authorities, dependent on income from fisheries, recreation and sector-based interest groups, had not asked for an integrated policy plan at the time.

Table 1   **Environmental responsibilities held by different agencies in the coastal zone of The Netherlands**

Organisation	Planning	Permitting/ Enforcement	Provision	Other
Ministry of Environment	National Environmental Plan and Programmes	Special and Complex Cases		Regulations of Products Measuring Air Quality
Ministry of Transport (Rijkswaterstaat)	Water Management Plans Coastal Defence Council (POK) Member	Regional Authorities for National Water, Coastline and North Sea		Measuring Water Quality Measuring the Basal (1990) Coastline
Ministry of Agriculture, Nature Conservation and Fisheries	Nature Conservation Plan Fisheries Management		Planning and Developing Nature Preservation Areas	
Ministry of Economic Affairs	Energy Plan	Mining Activities		
Provinces	Regional Environmental Plans Coastal Defence Council (POK) Chair	Larger Firms	Soil Sanitation, Waste Disposal and Incineration	
Water Boards	Regional Water Management Plans Coastal Defence Council (POK) Member	Water Discharges	Water Sewage Installations and Incineration	Measuring Water Quality
Municipalities	Local Plans	National Regulations Small Firms	Waste Collection	

Source: *Rhetoric and Reality in Environmental Policy.* Wintle & Reeve (eds.) 1994, Table 2.2

The policy plan was prepared by a co-ordinating group, comprising relevant state departments, provinces, municipalities and water boards. The finalised plan has a non-legal status, putting emphasis on the willingness of all authorities to co-operate in plan implementation and their acceptance of the policy outcome. Following public and political consultation, the policy plan was agreed in October 1993. In addition to a description of the policy and measures regarding different activities, the policy plan has been translated into a zonation scheme (Figure 1). The map enables local interest groups and the general public to understand the aims and policies of the Voordelta Plan. This interpretation is potentially one of the most important aspects of the project (see also Gubbay & Laffoley, this volume).

To ensure implementation, all parties signed a management agreement. This committed each organisation to specific actions (including research and monitoring) and to the assimilation of the plan into related regional, developmental, and sector plans. Supervising the action programme is a steering group (the former co-ordinating group, chaired by the Rijkswaterstaat). The group also assesses the permissibility of new developments and adjustments needed resulting from changing circumstances. The first evaluation report, prepared one year after signing the management agreement, indicates that initial implementation of the action programme has started successfully.

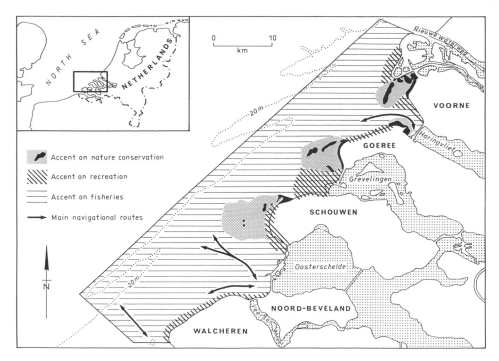

Figure 1   **Map of the Voordelta area showing the main categories of the zonation scheme**

Source: Ministry of Transport, Public Works & Water Management, The Netherlands

Coastal zone management in the United Kingdom

There is currently no explicitly 'coastal' component to general landuse planning and managementin the UK. Coastal management has instead been heavily dependent on private, voluntary efforts aimed at protection rather than managing competing uses. Existing local coastal planning and management initiatives are closely tied to the general planning system, which unlike the Dutch system is highly centralised. The lack of a centralised coastal programme has been responsible for the absence of clear policy goals, a plethora of alternative management proposals for competing uses of resources and an inflexibility in planning and designation policies (Mitchell, 1982). Consequently, there is a difference between what might be achieved within the present statutory planning framework and what is achieved by many local authorities (Department of the Environment, 1993).

During the past five years there has been considerable discussion and progress in the debate to develop a national CZM system. In 1991, voluntary organisations, sharing Dutch concern over the loss of coastal and estuarine resources, persuaded the House of Commons Select Committee on the Environment to investigate coastal planning. The Committee's findings (HMSO, 1992) prompted the government to undertake a number of initiatives, including a review of existing systems of development control below low water mark, and an examination of the role of coastal management plans. A 'Coastal Forum' (confined to England) has recently been launched to review coastal byelaws and produce a 'best practice guide' for coastal management plans (see Holgate-Pollard, this volume). A coastal policy guideline document has also recently been produced (Department of the Environment, 1995). Nevertheless, county and district councils continue to implement a variety of coastal planning and management initiatives (NCEAG, 1993, 1994).

As in The Netherlands, many urban and rural areas are dependent on coastal defences to protect against flooding and erosion. Coastal defences are administered similarly to the Dutch system. The Ministry of Agriculture, Fisheries and Food (MAFF) has overall responsibility, whilst operational responsibilities rest with the National Rivers Authority (NRA) and maritime district councils. Co-ordinating coastal defence activities, Regional Coastal Defence Groups operate on a voluntary basis (unlike the statutory POKs) to produce Shoreline Management Plans. These plans consider coastal processes and the impact of the built environment, and form the engineering input of the local planning process.

From a statutory and administrative perspective, the UK possesses a powerful system of landuse planning. Responsibility lies with the Department of the Environment (DoE), whilst coastal defence is MAFF's responsibility. This division also reflects the situation in the Netherlands, where coastal defence is the responsibility of the Rijkswaterstaat (Ministry of Transport and Public Works) and physical planning is organised by the Ministry of Housing, Physical Planning and the Environment. Likewise, the physical planning system is based on a three-tier hierarchical structure, each level contributing something distinctive to policy expression (Tewdwr-Jones, 1994). Each county council is required to produce a generalised structure plan (for approval by the relevant Secretary of State) to ensure that national and regional interests are respected. District councils are required to produce local plans to carry through policies for development control in local areas.

A change of emphasis in planning approach (from 'appeal-led' to 'plan-led') initiated by the Town and Country Planning Act 1990, and the introduction of Planning Policy Guidance Notes (PPGs), has placed local authorities in a key position when planning the coastline (Tewdwr-Jones, 1994). A governmental review in 1993 identified them as the "lead agency and natural nucleus of coastal management plans" (DoE & Welsh Office, 1993). Through the publication of PPG 20 (*Coastal Planning*; DoE & Welsh Office, 1992), the government also placed great importance on consistent planning policies between neighbouring authorities.

This account has been mainly limited to England and somewhat different arrangements exist for the management of the coastal zone in the rest of the United Kingdom (Wales, Scotland and Northern Ireland). Aspects of the management of the Welsh coastal zone are discussed by Ballinger *et al.* (this volume).

The Wash Estuary management plan

The Wash, lying between Lincolnshire and Norfolk, is the largest estuarine system in the UK (Davidson *et al.*, 1991). It is an internationally important area for nature conservation, and has national recognition as a Site of Special Scientific Interest and Area of Outstanding Natural Beauty. The coast performs a flood protection function and supports a nationally important shellfish industry, ports and industry, agriculture, military uses, tourism and recreation and water abstraction. The area therefore shares with the Voordelta a similar physical environment, ecological status, and complex range of competing uses. It forms an appropriate parallel through which to examine administrative responses to the needs of coastal management.

Government planning advice (through PPG 20) states that key issues to be addressed in coastal planning include natural environment conservation and developments requiring a coastal location. Regional Planning Guidance briefly considers coastal conservation and development, but does not highlight the Wash. Consequently, the Lincolnshire and Norfolk County Councils, together with English Nature, formed the Wash Estuary Strategy Group in 1993, to prepare an independent management plan. The Strategy Group brings together all local authorities and statutory bodies with an interest in the area, thereby confirming the local authorities' central position.

The management plan area principally relates to the statutory designated areas of the Wash, but also includes adjoining areas in relation to specific issues (landscape, water quality and development) (Figure 2). The policy plan has been developed by an Officers' Group, comprising the local authorities and organisations responsible for the area. Another group, composed of elected councillors, has been established to oversee final plan preparation once public consultation processes in each council area have been completed. On finalisation, individual authorities will be invited to endorse the non-statutory document. To be effective this plan will also rely on the goodwill and co-operation of landowners, local communities, user groups, and those with statutory responsibilities in the area.

Figure 2   Map of the Wash Estuary showing the area covered by the management plan
Source: Department of Planning & Transportation, Norfolk County Council, UK

The Wash Estuary Management Plan presents policy lines for flood defence, ports and navigation, nature conservation, fisheries, military use, water quality, agriculture and recreation. It is aimed to ensure that all planning aspects fully recognise the need to safeguard statutorily designated areas and that land and sea-based development is compatible with sustainable use. The intention is not to constrain industrial developments unnecessarily, because these can benefit the local economy. Rather, it is to make the environmental implications of a development a material consideration in the decision making processes. Likewise, tourism and recreational interests are to be maintained and enhanced where pressure for use does not conflict with nature conservation.

Implementation is fundamental to the plan's success and will require the involvement of numerous authorities, organisations and individuals. It is intended that all those involved will formally adopt the plan both as the general framework and detailed guide for the sustainable management of the Wash. The Strategy Group's role will be to ensure cross-agency co-ordination of effort, monitoring and (ultimately) plan review. A 'Forum' is also planned to raise, discuss, and where possible resolve, cross-topic issues. An Implementation Officer post is also being considered owing to the amount of local authority staff time required for implementation.

Discussion

Both management plans reflect the planning culture of their national systems. In the UK, local authorities have been the key agencies initiating and developing the plan (within a 'centralised' planning system), whilst central government undertook the role in The Netherlands (usually a 'decentralised' system). The apparent paradox is explained by the necessarily regional nature of CZM determining those authorities with the competence for each plan's area. Both plans ensure the sustainable use and development of similar environments, subject to a similar range of competing uses. The independent formation of both plans, and the similar nature of their policies, suggests a system that generates integrated planning and management (Figure 3).

The Voordelta Plan has been developed through a process of identifying coastal resources and conflicts, public participation, and administrative approval during policy decision making. Without a national CZM strategy, the governmental role has been central and significant. The Rijkswaterstaat is ensuring that implementation of the proposed policies takes place. Non-legal status is an appropriate instrument to involve all organisations since (it is suggested) they are able to withdraw should interests be seriously compromised (van Alphen, 1995). During consultations, objections were raised from harbour authorities, the military, fisheries, and recreational interests over the amount of ecological protection proposed and whether the plan was even necessary. Part of the work for the Steering Group and Voordelta 'forum' has consequently been to restore the motivation of these groups to implement the plan through compromise.

Development of the Wash Estuary Management Strategy mirrors the Voordelta Plan. The central governmental role deserves examination because MAFF and the MoD are observers in the Officers' Group, but the DoE is absent. The latter is a nominal consultee, but refused 'observer status' because the Department's presence might have been interpreted as official approval of management solutions that contradict national planning policies.

The inclusion of the Boston Port Authority and Eastern Sea Fisheries Joint Committee on the Officers' Group is notable as these organisations regulate the activities of the principle offshore users. There is the potential to avoid the difficulties experienced by the Voordelta Steering Group, although during public consultation no responses were received from fishermen despite the Committee's involvement. Concern remains that for plan implementation, compromises might have to be made, and if there is compromise the environment may suffer.

Whilst the Wash Management Plan has to be finalised, implementation mechanisms have already been suggested that are successful in the Voordelta. These include a Steering Group to oversee progress and find solutions to further

ACTION   ADMINISTRATIVE RESPONSE

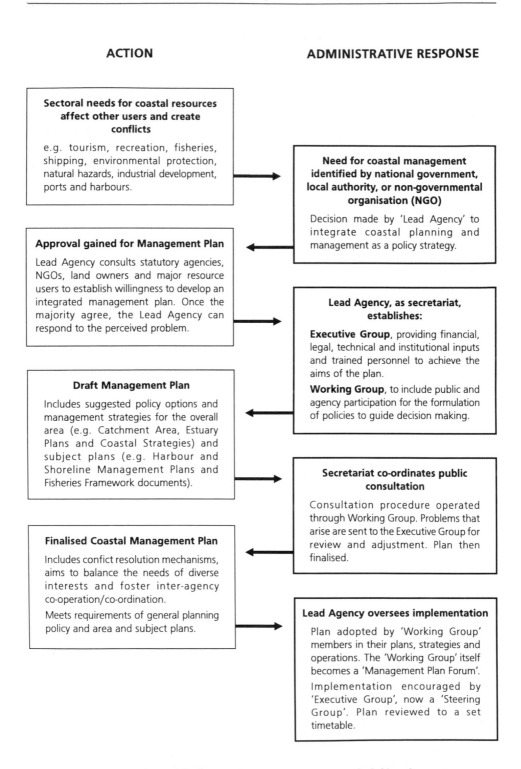

Sectoral needs for coastal resources affect other users and create conflicts

e.g. tourism, recreation, fisheries, shipping, environmental protection, natural hazards, industrial development, ports and harbours.

Need for coastal management identified by national government, local authority, or non-governmental organisation (NGO)

Decision made by 'Lead Agency' to integrate coastal planning and management as a policy strategy.

Approval gained for Management Plan

Lead Agency consults statutory agencies, NGOs, land owners and major resource users to establish willingness to develop an integrated management plan. Once the majority agree, the Lead Agency can respond to the perceived problem.

Lead Agency, as secretariat, establishes:

Executive Group, providing financial, legal, technical and institutional inputs and trained personnel to achieve the aims of the plan.

Working Group, to include public and agency participation for the formulation of policies to guide decision making.

Draft Management Plan

Includes suggested policy options and management strategies for the overall area (e.g. Catchment Area, Estuary Plans and Coastal Strategies) and subject plans (e.g. Harbour and Shoreline Management Plans and Fisheries Framework documents).

Secretariat co-ordinates public consultation

Consultation procedure operated through Working Group. Problems that arise are sent to the Executive Group for review and adjustment. Plan then finalised.

Finalised Coastal Management Plan

Includes conflict resolution mechanisms, aims to balance the needs of diverse interests and foster inter-agency co-operation/co-ordination.

Meets requirements of general planning policy and area and subject plans.

Lead Agency oversees implementation

Plan adopted by 'Working Group' members in their plans, strategies and operations. The 'Working Group' itself becomes a 'Management Plan Forum'.

Implementation encouraged by 'Executive Group', now a 'Steering Group'. Plan reviewed to a set timetable.

Figure 3   Framework model of coastal zone management administrative responses

problems identified by a 'Coastal Forum'. Through a proposed 'Implementation Officer', organisations might also be assisted in adopting relevant parts of the plan. There is, however, no proposal to develop a zonation scheme and associated map, the preferred option being to promote holistic planning across the general area from within organisations' policies and actions. Nevertheless, such a scheme would be worthwhile, promoting the plan amongst those affected by it. A map could represent the environmental sensitivity, areas of conflict, and thus the plan's aims (see also Gubbay & Laffoley, this volume). Even without such a technique, the (finalised) Wash Estuary Management Strategy should achieve the similar initial success which has followed the introduction of the Voordelta Plan.

References

Ballinger, R.C., Havard, M., Pettit, S. & Smith, H.D. 1996. Towards a more integrated management approach for the Welsh coastal zone. This volume.

Cicin-Sain, B. 1993. Sustainable development and integrated coastal management. *Ocean and Coastal Management*, 21:11-43.

Council of the European Communities. 1992. Council Resolution 92/C 59/01 on the Future Community Policy Concerning the European Coastal Zone. 25th February 1992. *Official Journal of the European Communities.*

Davidson, N.C., Laffoley, D.d'A., Doody, J.P., Way, L.S., Gordon, J., Key, R., Pienkowski, M.W., Mitchell, R. & Duff, K.L. 1991. *Nature Conservation and Estuaries in Great Britain.* Nature Conservancy Council, Peterborough, UK. 422 pp.

Department of the Environment. 1993. *Coastal Planning and Management: A Review.* Lee, M. HMSO, London, UK. 178 pp.

Department of the Environment. 1995. *Policy Guidelines for the Coast.* HMSO, London, UK. 65 pp.

Department of the Environment & Welsh Office. 1992. *Planning Policy Guidance: Coastal Planning.* PPG 20, HMSO, London, UK.

Department of the Environment & Welsh Office. 1993. *Managing the Coast: A Review of Coastal Management Plans in England and Wales and the Powers Supporting Them.* HMSO, London, UK.

Department of the Environment. *Wavelength* - Newsletter of the Coastal Forum (available from Department of the Environment [Room 913], Tollgate House, Houlton Street, Bristol BS2 9DJ, UK).

De Ruig, J.H.M. 1995. The Dutch experience: four years of dynamic preservation of the Dutch coastline. In: *Directions in European Coastal Management.* Eds: Healy, M.G. & Doody, J.P. Samara Publishing Limited, Cardigan, Wales, UK. pp. 253-266.

Godschalk, D.R. 1992. Implementing coastal zone management: 1972-1990. *Coastal Management*, 20:93-116.

Gubbay, S. & Laffoley, D. 1996. Improving integration and communication of coastal zone management: a case study for the Solent region, UK. This volume.

Holgate-Pollard, D. 1996. Coastal zone management in england: the policy context. This volume.

House of Commons Environment Committee, Second Report. 1992. *Coastal Zone Protection and Planning.* HMSO, London, UK.

Intergovernmental Panel on Climatic Change. 1992. *Global Climate Change and the Rising Challenge of the Sea*. (Report prepared for the IPCC by Working Group 3, the Coastal Zone Management Subgroup). Rijkwaterstaat, The Hague. 124 pp.

Low, N. 1991. *Planning, Politics and the State. Political Foundations of Planning Thought.* Unwin Hyman, London, UK. 313 pp.

Mitchell, J.K. 1982. Coastal zone management: A comparative analysis of national programs. In: *Ocean Yearbook*. Eds: Borgese, E.M. & Ginsberg, N. 3:259-319.

National Coasts & Estuaries Advisory Group. 1993. *Coastal Planning and Management: A Good Practice Guide*. NC&EAG, c/o Devon County Council, UK. 42 pp.

National Coasts & Estuaries Advisory Group. 1994. *Directory of Coastal Planning and Management Initiatives in England*. NC&EAG, c/o Kent County Council, UK. 58 pp.

Organisation for Economic Co-operation and Development. 1993. *Coastal Zone Management: Integrated Policies*. OECD, Paris. 128 pp.

Tewdwr-Jones, M. 1994. Policy implications of the "plan-led planning system". *Journal of Planning and Environmental Law*, July 1994, 584-593.

United Nations Conference on Environment and Development. 1993. *Agenda 21: Programme of Action for Sustainable Development*. United Nations Department of Public Information, New York, USA.

Van Alphen, J. 1995. Integrated Policy Plan: Administrative Aspects of Coastal Zone Management in The Netherlands. Unpublished Report.

Van Gelder, W.T. 1995. Regional planning for integrated coastal management in The Netherlands. In: *Coastal Management and Habitat Conservation*. Eds: Salman, A.H.P.M., Berends, H. & Bonazountas, M. EUCC Leiden, The Netherlands. pp. 201-206.

Studies in European Coastal Management. Jones, Healy and Williams (eds)
1996, Samara Publishing Limited, Cardigan. ISBN 1 873692 07 2

Improving Integration and Communication of Coastal Zone Management: A Case Study for the Solent Region, UK

S. Gubbay

Coastal Zone Management Specialist, 4 Bamford Cottages, Upton Bishop, Ross-on-Wye, UK

D. Laffoley

Marine Task Force, English Nature, Northminster House, Peterborough, UK

Abstract: As pressures on the coastal zone continue to grow, effective Coastal Zone Management (CZM) becomes increasingly important. New means of effective communication between players in coastal management can facilitate the management process. The use of colour coded multiple use zoning schemes is examined in the context of integrated management and information dissemination. It is concluded that management information charts, which provide an easily understood means of communicating environmental management information, can contribute to improved integration of CZM policies and management arrangements for coastal areas.

Introduction

Coastal Zone Management (CZM) has been the subject of much debate in the UK in the last five years. Two themes which recur are the need for more integrated planning and management and the need for CZM plans to be communicated effectively to planners, managers and users. Ways of tackling these include using national networks to exchange information, setting up multi–disciplinary coastal groups and a unit within government with specific responsibility for the task. The usual way of informing people about management arrangements is to advertise and distribute reports, leaflets and management plans. On-site promotion often involves the use of interpretation panels and, in some cases, posting of byelaws on notice boards. In this paper we examine the usefulness of colour coded multiple use zoning schemes in the preparation of integrated management plans, and as a way of communicating their subject matter to the general public, sea users and those with a special interest in CZM.

Multiple use zoning

Zoning schemes are used widely in the management of marine protected areas and the best known examples are probably from the Great Barrier Reef Marine Park in Australia (Kenchington, 1990). Two European examples are the scheme used in the Danish sector of the Wadden Sea and, on a more local scale, the Lundy Island Marine Nature Reserve off the coast of England (Ministry of the Environment, 1993; English Nature, 1994a). These schemes could be viewed as taking a sectoral approach to management because they identify areas where certain activities are welcome and others are limited or prohibited. In these examples, however, a range of activities have been considered and the cumulative effects of controls have been interpreted as a multiple use zoning table. The end result is an integrated representation of current management controls and what they mean for environmental protection.

An important feature of the three examples cited above is the use of colour to illustrate the management arrangements and different levels of protection in each zone. Blue is used to represent areas where virtually all activities can take place, subject to agreed regulations and Codes of Practice. Green, yellow and orange show increasing levels of restriction, with red areas the most highly protected. This approach, showing how existing controls can benefit marine nature conservation, has been used successfully for the Lundy Island Marine Nature Reserve. In 1994 English Nature commissioned a study to investigate whether it could be applied more widely.

The study area

An area of sea off the south coast of England, between Portland Bill and Selsey Bill, was chosen for the study (Figure 1). The boundaries of the study area were from Mean Low Water to the 12 nautical mile limit of UK territorial waters, bordering more than 200 km of coastline. This corresponds to the boundaries of two of the 'Maritime Natural Areas' identified by English Nature, which are based on the natural 'coastal cells' that are defined by erosion and deposition patterns along the coast (English Nature, 1994b). The most dominant geographic features are Southampton Water, the Solent and the Isle of Wight. Coastal and marine habitats include estuaries, natural harbours, cliffs, underwater gravel and sand banks. This is an intensively used area. Most of the activities that take place in UK waters are represented in the region and the management arrangements, legal provisions and jurisdiction of various authorities are complex. This mix made it ideal for a realistic study of whether a colour coded zoning scheme could provide a readily accessible and fully integrated representation of the environmental protection provided by current management arrangements.

Preparation of a management information chart (MIC)

There is a great deal of information on the use and management of the study area but no concise overview or summary, even though many organisations in the region have an interest in CZM. Instead, most of the material is geared to providing information on specific interests such as water based recreation, fisheries, nature conservation and archaeology. The exceptions tend to be coastal plans, directories and proceedings of meetings organised by groups such as the Solent Forum and the Dorset Coast Forum who have a multi-disciplinary membership. The most likely reason for this lack of overview is that the majority of organisations are either concerned with only part of the area or, if they do cover the whole region, are only responsible for certain activities. No organisation or consortium has jurisdiction over the whole area and all the activities taking place within it. The aim of this study was to determine the environmental controls provided by the current management arrangements and summarise these into a MIC.

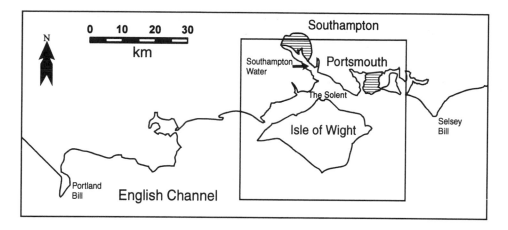

Figure 1   Location of the study area

A traditional starting point in the development of management plans is to identify the activities taking place in an area, where they occur and to what level. A parallel requirement is to be aware of any constraints which, as a minimum, are determined by legislation which specifies the conditions within which management arrangements must operate. Such controls are then added to by a host of other measures such as informal management agreements, codes of practice and recommended areas in which to operate. For the purposes of this trial, a decision was taken to limit the information on the MIC to baseline conditions i.e. those determined by legislative controls.

To get a comprehensive picture of the legal controls in an area it is necessary to be aware of both national legislation and local byelaws. This resulted in the first difficulty with the study as there is no central source of such information. National legislation is held by Parliament and Government Departments hold copies of model byelaws which can be introduced under their auspices. Individual organisations had to be contacted for regulations relating to their activities and to gather details of local byelaws it would have been necessary to contact every local authority in the region. As this was unrealistic in the time available and, because such byelaws are generally only concerned with a narrow strip of water adjacent to the coast, local authority byelaws were not included on the chart. Despite these byelaws being excluded from the study, the investigation revealed that a minimum of 42 regulations must be consulted to get an overview of the environmental controls in the region. These are: port and harbour byelaws and orders (12); fisheries byelaws and orders (19); Acts of Parliament (8) and miscellaneous (3). Additional information provided by more than 50 individuals who were familiar with various management arrangements for the region was also included.

A multiple use zoning scheme showing increasing levels of environmental protection was prepared for the region using this information. Six zone types were identified, namely General use, Recreation, Harbour, Refuge, Sanctuary and Protected zones. In each case details were given in relation to controls on thirteen different activities

(Table 1). The completed work was presented as an A3 size MIC. (Figure 2 shows a section of the MIC). Explanatory notes were needed to back up the multiple use zoning table but this was to be expected because of the number of activities taking place in the region, the fact that the management arrangements for each were determined independently and because the zoning scheme was being developed retrospectively rather than when the regulations were agreed.

Discussion and conclusions

The trial was successful in that it showed it was possible to prepare a MIC for the region which summarised the baseline management conditions and interpreted them into levels of environmental protection. The format gives an easily understood overview of the spatial controls relating to 13 marine activities.

Two interesting features illustrated by the chart are worth highlighting:

1. Environmental protection: With the exception of one local nature reserve, the most highly protected sites are those covered by the Protection of Wrecks Act (1973) or under the jurisdiction of the Ministry of Defence. In addition, disturbance to benthic communities is reduced by certain fishing controls and in areas laid with cables and pipelines where bottom fishing and anchoring is prohibited. These areas can be categorised as 'Sanctuary Zones'. The chart therefore illustrates very clearly that the management controls introduced by bodies other than those responsible for nature conservation can be used to assist environmental protection.

2. Freedom to operate: The Solent region was selected for the trial because it is used intensively. Despite this, the MIC shows that there are no limitations on the thirteen activities throughout much of the region. In the case of oil and aggregate extraction, for example, licences need to be sought and conditions may be applied before permission is granted. There are also recommendations and voluntary agreements, such as those agreed by the Solent Oil & Gas Consortium to oppose oil extraction in the Solent and the recommendations relating to minimum depth for aggregate extraction. The notes on the MIC explain that restrictions may apply in shipping lanes and fairways. However, as the zoning table illustrates, there are no areas where these activities are prohibited by statute.

Several limitations of MICs were highlighted during the study. The most significant is probably that a chart is designed to give a simplified overview of the legal controls in the area. In the case of the Solent chart, for example, it was not possible to include all activities taking place in the coastal zone. Other limitations are that charts such as these will only deal with area based restrictions and the level of detail will not be sufficient as the only source of information for those preparing CZM plans. This is to be expected from any document which summarises information and serves to emphasise that charts such as these should not be used in isolation. Another difficulty is that the zoning scheme was developed on pre-existing regulations whereas the ideal situation is to consider the sorts of controls required in different types of zones and introduce such controls at the same time as the zoning system. This may become the case in future marine protected areas, but for the purposes of this study the zones had to be interpreted retrospectively and may not reflect

Table 1   Multiple use zoning table for the Solent region

Activity	General use GU	Recreation zone RE	Harbour zone HZ	Refuge zone RF	Sanctuary zone SA	Protected zone PZ
Fisheries						
Potting	Yes	Limited	Limited	Limited	No	No
Beam trawling	Yes	Limited	Limited	Limited	No	No
Dredging	Yes	Limited	Limited	Limited	No	No
Recreation						
Waterskiing	Yes	Yes	Limited	Limited	Limited	No
Jet-skiing	Yes	Yes	Limited	Limited	Limited	No
Sub-aqua	Yes	Yes	Limited	Limited	Limited	No
Windsurfing	Yes	Yes	Limited	Limited	Limited	No
Sailing	Yes	Yes	Yes	Yes	Yes	Limited
Industry						
Aggregate extraction	Yes	Yes	Yes	Yes	Yes	No
Dredge spoil disposal	Yes	Yes	Yes	Yes	Yes	No
Oil and gas extraction	Yes	Yes	Yes	Yes	Yes	Limited
Research	Yes	Yes	Yes	Yes	Yes	Permit
Military	Yes	Yes	Yes	Yes	Yes	Yes

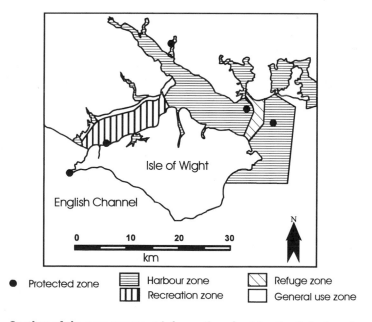

Figure 2   Section of the management information chart for the Solent region

the levels of protection which different groups may require. On the positive side, the MIC gives a rapid, easily interpreted, introduction to the management arrangements for the area and translates these into levels of environmental protection. The alternative would be to read 42 pieces of legislation and, even then, the outcome is likely to be a good understanding of how the legislation relates to one particular activity, such as fisheries, rather than getting a clear picture of how they all interrelate. Benefits of this approach are that it is multi-disciplinary and presents relatively complex management information in an accessible and easily understood format. There are also opportunities to improve integrated planning and management at the coast. One simple example is that by providing information on the boundaries of existing zones, managers considering new controls could quickly become aware of the possibilities of combining their efforts, simplifying arrangements and developing a more integrated system of management. There is no need for any legislative framework to carry out such analyses and the modest costs involved mean that it would be possible to prepare a full set of charts for UK waters relatively rapidly.

In conclusion, the MIC summarises the area based statutes which control activities in the region, and the level of environmental protection they provide, on a single sheet of paper. By mapping the spatial coverage of the management arrangements, it shows where and how those planning or managing sea use might combine their actions. This is a practical way to improve integration. The format provides an easily understood way of communicating key environmental management information to interested parties. The trial confirmed that while this approach is not a replacement for management plans and legal provisions for coastal management, it can contribute to better integration of CZM policies and improve understanding of the management arrangements for an area of sea.

Acknowledgements

We would like to thank the many individuals and organisations who supported this research. Particular thanks are due to Alan Inder and Tim Badman of Hampshire County Council, Richard Bushell (Ministry of Agriculture, Food and Fisheries), Mark Whitley (Southern Sea Fisheries Committee), Laurence Talks (National Rivers Authority) and English Nature staff in the headquarters and regional offices, all of whom gave their time, interest, and expertise to the study.

References

English Nature. 1994a. *Lundy Marine Nature Reserve Zoning Scheme*. English Nature, Peterborough, UK.

English Nature. 1994b. *Natural Areas. Strategy for the 1990s*. English Nature, Peterborough, UK.

Kenchington, R.A. 1990. *Managing Marine Environments*. Taylor & Francis, London, UK. 248 pp.

Ministry of the Environment (The National Forest & Nature Agency). 1993. *The Wadden Sea. Portrait of a Wetland*. Ministry of Environment, Esbjerg, Denmark.

Studies in European Coastal Management. Jones, Healy and Williams (eds)
1996, Samara Publishing Limited, Cardigan. ISBN 1 873692 07 2

A Management Plan for the Southern Albanian Coast

A. Bako

Urban Planning Institute, Tirana, Albania

Abstract: The new political system which operates in Albania, coupled to the high environmental quality of the Albanian coastal zone, necessitates the development of a new environmental approach to coastal planning. The proposals for planning and management contained in the Coastal Zone Management (CZM) Plan for the southern Albanian coast can provide sustainable development and environmental protection in this area. The main objectives of this plan are to promote the conservation of biodiversity and socio-cultural heritage, to promote tourism and other development activities in selected areas and to strengthen institutional arrangements for the implementation of CZM policies. This paper provides an overview of CZM planning for the southern Albanian coast within the context of the national CZM Plan.

Introduction

The coast of Albania borders the Adriatic and Ionian seas and for the purposes of coastal management planning may be divided into three regions, north, central and south (Figure 1 - inset). The southern Albanian coast (Ionian coast) is *c.* 170 km long, extending from the Karaburun Peninsula in the north to Cape Stillo in the south. In the northern part of this area rocky, steeply sloping shores prevail. The central portion is characterised by shingle and sandy beaches inter-spersed with rocky shoreline, while the southernmost part of the coast exhibits low-angle coastal plains, including the Butrinti Lagoon. Several sites of high nature conservation value occur on the Ionian coast, including the Llogara National Park (Karaburun Peninsula), Kakome Bay, Stillo Bay and Butrinti Lagoon (Figure 1). In addition, sites of cultural and archaeological importance which demonstrate the ancient civilisation of Albania are to be found at Gjipeu Canyon, Vuno and Dhermi villages, Butrint and Orikum as well as on the Karaburun Peninsula. The area has a generally high environmental quality and has not been significantly affected by modern development activities. This paper concentrates on the southernmost part of the Albanian coast.

Administration

The landward boundary of the study area is defined by a north-south trending mountain range which separates the coastal plain from the hinterland. There are two administrative units in this area; Himara commune and Saranda district. They share a total population of *c.* 60,000 inhabitants and approximately 65% of the population is rural. Since 1990, there has been considerable emigration from the area for political reasons, causing a general decline in population. Local administrative

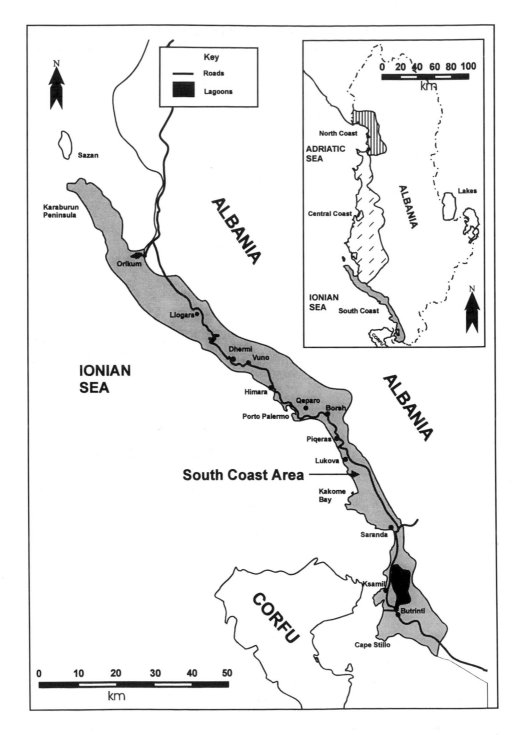

Figure 1 Inset map of the Albanian coast showing the location of the northern, central and southern regions and larger scale map of the southern coastal area showing the location of sites referred to in the text

divisions are used for economic, demographic and institutional functions. Regional administrative divisions are responsible for infrastructural issues. For the purpose of natural resource analysis and environmental issues an ecosystem approach is employed.

Coastal landuse and infrastructure

Agriculture and aquaculture, fisheries and industry are pursued in the study area, with agriculture being most significant. Cultivation of olives, citrus, maize and vegetables is common, as well as livestock production. Mountainous areas are mainly occupied by pastures and forestry, while Mediterranean maquis, composed of pine and oak, is common close to the coast. Marine fishery activities are common in the area, but the main concentration occurs at the port of Saranda.

Infrastructural problems limit economic activity. Water and sewage facilities are inadequate due to lack of investment and maintenance. Waste is frequently discharged untreated into the sea. Port facilities are present at Saranda, Porto Palermo and Himara. A military airport, with potential for civilian development, occurs close to Saranda. The coast is serviced by a single road which runs roughly parallel to the shoreline but there are no rail facilities.

Human activities which endanger the quality of the coastal zone include the discharge of untreated waste waters into the sea, agricultural runoff, illegal fishing and hunting and the unlawful construction of buildings.

The need for a coastal management plan

Although intense human activity has not yet reached the southern Ionian coast, the anticipated future development of this area may have a considerable impact on the physical, biological and socio-economic resources of the coastal environment. Development proposals for some coastal areas are already in existence. The development of tourism, as well as biodiversity and heritage conservation, would be best achieved through a Coastal Zone Management (CZM) Plan. Such a plan may provide a framework to assist policy and decision makers and national and local authorities involved in coastal development planning. It would ensure the protection of natural values, the wise use of resources, sensible development activities with sustainable use of the environment and help avoid conflicts between conservation and development.

Coastal zone management planning in Albania

Plans for the northern and southern areas of the Albanian coast are being developed and implemented by the Albanian government in co-operation with the World Bank. The plan for the central coastal area is being developed in co-operation with the United Nations Environment Programme (UNEP) and the Mediterranean Action Plan (MAP). The main aims of the CZM Plan for the southern coastal area may be summarised as follows.

The conservation of biodiversity

Many of the sites within the study area are of considerable importance for nature conservation. An example occurs at the Karaburun Peninsula where a monk seal (*Monachus monachus*) colony of 5–10 individuals has been recorded; a further example is Llogara National Park which has a distinctive flora and fauna linked to three separate climatic zones (Mediterranean field, hill and mountainous climates) which occur within a relatively small geographical area. Kakome Bay, Stillo Bay and the Butrinti Lagoon are also important in a biodiversity context. Other sites such as the Orikumi lagoon, Porto Palermo and Ksamil Bay are of secondary importance for nature conservation as a result of human impacts. Nevertheless, such sites are still significant because there is much scope for ecosystem rehabilitation.

The CZM Plan needs to encourage the conservation and development of this aspect of the coastal resource. One important task concerns the preparation of an appropriate biodiversity strategy to focus both on the protection of the most environmentally sensitive areas and the rehabilitation of areas damaged by human activity.

Cultural, historical and archaeological conservation and tourism development

A very significant part of Albania's cultural heritage is represented by sites within the study area. These sites require restoration and conservation and have the potential to serve as a major attraction for tourists. Along with the added benefits of a relatively unspoiled coastal environment, the use of the cultural, historical and archaeological resource of the coastal area urgently needs careful planning through the agency of a CZM Plan.

Infrastructure

Future developments within the coastal zone would firstly require extensive improvements to the infrastructure of the area. Transportation and municipal service infrastructure are key areas in need of improvement, not least because this will help to reduce negative impacts on the environment such as pollution. A good example of the transportation problem concerns the scenic road connecting the three coastal regions of Albania which is in urgent need of improvement. Other infrastructure issues concern the need for improved airport, seaport and marina facilities. The location and development of such services requires careful planning to minimise impacts and prevent habitat loss.

Institutional strengthening

The legal framework within Albania is still under review and development following the democratic changes which took place in 1991 (Bako, 1995). This has resulted in the absence of executive administrative bodies at national and local level. The CZM Plan will provide guidelines for institutional arrangements. These will help clarify the duties of decision makers and link their activities to environmental conservation. The CZM Plan will need to take into account the nature of an administrative framework for its own implementation, as well as identifying any proposed policies which can be put in place under existing laws.

Conclusions

The sustainable development of the study area and the Albanian coast in general, requires careful conservation and development planning. An holistic approach to the coast is needed with appropriate administrative frameworks for coastal management. This approach includes the need to identify environmentally sensitive areas and sites of nature conservation interest. Some sites, such as Sazan Island, Karaburun Peninsula, Kakome Bay, Stillo Bay and Butrinti Lagoon are of prime importance. Others, including Orikumi Lagoon, Porto Palermo and Ksamili Bay are worthy of improvement and rehabilitation. Management strategies need to take into account the varied requirements of sites of different coastal resource value. Future coastal development needs to be restricted to less sensitive areas, thereby protecting sites of nature conservation and socio-cultural value. The adoption of this policy will bring substantial benefits to the Albanian coast, both now and in the future.

References

Bako, A. 1995. Coastal conservation in Albania. In: *Coastal Management and Habitat Conservation*. Eds: Salman, A.H.P.M., Berends, H. & Bonazountas, M. European Union for Coastal Conservation, Leiden, The Netherlands. pp. 39-44.

Studies in European Coastal Management. Jones, Healy and Williams (eds)
1996, Samara Publishing Limited, Cardigan. ISBN 1 873692 07 2

Factors Influencing the Development of the Recreation and Tourism Industry on the Coastline of Kaliningrad Region

H. Kropinova & V. Litvin

Kaliningrad University, Kaliningrad, Russian Federation

Abstract: The development of the tourism and recreation industry on the coast of Kaliningrad is viewed as an urgent economic priority. Although the climate favours the development of the industry, many other factors have retarded its growth. Limited accommodation and a generally inadequate tourism infrastructure constitute major problems and are being addressed by a programme of construction and refurbishment. Poor organisation has also led to the inadequate management of the regions' natural resources. While some beaches are subject to considerable visitor pressure, others are underused or are physically unsuitable for tourism and recreational use because of their narrow width. Accordingly, sand nourishment is already being used to create wider sandy beaches. Although the utilisation of un-developed areas for tourism may appear economically attractive, careful management will be required to balance economic gain against the loss of natural coastal habitats.

Introduction

The utilisation of the oceanic and coastal resource for recreation and tourism is technologically simple, profitable and causes the least damage in ecological terms when compared to other forms of use (Eltzina & Litvin, 1993). It is for these reasons that the development of tourism and recreation on the coast of Kaliningrad is regarded as a socio–economic priority.

In spite of the many factors favouring tourism and recreation on the Kaliningrad coastline, including numerous sandy beaches and an equable climate, the development of this resource has been limited by:

a) the small size of the region (15,100 km^2), of which only 15% can be used for recreational purposes;

b) the vulnerability of the area, especially the spit complexes, to natural processes such as wave overwash; and

c) the deficient level of organisation in relation to the management of natural resources.

A range of other factors also limit the development of the tourism and recreation industry in the region. This paper will review these and will also discuss ways in which the growth of the industry can be promoted in the future.

Factors influencing the development of tourism and recreation in the region

The coastline of Kaliningrad fringes the southeastern part of the Baltic Sea and extends over a distance of 157 km. This coastline encompasses the northern part of the Vistula Spit, the western and northern sections of the Sambian Peninsula and the southern section of the Curonian Spit. Cliffs dominate the coast of the Sambian Peninsula and sand beaches of various widths occur between the numerous cliffed headlands (Table 1). These contrast sharply with the dune backed beaches of the Kaliningrad coast spit formations.

In comparison to other Russian and Baltic coast resorts, the climate of the region is favourable. The warmest month is July with a mean temperature of 17°C for Svetlogorsk and winter temperatures are some 4-8°C higher than on the coast of the Gulf of Finland. The average period of sunshine is 1,830 hours/yr, although in 1968 a peak of 2,200 hours was recorded.

These warm and sunny conditions favour sun-bathing and also favour bathing in the sea from mid-June until mid-September. This length of season is similar to that observed in Poland and Germany, but is much longer than the sea bathing period for Estonia and St. Petersburg (Russia). In spite of this, heated saltwater swimming pools are still provided.

The presence of sandy beaches, warm sea water and a mild and sunny climate are all factors which have favoured the development of the area as a centre for tourism, recreation and health care (convalescence). This is reflected by the presence of numerous well established resorts along the northern coast of the Sambian Peninsula, including Zelenogradsk, Pionerski, Svetlogorsk, Otradnoye and Primorie (Figure 1). In contrast, the beaches of the western coast of the peninsula are mainly used by local inhabitants, while little development has occurred along the Curonian Spit. The beaches of the Vistula Spit in particular are very infrequently used (Boldyrev, 1981; Anon. 1988; Kucheryavy & Fyodorov, 1989).

Accommodation and transport infrastructure

Economic and ecological parameters are the main limiting factors concerning tourism, essentially relating to health resort capacities and nature conservation respectively. As an example, during the summer only 20,000 convalescent home places are available in the area but this falls to 8,000 during the winter. Another 21 convalescent homes would allow 3,300 people to be treated simultaneously, thus giving rise to 45-50,000 additional visitors per year. This additional capacity could be provided through the construction of new and the restoration of existing structures, many of which pre-date World War II and are of historic or architectural interest. Such a major programme of work should also be accompanied by general improvements to the healthcare, industrial and socio-cultural infrastructure.

The growth of family tourism is also being promoted in the region. Currently, there are plans to increase the capacity of hostels and boarding houses to over 20,000 places along the northern and western coasts of the Sambian Peninsula. Furthermore, the construction of tourist villages, each composed of *c.* 300 cottages, has been proposed for a number of coastal locations including Morskoe (on the Curonian Spit), Kulikovo and Primorie. Another way of increasing tourism is to encourage more visitors during off-peak periods through competitive pricing arrangements. Currently very few people visit the area during the autumn, winter or early spring periods.

The location of the area on the Baltic coast offers many opportunities for linking land-based tourism to the international sea routes connecting the countries of Northern Europe. In order to achieve this it will be necessary to undertake improvements to the infrastructure of seaports, organise the sea links and provide a range of tourism services for passengers. One sea route which could prove especially attractive to Russian tourists would run from Kaliningrad to St. Petersburg, with visits to the seaports of the new Baltic states, Sweden and Finland.

The impact of tourism and recreation developments on nature conservation

The development of new tourist complexes has an inevitable ecological impact. It is therefore essential to strive for a compromise between development and conservation in order to preserve the essential quality of the coastal resource. Numerous organisations are involved in this process and their activities are co-ordinated by the Administration for Architecture and Town Construction for the Kaliningrad Region. At the current time, the general plan for the coastal recreation district is reaching an advanced state of preparation. Through its treatment of the coast as a distinct entity with specific problems, this plan represents a stage in the development of a Coastal Zone Management approach, but conflicts are still apparent. As an example, the general plan for the Vistula Spit area has met with opposition from ecologists defending the status of the region as a National Natural Park. Despite this, the potential of the area for development as a tourism and recreational resource is considerable. In the future it will be important to optimise such developments to conserve as wide a range as possible of natural habitats.

The visitor capacity of beaches and coastal habitats

One important natural factor which could limit the number of visitors in the future is beach capacity. The average width of beaches on the coast of Kaliningrad region is 28 m. However, beach width varies from a minimum of 5-15 m on the capes of the Sambian Peninsula, to 70 m or more at locations subject to artificial sand nourishment or where abundant sand has been made available as a by-product of the amber extraction industry (see Boldyrev, Dimitriev & Shelkov, this volume). Beach substrate can also have an important effect on visitor capacity, but this does not impose a serious limit on visitor numbers as 140.7 km of the 157 km coastline is composed of beaches with a predominantly sandy (coarse, medium and fine) substrate. This equates to a total beach area of 480 ha which is theoretically available for visitor use. If each visitor is assumed to occupy a space of $c.$ 6 m^2, and if a strip 10 m wide is left for pedestrian movement, then this allows a total theoretical visitor capacity of more than 510,000 people (Boldyrev & Kropinova, 1993). This total value is based on the assumption that all suitable beaches would support an equal density of visitors. In practice, some beaches are subject to much higher visitor pressure, while at others there are important reasons for restricting visitor numbers to a much lower level. Examples of both cases can be cited.

Table 1   The principle characteristics of beaches around the coast of Kaliningrad

Number	Beach name	Average width (m)	Width range (m)	Length (km)	Area (ha)	Substrate	Theoretical visitor capacity (x 10³)
1	Vistula	30	15 - 45	25.0	75.0	Sand	83.0
2	Baltyisk	30	25 - 50	9.0	27.0	Sand	30.0
3	Khmelevka-Obzorny	40	35 - 80	10.0	30.0	Sand	50.0
4	Yantarny	23	20 - 50	10.0	25.0	Sand	21.0
5	Bakalny	23	20 - 50	0.5	1.3	Boulder/pebble	-
		23	20 - 50	0.5	1.3	Sand/pebble	-
6	Donskoy	23	20 - 50	3.6	5.0	Sand	7.8
7	Cape Taran	6	5 - 7	0.5	3.0	Sand/pebble	-
		6	5 - 7	1.0	6.0	Boulder/pebble	-
		6	5 - 7	0.5	3.0	Sand/pebble	-
8	Primorie	70	60 - 80	3.2	22.4	Sand	32.0
9	Otradnoye	11	8 - 20	1.5	1.5	Boulder/pebble	-
		11	8 - 20	0.5	1.5	Sand/pebble	-
10	Svetlogorsk	33	30 - 45	4.5	16.0	Sand	17.0
11	Pionerski	23	20 - 45	6.4	15.0	Sand	14.0
12	Cape Gvardeysky	11	8 - 15	0.5	0.5	Sand/pebble	-
		11	8 - 15	0.5	0.5	Boulder/pebble	-
13	Cape Gvardeysky - Kulikovo	11	8 - 15	2.2	2.2	Sand/pebbles	-
14	Kulikovo - Zelenogradsk	30	25 - 45	11.0	34.0	Sand	56.7
15	Edge of the Curonian Spit	33	30 - 50	3.8	12.5	Sand	14.5
16	Lesnoye	33	30 - 50	3.8	12.5	Sand	14.5
17	Curonian	40	35 - 60	34.4	138.0	Sand	173.0
Total				**132.9**	**433.2**		**513.5**

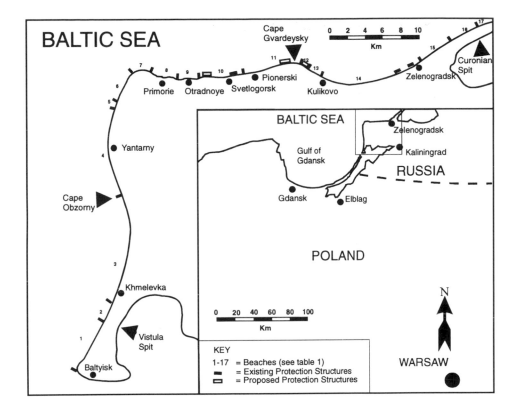

Figure 1   The coast of Kaliningrad

The beaches of Zelenogradsk and Svetlogorsk are subject to intense visitor pressure. With an area of 12 ha the 4 km long beach at Zelenogradsk should support a theoretical maximum of 13,000 visitors. Despite this 60,000 visitors have been recorded. The beach at Svetlogorsk is similar with 33,000 people using an area which should theoretically only support a maximum of 17,000 visitors. Visitor pressure at these sites could be reduced by promoting the use of suitable beaches at other sites. For example, the beaches of Kulikovo-Zelenogradsk and Primorie and the beach running between Khmelevka and Pokrovskoe have a total visitor capacity of 130,000, but are currently underused.

The beaches of the Curonian Spit have a mean width of 35 m and occupy a total area of 150 ha. According to the method for estimating visitor capacity, these beaches should be able to support a theoretical maximum of more than 180,000 people. However, due to the vulnerability of the area and its status as a National Natural Park, beach capacity should be restricted to no more than 10,000 people, including local inhabitants. Similar arguments apply to the beaches of the Vistula Spit. With a total area of 75 ha this beach system could support a theoretical maximum of more than 80,000 people, but a limit of 10,000 is recommended in order to safeguard its unique character.

When these are taken into account, the total visitor capacity of beaches in the Kaliningrad Region is reduced from more than 510,000 to 360,000.

Another factor which influences visitor numbers is the carrying capacity of land backing the inter-tidal zone. In this region, the maximum permissible number of visitors is considered to be 50 people/ha.

Areas with considerable potential for tourism and recreation development occur on the western coast of the Sambian Peninsula to the south of Yantarny. However, the promotion of access to this area would need to be accompanied by measures such as path construction and the protection of valuable natural features such as coastal woodland. Opportunities for development also occur on the northern coast of the peninsula. Here beach nourishment programmes are being planned to increase beach width by using 0.3-0.5 million m³/year of sand overburden sediment derived from the amber mines at Yantarny (see also Boldyrev, Dimitriev & Shelkov, this volume). Other sediment sources such as the seabed and land-based quarries may also be used, whilst substantial sources of sediment could come from the reconstruction of the port of Pionerski (Boldyrev, 1981).

Conclusion

The development of the Kaliningrad Region as an international resort of the Baltic is feasible, but will depend on a range of factors. Improved sea links with other states fringing the Baltic is one important measure, whilst a range of building and development programmes will be required to increase accommodation space and provide a varied range of resort facilities. More efficient use of the overall coastal resource is also required, with underused areas being promoted, where appropriate, to increase overall visitor capacity and reduce pressure at well known sites. All of these measures need to be carefully planned to minimise the impact on natural habitats and landscapes.

References

Anon. 1988. *The Kaliningrad Region.* Kaliningrad, Russian Federation. 280 pp.

Boldyrev, V.L. 1981. The Kaliningrad coastline from the industrial point of view. In: *The Coastline of the Sea.* Moscow, Russia. pp. 126-133.

Boldyrev, V.L. & Kropinova, H.G. 1993. Sand spits and beaches of coastline. In: *Recreational Complex of Kaliningrad Region.* Kaliningrad, Russian Federation. pp. 10-16.

Boldyrev, V.L., Dimitriev, A.E & Shelkov, I.A. 1996. New approaches to shoreline protection along the Baltic Sea coast of Kaliningrad Region. This volume.

Eltzina, G.N. & Litvin, V.M. 1993. *Resources of the World Ocean.* Kaliningrad, Russian Federation. 86 pp.

Kucheryavy, P.P. & Fyodorov, G.M. 1989. *The Geography of the Kaliningrad Region.* Kaliningrad, Russian Federation. 142 pp.

Studies in European Coastal Management. Jones, Healy and Williams (eds)
1996, Samara Publishing Limited, Cardigan. ISBN 1 873692 07 2

Green Globe: A New Approach to Environmentally Responsible Tourism

R. Hawkins

World Travel & Tourism Environment Research Centre, Oxford, UK

Abstract: The tourist and travel industry values coastal resources and utilises the coastal zone for its primary products. Degradation of the coast presents a serious threat to the industry. The World Travel & Tourism Council, together with its Environment Research Centre, is attempting to initiate improved environmental practice among travel companies and host coastal destinations for the benefit of the travel and tourism industry and the coastal zone worldwide. Sustainability of the coastal resource will only become a reality when these groups work together for mutual benefit.

Introduction

With a few exceptions, the history of coastal management illustrates a failure of formal planning and regulatory systems. A wide range of action plans and regulations have been introduced at both international and national level with the aim of reducing marine pollution and protecting the coastal zone. These have brought about some improvements in water quality, but have, for the most part, failed to control pollutants entering the seas and to protect land based systems in the coastal zone.

Threats to coastal ecosystems are posed on a number of fronts. Firstly, there is intense pressure on land to house the 60% of the world's population who live within 60 km of the coast and to provide the agricultural, fishing, industrial and service activities that they require. Secondly, there is marine pollution emanating from these urban developments, from industrial and agricultural activities inland, from marine based activities, such as oil drilling and indirectly from atmospheric fallout. Thirdly, there is increased pressure for development space for travel and tourism, the world's largest service industry. Finally, there is the threatened loss of coastal lowlands and changes to marine ecosystems if the rise in sea level predicted by the Intergovernmental Panel on Climate Change (IPCC) occurs.

The interrelationships between these activities and the interaction between inland river flows, coastal development and marine degradation are complex and not yet fully understood by the scientific community. It is, however, clear that the oceans and the coastal zone are under threat from a combination of pollution and development pressures worldwide and that in some areas, such as the Mediterranean and Baltic Seas, ecosystems are in danger of collapse. It is also clear that traditional approaches to coastal management around the world have failed to deliver results and that a new approach is necessary to tackle the problems which are evident and to protect the remaining natural areas of the coastal zone.

This paper presents information on the scale and nature of the problems facing the coastal zone and the likely implications of these for the travel and tourism industry. It will also provide details of a programme devised for the travel and tourism industry to bring about improvements in environmental quality.

Traditional approaches to coastal management in Europe

The regulatory system to protect the environment in Europe is one of the most comprehensive in the world. Regulations are supported by initiatives, such as the ten United Nations (UN) Regional Seas Programmes which involve 130 nations. The regional seas programme for the Mediterranean is known as the Mediterranean Action Programme (MAP). For this initiative, coastal nations surrounding the Mediterranean have set a series of objectives to clean up the Mediterranean Sea within ten years (1985-1995) and these objectives include:

a) measures to reduce contaminated water discharge by ships into the sea and to improve facilities at ports;

b) sewage treatment works for all urban centres with over 100,000 people, plus 'appropriate' sewage outfall pipes for treatment plants in centres with over 10,000 people;

c) environmental impact assessments for development projects such as new ports, marinas and holiday resorts;

d) improved navigation safety;

e) protection of endangered marine species;

f) reduced industrial pollution;

g) identification and protection of 100 coastal historic sites and 50 marine and coastal conservation sites;

h) more protection against forest fires and soil loss to minimise run-off into rivers; and

i) reduction of acid rain.

Despite agreement among the nations involved on the steps necessary to clean up the Mediterranean, MAP acknowledges that none of these objectives have been achieved (Pearce, 1994). According to the UN, swimming in the Mediterranean could result in ear and throat infections and serious diseases. Illness arising from such recreation is not confined to the Mediterranean alone, a recent study of boat users in Plymouth Sound (southwest England) showed that 33% of those interviewed had experienced health problems associated with their recreational use of the water resource (Newman & Foster, 1993).

Health risks have brought coastal pollution to the notice of the public. During a recent survey, 38% of a UK resident study group were so concerned about pollution that they said they would stop buying products linked to its source (Newman & Foster, 1993). In 1988, 47% of a German holiday maker study group noted that they had encountered serious environmental problems and that the main problem was pollution of seas, lakes and streams (Table 1). Furthermore, during a recent questionnaire survey in Wales, Morgan & Williams (1995) found that 60% of people rated clean sand and water as their highest priority from a list of five overall characteristics of the beach environment.

Table 1 **Environmental problems cited by German holiday makers**

Source: Newman & Foster (1993)

Year	1985 (%)	1988 (%)
Serious environmental problems cited	21.9	46.8
Problems experienced with:		
seas, lakes and streams	13.8	30.1
rubbish	7.5	17.1
dirty beaches	6.3	13.0
dead trees	6.3	12.8
degraded landscapes	4.5	13.5
noise	3.9	11.5

The travel and tourism industry

The coastal zone has been a major focus for the tourism industry and is likely to remain so for the foreseeable future. The Mediterranean Basin, for example, received more than 100 million international visitors during the peak season in 1990 and this number is expected to more than double by the year 2025. The Mediterranean currently attracts 35% of global tourist activity and most visitors (90%) stay in the European Union states of France, Portugal, Spain, Italy and Greece. The coastal zone in the northern European countries, such as the UK, Germany and The Netherlands, is also important for domestic tourism. Most visitors are accommodated in close proximity to the coast. According to the findings of the World Travel & Tourism Council (WTTC, 1995) many countries now rely heavily on tourism as a source of income and employment; for example in 1995 tourism accounted for 12.3% of the UK Gross Domestic Product (GDP). Tourism in turn relies on the quality of the environment, but the coast is being transformed by urban, industrial, agricultural and recreational pressures which threaten the future of the tourism industry.

Degradation of the coast has been most severe in the Mediterranean, but evidence for coastal damage is found throughout Europe. Degradation includes loss of landscapes and habitats, shortages of fresh water in some areas, discharge of waste water without treatment, routine spills of hydrocarbons from shipping and extractive industries, increased incidence of algal blooms (or red tides) and pollutants in fish and shell fish. By the late 1980s it was apparent to some European tour operators that the long term viability of the coastal zone for tourism could be threatened by environmental degradation. The challenge was to find new approaches to coastal management which would guarantee business profitability, long term resort viability and also have the potential to retrofit old resorts, work with other industrial sectors to prevent pollution and ensure that new resorts did not repeat mistakes of the past.

Green Globe: A new approach to environmental management in the travel and tourism industry

The WTTC is a coalition of 70 travel and tourism companies whose goals are to convince governments of the economic and strategic importance of travel and tourism, to promote environmentally compatible development and to eliminate barriers to the growth of the industry. In 1992, the WTTC took up the challenge to find new ways to make all travel and tourism environmentally responsible. It had already incorporated environmental quality into its own mission statement in 1991 by its commitment to the promotion of 'environmentally compatible growth'. This commitment was supported by the development of comprehensive environmental guidelines providing advice on issues such as corporate commitment and environmental improvement. WTTC members were invited to make a signed commitment to use these guidelines in their business decisions.

WTTC then established a World Travel & Tourism Environment Research Centre (WTTERC) at Oxford Brookes University. Charged with becoming a centre of excellence for travel and tourism and the environment, WTTERC began building up a database tracking the initiatives that leading travel companies and host destinations had taken to improve environmental performance. In this way, the components of good environmental practice could be learnt and communicated industry-wide.

Using the experience gained in these activities, WTTC developed 'Green Globe', a comprehensive environmental management and awareness programme to help travel and tourism companies to protect the environments on which their products depend. In joining Green Globe, member organisations make a commitment to progressively improve their environmental performance. The current status of their environmental programme is assessed as they join and practical advice which meets their specific needs is provided through the Green Globe Office in London. Progress is tracked through a comprehensive database system enabling further targeted advice to be provided as required. The path that companies take within the Green Globe programme is illustrated in Figure 1.

This programme provides a comprehensive approach to environmental management across the travel and tourism industry and has been designed to address key issues identified at tourism destinations. The first step for those companies which have as yet taken little action to improve their environmental performance, is the development of an environmental management system. This starts with the completion of simple checklists which help companies to assess the full environmental impact of their business operation and moves on to offer advice on identifying areas for improvement, motivating staff and establishing a policy or mission statement.

Once a management structure is in place, the most significant contribution that companies can make to improving coastal zone environmental quality is to reduce energy use, waste production, water consumption and waste water production. Companies are provided with sector specific, targeted guidance through a series of simple practical management guidelines. This guidance will help them to achieve the greatest environmental benefits and cost savings in these areas.

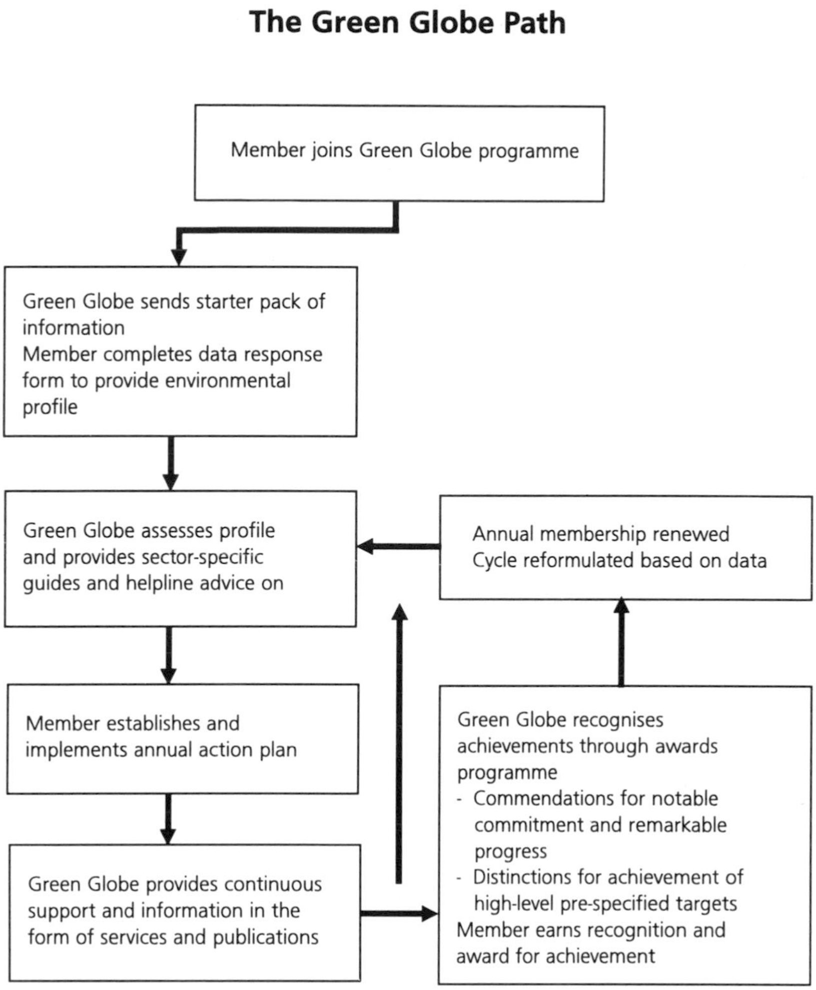

The Green Globe Path

```
        ┌─────────────────────────────────────────┐
        │   Member joins Green Globe programme     │
        └─────────────────────────────────────────┘

┌──────────────────────────────────┐
│ Green Globe sends starter pack of │
│ information                       │
│ Member completes data response    │
│ form to provide environmental     │
│ profile                           │
└──────────────────────────────────┘

┌──────────────────────────────┐        ┌──────────────────────────────┐
│ Green Globe assesses profile  │◄───────│ Annual membership renewed    │
│ and provides sector-specific  │        │ Cycle reformulated based on  │
│ guides and helpline advice on │        │ data                         │
└──────────────────────────────┘        └──────────────────────────────┘

┌──────────────────────────────┐        ┌──────────────────────────────┐
│ Member establishes and        │        │ Green Globe recognises        │
│ implements annual action plan │        │ achievements through awards   │
└──────────────────────────────┘        │ programme                     │
                                         │ - Commendations for notable   │
┌──────────────────────────────┐        │   commitment and remarkable   │
│ Green Globe provides continuous│       │   progress                    │
│ support and information in the │──────►│ - Distinctions for achievement│
│ form of services and publications│     │   of high-level pre-specified │
└──────────────────────────────┘        │   targets                     │
                                         │ Member earns recognition and  │
                                         │ award for achievement         │
                                         └──────────────────────────────┘
```

Figure 1   **The path taken by travel and tourism companies upon joining the Green Globe programme**

The savings which are achieved will be continuous and often increase in the face of more stringent environmental regulations and the use of economic instruments by governments. Programmes to manage water use and waste water production will bring additional benefit as environmental costs rise. German companies which adopt water management programmes, for example, will benefit as prices charged for effluent treatment are predicted to rise by 28% before the end of the century. Savings made at this stage of the programme can be used to finance further environmental improvements. Such programmes may, for example, include guidance on working with suppliers to purchase environmentally benign products, or to work with and manage visitors to enhance positive impacts.

Through its publications and award programmes, Green Globe will challenge travel companies and destination managers to improve environmental performance. Guidance is being developed to address changing company needs and Green Globe offers a help line for companies with specific environmental problems which are not addressed in the guidelines or fact sheets. If companies require site or region specific assistance which cannot be provided directly from the Green Globe team, it is provided through a network of advisers based around the world and co-ordinated by the international tourism and conservation group Green Flag International.

Working through Green Globe, travel and tourism companies have an opportunity to help to protect the coastal zone. The potential of travel and tourism to protect the environment will not, however, be realised by the industry in isolation. Governments have a fundamental role to play in establishing a baseline from which companies can take action and through the provision of incentives where appropriate. Other industries have a role to play in ensuring that their activities do not damage the environment upon which the tourism industry depends and communities have a role to play in protecting the environment on which their livelihood depends.

Conclusions

Sustainability will only become a reality when all parties work together for mutual benefit. There are only isolated examples of truly mutual programmes involving the travel and tourism industry and host destinations. The next step for WTTERC is the development of a series of pilot programmes in the coastal zone which establish and examine the development of effective and self perpetuating partnerships which have long term sustainability as their goal. The messages learnt from these pilot programmes will be developed as further advice within the Green Globe programme and should help to make travel and tourism not only the worlds largest, but also the worlds most environmentally responsible and influential service industry.

References

Morgan, R. & Williams, A.T. 1995. Socio-demographic parameters and user priorities at Gower beaches, Wales, UK. In: *Directions in European Coastal Management*. Eds: Healy, M.G. & Doody, J.P. Samara Publishing Limited, Cardigan, Wales, UK. pp. 83-90.

Newman, O. & Foster, A. 1993. *European Environment Statistics Handbook*. Gale Research International, Ipswich, UK. 151 pp.

Pearce, F. 1994. Dead in the water. *New Scientist*, 1963:29.

World Travel & Tourism Council. 1995. *United Kingdom Travel & Tourism*. WTTC, Brussels.

Shoreline Management

Studies in European Coastal Management. Jones, Healy and Williams (eds)
1996, Samara Publishing Limited, Cardigan. ISBN 1 873692 07 2

The Sustainable Use of Coasts: Monitoring, Modelling and Management

J. Pethick

Coastal Research Unit, Department of Geography, University of Cambridge, UK

Abstract: Shoreline management, whether for nature conservation or more directly for socio-economic aims, puts coastal defence as its primary objective. In this paper it is argued that Coastal Zone Management (CZM) and Shoreline Management, as a subset of CZM, should share the same ultimate objectives - defined by many authorities as Sustainable Use. The objectives both strategic and pragmatic which follow from such an aim may appear to conflict with a reading of many of the texts for international and national CZM or designated area management which emphasise stability rather than sustainability - with the result that coastal defence is seen not merely as a means to an end but as an end in itself.

Sustainable use of the coast, however, demands both spatial and temporal flexibility of its component systems and management for change must therefore be the primary objective. Response of the natural system to independent forcing factors must be encouraged under this objective, whether such forces are natural or anthropogenic.

In achieving such an objective the concept of shoreline vulnerability may prove useful. This provides a measure of the temporal variability which may be expected in landform components of the shoreline system, so allowing management to provide more realistic objectives for long term sustainability in response to both natural and artificial forces.

Introduction

Shoreline management is one aspect of environmental management which appears to have avoided much of the philosophical breast beating of the past decade. In England, shoreline management is the responsibility of the Ministry of Agriculture, Fisheries and Food (MAFF) - a responsibility which the Ministry delegates to its operating authorities: local maritime district councils on high, potentially eroding, coasts and the National Rivers Authority for low, potentially flooding coasts. These authorities, while they have a duty to consider the nature conservation implications of their management activities, nevertheless regard it as their primary duty to reduce risks to people and property (MAFF & Welsh Office, 1993). Thus, although shoreline management may be seen as a sub-set of Coastal Zone Management (CZM) it possesses a very different set of aims and objectives. The aim of CZM, as set out, for example, in the UK by the Department of Environment (DoE) in its strategy for the management of the coast (DoE & Welsh Office, 1993), is to achieve sustainable use of the coastal environment, while that of shoreline management is to achieve shoreline stability. Although the distinction between these two aims may appear slight, nevertheless it is argued here that it is in fact fundamental.

Sustainable use of the coast

The most familiar of the many interpretations of sustainable use is the so-called Brundtland definition (WCED, 1987):

> Sustainable development that meets the needs of the present without compromising the ability of future generations to meet their own needs.

Two of the major issues to which such a definition has given rise are, first, the confusion it engenders between the concepts of sustainable and permanent and, second, the implication that the needs of the present generation may indeed be met as a right.

Far from implying permanence it can be argued that the primary objective of a sustainable use policy must be management for change. It is only when the natural system is allowed time and space to develop naturally that true sustainability will be engendered. This concept has become known as **Strong Sustainability** while the alternative view, that of merely preserving our existing capital assets, is referred to as **Weak Sustainability** (Pearce & Warford, 1993; O'Riordan, 1995; Turner, 1993).

- **Strong Sustainability** in which the ecosystem is allowed to function in as natural a manner as possible both for functional and ethical reasons.
- **Weak Sustainability** in which the overall stock of natural assets are preserved, often requiring substitutions to be made.

The tendency, especially by shoreline managers, to adopt the former, weak sustainability definition rather than the latter may be, in some measure, attributable to a reading of the various documents providing guidance or outlining legislation for coastal areas. In many cases temporal change at the coast is seen as the converse of sustainable use and, moreover, such change is often explicitly defined as erosion or deposition (sometimes even referred to as degradation). For example, Chapter 17 of the Agenda 21 (UNCED, 1992) states that:

> Para 17.3 Current approaches to the management of marine and coastal resources have not always proved capable of achieving sustainable development and coastal resources and the coastal environment are rapidly being *degraded and eroded* in many parts of the world.

> Para 17.29 As concerns physical destruction of coastal and marine areas...priority action should include control and *prevention of coastal erosion and siltation* due to anthropogenic factors.

The Ramsar Convention includes the following enjoinder to guard against change (Article 3:2 of the Convention on Wetlands of International Importance especially as Waterfowl Habitat. (Ramsar) 1971):

> Each contracting party shall arrange to be informed at the earliest possible time if the ecological character of any wetland in its territory has changed, is changing or is likely to change as the result of technological developments, pollution or other human interference.

These statements raise two major issues: first erosion and siltation should be seen not as degradation, but as a natural response to external changes leading to a steady state which should be encouraged by managers who wish to achieve strong sustainability. Second, these changes to the coastal system may, as acknowledged in the excerpts given above, be due to anthropogenic causes as well as natural, but the response of the system is identical in both cases. Distinguishing between natural and anthropogenic causation is an academic and usually futile occupation; indeed, it may be suggested that attempting to stifle the response of a natural system to changes which we have introduced in the first place actually compounds the felony. This emphasises the negative impacts of human intervention without allowing the system time to adjust to such modification.

Anthropogenic inputs

Instead of continuing this anthropophobic attitude, we should see ourselves as an integral part of the coastal system and that changes which we introduce in order to maintain our own position within it are perfectly acceptable as long as we allow the system the time, the space and the materials (usually in the form of sediments) to be able to adjust to such changes. Thus, for example, introduction of a hard coastal defence in order to protect an important asset may lead to the reshaping of adjacent shorelines; a process which may take several decades to achieve but will eventually result in a new, stable, coastal morphology into which the artificial element has been incorporated. Examples of such incorporation include many of the 18th century fishing harbours around the UK coast which now appear to be moulded into their coastline but which, initially, presented a major disruption to natural processes.

This *laissez faire* approach to the development of strong sustainability is appealing, but it may involve the loss of existing infrastructure, natural, industrial or urban, which we possess on adjacent coastlines and which may be threatened by erosion, deposition, flooding or other processes set in motion by the introduced change. Such losses may be considered unacceptable, but, in order to assess whether or not to proceed with coastal defence construction we should first be able to predict the medium to long term effects of any modifications which we make to the natural system. Unfortunately we do not, at present, possess such predictive power for the medium to long term development of coastal morphology. A strong sustainable coastal system is, therefore, one which we cannot design since we are unable to predict its optimum morphology and, since we are forced to continue to make adjustments to the coastal system in order that we may meet our own needs, it appears that we are thrown back to the protectionist philosophy of weak sustainability.

Monitoring and sustainable use

There is, however, a middle road which we may adopt, allowing us to move towards strong sustainable coastal systems which function with a mixed input of anthro-pogenic and natural inputs. Careful monitoring of the coastal system can be used to fine tune our inputs so that we avoid progressive deterioration of natural and human assets but at the same time allow the system to change in response to variations in inputs. This implies that, while we may not be able to predict or design sustainable coastal systems, we can recognise an unsustainable system when we see one and take appropriate remedial action. This middle road considers the attainment of sustainable coastal systems as a 'process' not as a 'plan' - a process which manages change in the coastal system.

The recognition of an unsustainable coastal system is, however, more complex than may at first be supposed. Deterioration cannot be equated simply with erosion as suggested in Agenda 21; the erosion of a sand dune or saltmarsh may be part of the internal functioning of the wider coastal system, allowing it to adjust to changes in energy or sediment caused by natural or anthropogenic factors. On the other hand, the progressive loss of coastal landforms such as dunes, marshes or mudflats may be seen as deterioration in that the resulting system is less capable of responding to imposed changes. The problem facing coastal managers is to be able to distinguish between progressive deterioration and system adjustments to changing inputs.

Temporal change in coastal systems

Natural coastal systems have to respond to constantly changing environmental conditions imposed by such factors as tidal cycles, wave action or biological seasonality. Most of these low level, quasi-continuous changes in the environment do not result in morphological changes in the coast since their energy levels lie below the threshold strength of the coastal form. In most cases this threshold coastal strength has developed as a direct response to such environmental inputs - as in the depositional mudflat environment, for example - so that a short term balance is achieved between environmental inputs and system response. Infrequent but high energy events such as extreme storms may, however, exceed this threshold strength and cause changes in the coastal morphology. If such events were to persist, such change would represent the natural development towards a sustainable form; but, since they are relatively rare, they are separated by periods of low energy during which the coast can recover from the effects of the extreme event. This period of recovery, often referred to as the relaxation time of the system, is crucial to the long term sustainability of the coast, since, if insufficient time elapses for recovery between threshold events, the coast will suffer progressive change. The ratio between relaxation time and the return interval for threshold events, referred to here as the Vulnerability Index, provides an important measure of the manner in which coastal landforms respond to imposed changes and can allow assessment of the potential for long term progressive change in the system.

A coastal vulnerability index

Despite the crucial importance of the assessment of change in coastal systems, no extensive research has been undertaken into the response of these landforms to imposed change. Table 1 sets out a preliminary data set showing some estimates of the return intervals and corresponding relaxation times of a range of coastal forms. The ratio between return interval and relaxation time, the vulnerability index, provides an indication of the sensitivity of the landform to slight changes in its environment. Saltmarshes, for example, were shown by Pethick (1992) to

Table 1   Shoreline vulnerability index = event frequency/relaxation time

Shoreline	Event frequency	Relaxation time	Vulnerability index
Cliff shores	250,000 years	>250,000 years	<1
Sand dunes	10 years	5 years	2
Mudflats	2 years	1 year	2
Spits	1,000 years	200 years	5
Saltmarshes	30 years	5 years	6
Estuaries	100,000 years	10,000 years	10
Shingle ridges	1 year	1 month	12
Beaches	4 months	1 week	16

suffer surface erosion under vegetation cover only during rare events when a high tide combined with storm wave conditions. The return interval for such an event was calculated at >30 years, but the marsh recovered from the erosion by rapid deposition in less than 5 years. The resultant vulnerability index (6.0) suggests that an increase in the return interval of such storm events or a decrease in the deposition rate would not result in progressive deterioration of the marsh system which may thus be described as robust.

On the other hand, Table 1 shows that sand dunes, located in high energy environments and with relatively slow recovery time, have a vulnerability index approaching 1.0. This implies that even a slight random variation in the return interval of erosive wave events could mean that re-erosion of the foredune ridge may occur before the system has fully recovered from previous erosive events. However, the opposite is also true, a slight increase in the return interval of threshold events can allow the sand dune system to prograde seaward. This sensitivity of the sand dune system may explain why they are commonly observed with eroding seaward margins and yet with extensive dune ridges landwards.

Sand dune vulnerability

The type of information shown in Table 1 could be used as the basis for interpretation of data bases assembled as part of a monitoring programme from remote, terrestrial or marine sources. Simple observation of the temporal variability of coastal landforms is insufficient to allow assessment of long term deterioration; instead, temporal changes in each landform must be assessed in conjunction with its expected behaviour as summarised in the vulnerability index. For example, based on the discussion given above, observation of erosion of the foredune ridge in a sand dune system need not be taken as an indication of long term deterioration of the system. The sensitivity of sand dunes to slight random changes in environmental conditions means that such change is to be expected and may continue for several years before a period of accretion ensues.

Saltmarsh vulnerability

Observations of the continued erosion of a saltmarsh should be taken much more seriously than those of a sand dune system since the high vulnerability index of this landform implies that only relatively massive changes in the return interval of erosive events, or the ability of the marsh to recover from such events, can result in progressive loss of the marsh surface. Determining whether observations of erosion are progressive or merely part of a periodic adjustment to storm damage is, however, extremely difficult in this case due to the time intervals involved. The probability of a measurement of the areal extent of a saltmarsh falling in a period of recovery from storm damage is 1:6 (5 years in 30 years). Comparison of a single measurement taken during this period of 5 years when a reduced marsh area is present, with one taken during a previous stable period when marsh area would be at a maximum, would immediately, but mistakenly, be construed as marsh deterioration. Repeated annual observations over at least 10 years would be needed to establish a progressive change in marsh extent.

It is clear that monitoring coastal landforms such as saltmarshes requires that the periodicity of measurement is carefully adjusted to fit the vulnerability index and the relaxation time period of the landform. Monitoring programmes which do not incorporate such periodicity may result in erroneous conclusions and stimulate coastal managers to take wholly inappropriate defensive action resulting in a reduction in the ability of the marsh to respond to future events.

Beach vulnerability

Similar conclusions could be made in the case of beaches whose high vulnerability index imply a robust response to environmental changes. Recovery of beaches after storm events can take hours and thus gives an apparent permanence to this highly volatile environment. Beach erosion which is not matched by such recovery must therefore be taken as an indication of a major environmental shift which is leading to progressive deterioration. Such changes are often ascribed to anthropogenic interference in the system, particularly to sediment inhibition by coastal defence works which can significantly increase the relaxation time of adjacent beach systems.

Large scale coastal landforms

Large scale coastal landforms, such as estuaries, respond to environmental changes in the same way as do the smaller scale forms already discussed, sand dunes, beaches and saltmarshes. The difference in spatial scale, however, is reflected in the temporal scale of such adjustments and, since the smaller scale forms are nested within the larger systems, this means that a complex series of internal responses are set up.

Estuaries

Monitoring and assessment of the long term sustainability of larger coastal landforms, such as estuaries or cliffed coasts, presents much greater problems than those involved in smaller scale marshes, beaches or sand dunes. Table 1 includes estimates of relaxation time and event return interval for such large scale systems which, although speculative, may indicate some of the issues involved. Estuaries for example are a response to the major change in postglacial sealevel and in many cases, especially those estuaries with high sediment loads, appear to have achieved a form of steady state in the 10,000 years of the Holocene period. Assuming that such major changes in sealevel have taken place only in interglacial periods, the return interval for the threshold event here may be as long as 100,000 to 200,000 years. This would mean that the vulnerability index for such an estuary could be 1:10, well within the range for much smaller scale landforms and implying that slight changes in sealevel or deposition rates would have no long term progressive impact on the estuarine system.

Open coasts

At the opposite extreme, rocky, cliffed coastlines also respond to major changes in sealevel, again perhaps with an interglacial return interval but here the strength of the cliffs prevent any rapid response to such changes so that the relaxation time is extremely long. In some cases cliff erosion appeared to have continued throughout the last interglacial period, implying that the relaxation time of these large scale hard rock systems is greater than the threshold return interval and that the vulnerability index might be <1.0. If this is the case then continued erosion of cliff coasts may be expected during the present interglacial, despite the negative feedback in the system in which widening abrasion platforms reduce incident wave energy at the cliff foot.

Nested responses

In both these cases the large scale landform, estuary or open coast has, nested within it, a number of smaller scale forms such as beaches, shingle ridges, sand dunes, mudflats or marshes. Each of these smaller scale components must respond to the changes in environment which result from the adjustment of the larger unit. Thus beaches located on a cliff coast must respond to the gradual changes in sediment supply and wave energy which are imposed upon them as the cliffs recede and abrasion platforms widen. It may be that the gradual, world-wide erosion of beaches noted over the past 100 years could be a response to this large scale change in environment. If this is so then the causes of the present observed deterioration in beaches may be internal to the larger system and not to any recent changes in environmental inputs.

In the case of the estuarine system, the robustness implied by the high vulnerability index means that, once the system has recovered from its postglacial sealevel shock, further minor changes in energy or sediments will not be significant. To the small scale components of the estuary, however, these environmental changes may represent major shifts in the environmental conditions and they will respond accordingly. Thus an increase in sealevel may be expected to decrease the joint probability of wave and tide events which threaten saltmarshes and inter-tidal mudflats. The result may be a progressive decrease in inter-tidal area, such as is now being observed in southeast England. Although the change in sealevel itself may not affect the wider estuary system directly, such reduction in the inter-tidal zone may have an indirect effect in widening the estuary. In this case the response of the small scale components may be seen to drive the larger scale system: a holistic response in which the whole is greater than the sum of its parts.

Monitoring and management

It is apparent from these examples that the recognition of progressive change in coastal systems depends to a large extent on our ability to determine the periodicity of regular adjustments to threshold events for coastal landforms and only to interpret any longer periods of change as deterioration. Provision of a suitable data base, whose measurement periodicity is designed to coincide with coastal adjustments and which will therefore allow such interpretation, must be seen as a major challenge for the immediate future. The rigorous requirements of such a data base calls into question the utility of infrequent or randomly spaced observations. For this reason many types of remote sensing which depend upon cloud cover or tidal states can only be used if they are combined with more frequent and regular terrestrial observations. Such a monitoring programme, composed of a variety of different types of observation, could be devised to allow minimum cost commensurate with maximum temporal cover.

Identification of deterioration, as opposed to adjustment, is the primary goal of such monitoring and the complexities of such an assessment have been outlined in an introductory way. If progressive changes in a coastal system are suspected then identification of possible causal factors is necessary before any remedial action may be taken. A decrease in the vulnerability index of a coastal landform to below the critical level of 1.0 may be caused by one or both of two groups of factors: a decrease in return intervals of energy events or an increase in the length of the response time of the landform. Progressive change in a natural system cannot be defined as deterioration since eventually some new steady state form will be attained. Progressive change which is due to anthropogenic causes may, however, be defined as deterioration and here interference in natural coastal systems can have three effects:

1. An increase in the frequency or magnitude of energy inputs (waves or currents). This may be caused by such modifications as an increase in water depth due to dredging or channel straightening or reclamation in an estuary.

2. A decrease in the sediment supply to a coastal area caused by coastal defence of eroding cliffs, aggregate dredging, fluvial dams, or loss of sediment-trapping vegetation due to pollution.

3. A decrease in the area available for coastal landform development. This is perhaps the most prevalent cause of system deterioration and can involve such structures as reclamation banks for agriculture; coastal defences; estuarine training walls; or port and harbour constructions.

In each case such interference results in a lowering of the vulnerability index until the critical level is attained when progressive deterioration is initiated. In the case of extremely sensitive landforms, such as sand dunes, such a process may be initiated by relatively small changes in the environment. In other cases, such as beaches, major changes must be introduced before deterioration is affected. Such considerations may allow a more positive approach to the introduction of artificial elements into our coastal system. It is not necessary to attempt to return to some ideal utopian natural system in order to provide a sustainable coastal morphology. Anthropogenic changes can be introduced as long as the impacts allow the vulnerability index to remain above the critical threshold. This means that we should be more careful in our treatment of sensitive coastal areas but need to be less so in robust areas. In cases where progressive deterioration is noted then it will be necessary to adjust our impacts to a safe level, rather than remove the impact altogether.

Conclusion

This paper has attempted to provide an approach to the problems involved in the attainment of a sustainable coastal system. Anthropogenic interference in the natural system must be viewed in the same way as any other input and the system allowed or even encouraged to adjust to such inputs. The prediction of a sustainable coastal morphology over long time periods must remain an elusive goal for the present; instead, it is recommended that a programme of monitoring is initiated which allows the identification of coastal deterioration - in time for remedial action to be taken. This implies that the attainment of sustainable coastal systems is more of an ongoing process than the implementation of well defined plans. Such a programme does not entail protectionism or preservation but is intended to manage change in the coastal system so that it is allowed to adjust to the various environmental changes which occur, both natural and human. In order to determine the levels at which our interference might be sustainable a vulnerability index is proposed which would allow the sensitivity of coastal landforms to be assessed and to which monitoring results could be referred.

Coastal systems are remarkably robust and can tolerate major changes in environmental conditions before they begin to suffer long term deterioration. The task which faces us over the next few years is to provide a carefully constructed research base which is capable of defining the precise limits of such tolerances, only then will we be able to utilise our coastal resources in a sustainable manner over the long term.

References

Department of the Environment & Welsh Office. 1993. *Managing the Coast: A Review of Coastal Management Plans in England and Wales and the Powers Supporting Them.* HMSO, London, UK.

Ministry of Agriculture, Fisheries and Food & Welsh Office. 1993. *Strategy for Flood and Coastal Defence in England and Wales.* MAFF Publications, PB 1471.

O'Riordan, T. (Ed.). 1995. *Environmental Science for Environmental Management*. Longman Scientific and Technical, Wiley, New York.

Pearce, D.W. & Warford, J.J. 1993. *World Without End: Economics, Environment and Sustainable Development*. Oxford University Press, Oxford, UK.

Pethick, J.S. 1992. Saltmarsh geomorphology. In: *Saltmarshes*. Eds: Allen, J.R.L. & Pye, K. Cambridge University Press, Cambridge, UK. pp. 41-62.

Turner, R.K. 1993. Sustainability: principles and practice. In: *Sustainable Environmental Economics and Management*. Ed.: Turner, R.K. Bellhaven Press, London, UK.

United Nations Conference on Environment and Development (UNCED). 1992. *Agenda 21: Programme of Action for Sustainable Development*. United Nations Department of Public Information, New York, USA.

World Commission on Environment and Development (WCED). 1987. *Our Common Future*. Oxford University Press, Oxford, UK.

Studies in European Coastal Management. Jones, Healy and Williams (eds)
1996, Samara Publishing Limited, Cardigan. ISBN 1 873692 07 2

The Stabilisation of Coastal Sands in Iceland

S. Greipsson & H. El-Mayas

Soil Conservation Service of Iceland, Hella, Iceland

Abstract: The dynamic physical environment of Iceland has led to the formation of extensive coastal sand deposits. A large volume of sediment is brought to the coast each year by glacial meltwater rivers. Also, sediments generated by volcanic activity can lead to the rapid formation of new coastal sand plains. Civil engineering works are reducing the volume of sediment carried to the coast in glacial meltwater. Furthermore, recent work suggests that relative sealevel may be rising by between 2.4 and 5 mm/year. The combination of these two factors indicates that coastal erosion is set to become a major coastal management issue in the coming decades.

The vegetation of coastal sands is often sparse and species-poor. Careful management of coastal sand deposits centres around the use of certain plant species (mainly *Leymus arenarius* and *Lupinus nootkatensis* to stabilise the sand surface. Overgrazing of vegetated coastal dunes by livestock is prohibited. Sand stabilisation has prevented the loss of several coastal villages and farming communities through sand inundation.

Introduction

Geomorphological processes operating in Iceland determine the distribution of coastal sands (Tómasson, 1994). The sandy coastline of southern Iceland is characterised by large plains of black sand (sandur) derived from basaltic rocks. In other parts of the country coastal sand deposits are usually found in close proximity to glacial meltwater rivers. Glacier bursts (jökulhlaup) also contribute sediment to the coast. Together these processes create large unvegetated sandy plains.

This paper examines some of the processes which contribute to the dynamic nature of Iceland's sandy coasts. It also discusses the technologies employed in sand stabilisation using native plant species. Finally, a discussion of the likely effects of civil engineering works and relative sealevel rise on the deposition and movement of coastal sands in Iceland is presented.

Sand deposition

The coastal sands of Iceland originated mainly as glaciofluvial outwash deposits (Tómasson, 1986a). The expansion and contraction of glaciers over time, responding to small scale climatic changes, has produced large volumes of sediment (Björnsson, 1979) and seasonal variations in meltwater flow also generate periodic peaks in sediment transport. The combined sediment load of Icelandic rivers is approximately 50 million tonnes per annum (mtpa), of which 38 mtpa is deposited along the south coast (Tómasson, 1986a; 1994).

The river Jökulsá á Brú (Figure 1) has the greatest sediment load, transporting 9 mtpa of sediment to the coast (Tómasson, 1986a, 1994).

River sediment load is also affected by volcanic activity. With an average of one eruption every five years, volcanic activity has both direct and indirect impacts on the geomorphology of the coast (Thórarinsson & Sæmundsson, 1979). Coastal sand plains receive volcanic ash (tephra) directly through aerial fallout and also from the deposition of ash in river catchments (Tómasson, 1986a). Indirect impacts result from the eruption of volcanoes located beneath glaciers, with rapid ice melt often causing extensive coastal flooding and the deposition of large volumes of fluvial sediment in the coastal lowlands (Björnsson, 1974, 1979).

The largest sand plains are Skeiðarársandur (1,000 km^2) and Mýrdalssandur (700 km^2), both located on the south coast of Iceland (Figure 1). The sand plain at Skeiðarársandur has been created by sediment deposition from glacier bursts. These occur at *c.* 10 yearly intervals as the Grímsvötn volcano erupts beneath the Vatnajökull glacier (Björnsson, 1974) (Figure 1) and each glacial burst is estimated to add 30 million tonnes of sediment to the sand plain (Björnsson, 1979). As a result, the shoreline of central Skeiðarársandur has advanced by more than 300 m during the last century (Nummedal *et al.*, 1974).

The second largest sand plain, Mýrdalssandur, has been created by glacier bursts which occur at *c.* 50 year intervals following eruptions of the Katla volcano beneath the Mýrdalsjökull glacier (Björnsson, 1979). In 1918 a catastrophic glacier burst on Mýrdalssandur caused a meltwater flow which produced a peak flow of 200,000 tonnes per second, and 500 million tonnes of volcanic debris were deposited on the sand plain (Tómasson, 1994). As a result, the shoreline advanced seaward by 4 km, although 3 km of this land has since been eroded (Víkingsson, 1986). A significant meltwater flood from the Vatnajökull glacier also created the Öxarfjörður sand plain on the north coast (Figure 1) *c.* 2,500 years ago (Tómasson, 1973). Here the coast has advanced at an average rate of 70 m per 100 years.

Nearshore and shallow marine processes can entrain and redistribute large volumes of sedimentary material along the shore. For example, the shoreline around the village of Vík on the south coast of Iceland prograded 1 km seaward after the glacier burst caused by the eruption of the Katla volcano in 1918. After 1971 the coast began to erode (Figure 2). As a result the village of Vík is now under threat from coastal erosion.

Coastal vegetation

The sandy coast of Iceland supports a sparse and species-poor vegetation (Steindórsson, 1954, 1976; Tüxen, 1970). The dune building grass *Leymus arenarius* thrives in rapidly accumulating sand, occurring on foredune, backdune and inland areas. *Leymus arenarius* can colonise single dune ridges, whole sand dune systems or scattered dunes, depending on the extent of sand accumulation and the frequency of disturbance events. The nitrogen fixing plant *Lathyrus japonicus* ssp. *maritimus* often occurs in association with *L. arenarius* and is thought to improve the nitrogen status of dune sediments (Sigurbjörnsson, 1960). Above the tidemark the natural vegetation is mainly composed of *Honckenya peploides*, *Cakile arctica* Pobed. and *Mertensia maritima*.

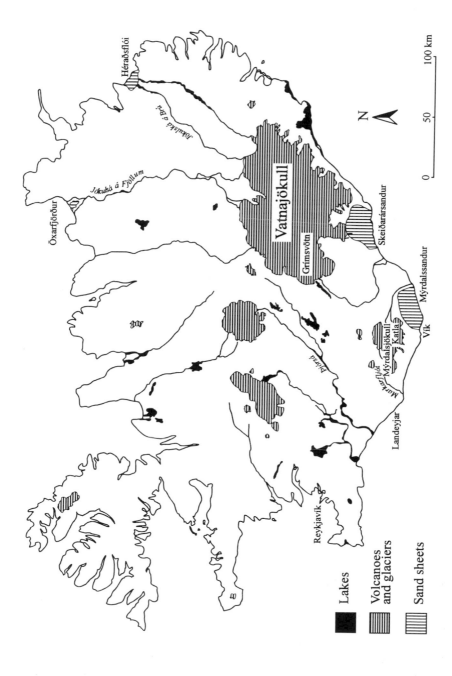

Figure 1   Map of Iceland showing the location of major meltwater rivers, lakes, coastal sand plains, volcanoes and glaciers

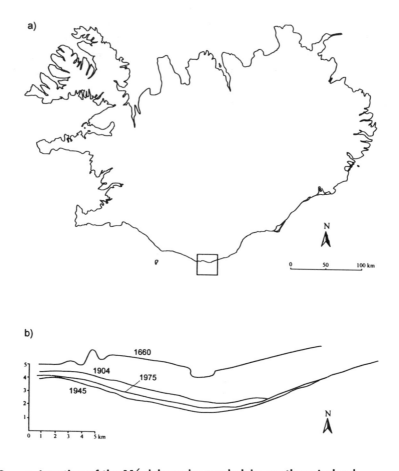

Figure 2   **a Location of the Mýrdalssandur sand plain, southern Iceland**
             b Changes over time in the position of the Mýrdalssandur sand plain shoreline near the village of Vík

Sand stabilisation techniques

A feature of the dynamic nature of the Icelandic coast is the mobility of coastal sand deposits. To stabilise drifting sands, the Soil Conservation Service of Iceland (SCSI) frequently utilises the 'dune building' qualities of the native *Leymus arenarius*. This species is used to stabilise dune ridges, retarding the inland displacement of dune sediments. Seed material of *L. arenarius* is collected from natural stands using special harvesting machines (Greipsson & Davy, 1994), as it has not yet proved possible to cultivate *L. arenarius* for seed. An area of 1,500 ha of mobile sand is sown each year with *L. arenarius*. The low nutrient status of the sand (particularly with respect to phosphorous and nitrogen) has required the use of chemical fertilisers to promote seedling establishment and plant vigour. However, the use of beneficial symbiotic micro-organisms, such as arbuscular mycorrhizal (AM) fungi, is now replacing the extensive application of chemical fertilisers.

Arbuscular mycorrhizal fungi supply the host plant with nutrients, mainly highly immobile phosphorous. These fungi play a key role in the establishment of pioneer species on sand dunes (Koske & Polson, 1984). Currently, experiments are in progress to devise methods for coating *L. arenarius* seed with inoculate composed of AM fungi.

The nitrogen fixing legume *Lupinus nootkatensis* is also used extensively by the SCSI as an alternative to expensive fertilisers. This plant does not require fertiliser applications because of its symbiotic association with nitrogen fixing *Rhizobium* bacteria. Once inoculated with the appropriate bacterial strain, *L. nootkatensis* can fix large amounts of atmospheric nitrogen and has been found to increase both sediment fertility (Palaniappan *et al.*, 1979; Halvarson *et al.*, 1991) and the rate of plant succession on dunes (Palaniappan *et al.*, 1979). Seed material is collected from cultivated fields of *L. nootkatensis* and after being inoculated with *Rhizobium* is sown on coastal dunes in the vicinity of *L. arenarius* stands.

In addition to the above taxa a variety of other species, including *Festuca rubra*, *Deschampsia* spp., *Poa* spp. and the native legume *Lathyrus japonicus*, are used to aid the development of a complete vegetation cover. When dune surfaces become stabilised, other grasses such as *Festuca rubra*, *F. ovina.*, *Agrostis stolonifera* and *Poa* spp. begin to colonise and may eventually replace *L. arenarius* (Steindórsson, 1954; RunÂlfsson, 1978). Under these more stable conditions *L. arenarius* typically becomes less vigorous, increasing the risk of sand erosion. However, careful use of nitrogen fixing species improves soil fertility which allows other plants to become established, negating the erosion risk.

Management of coastal sands

The earliest attempt to stabilise coastal sand deposits took place in 1677 when stone walls were erected to protect meadows from sand blast (RunÂlfsson, 1978). The first legislation on sand stabilisation dates back to 1885 (RunÂlfsson, 1978). In 1907 the Sand Reclamation Service was established. This became the Soil Conservation Service under legislation passed in 1965, with its main task being to stabilise drifting coastal sands (Greipsson, 1993). Overgrazing by livestock on coastal dunes led to vegetation degradation in the past, which in some cases initiated erosion. To date, the SCSI has fenced off an area of approximately 80,590 ha to prevent access by livestock. This measure, in combination with the stabilisation programme, has prevented settlements and infrastructure from becoming inundated by sand.

Stabilisation of coastal sands has also been achieved indirectly by major civil engineering projects. Artificial embankments have been erected to control the course of glacial meltwater rivers. This work has protected agricultural districts from devastating floods, especially in Landeyjar. However, in this area the embankment of the river Markarfljót redirects its outlet to a single location on the coast. Here it deposits around 2.5 mtpa of sediment, creating a large sand plain at its mouth (Haraldsson, 1981).

Several hydro-electric dams built in the interior of Iceland have reduced glaciofluvial sediment transport. This is because the retention time of water in artificial lakes is sufficient for sediment deposition to occur (Tómasson, 1986b). This has decreased sediment supply to some parts of the coast. For example, the sediment load of the River Þjórsá is reduced by 73% having passed through a series of artificial lakes (Tómasson, 1986b). One planned hydro-electric project, involving two large inland reservoirs, will harness the power of the two largest rivers in Iceland, Jökulsá á Fjöllum and Jökulsá á Brú in the northeast of the country (Figure 1). This project will reduce by one third the flow of sediment to the Öxarfjörður sand plain (Aðalsteinsson et al., 1994). It has been predicted that consequent sediment loss at Öxarfjörður and Héraðsflói will cause coastal erosion of 200 and 600 m respectively in the next 100 years, with rapid shoreline retreat in the first decades of this period (Aðalsteinsson et al., 1994).

The effect of relative sealevel movements

According to Jónsson (1994) crustal movements are leading to a land subsidence rate of 3–5 mm/year in Iceland. However, measurements by Einarsson (1994) in Reykjavík harbour suggest a relative sealevel rise of 2.4 mm/year (Figure 3) unconnected to crustal movement. Sealevel movements in Iceland are probably caused by a combination of factors, including land subsidence and global warming. Irrespective of the cause, relative sealevel rise leads to increased coastal erosion which needs to be taken into consideration in long term coastal management.

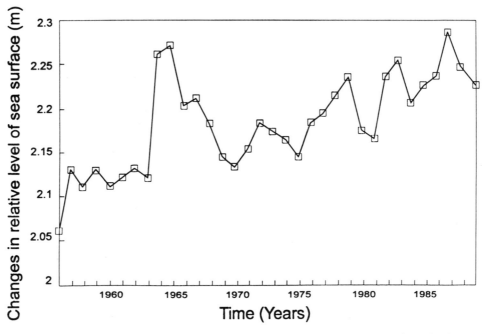

Figure 3   Changes in relative sea surface level over time in Reykjavík harbour (redrawn from Einarssson, 1994)

Conclusions

The establishment of vegetation on coastal sand deposits is vital to ensure stability and to prevent the loss of property through inundation by sand. A mixture of old and new technologies is used to encourage the rapid development of vegetation, an important consideration in view of the dynamic physical environment of Iceland. Natural processes such as volcanic eruptions, meltwater discharge and the redistribution of coastal sediments lead to rapid shifts in the deposition and erosion of sand at the coast. However, a range of major civil engineering projects have reduced the sediment load of meltwater rivers in many areas and this effect will increase in the coming decades. When this factor is combined with the effects of relative sealevel rise, an increase in coastal erosion is predicted. Such factors require the adoption of a long term approach to coastal management in Iceland.

References

Aðalsteinsson, H., Sigurðsson, O. & Jónsson, B. 1994. Coastal changes in Öxarfjörður and Héraðssflói bays due to hydropower development in NE Iceland. In: *Proceedings of the Hornafjörður International Coastal Symposium, Iceland.* Ed.: Viggósson, G. pp. 305-316.

Björnsson, H. 1974. Explanation of jökulhlaups from Grímsvötn, Vatnajökull, Iceland. *Jökull,* 24:1-26.

Björnsson, H. 1979. Glaciers in Iceland. *Jökull,* 29:74-80.

Einarsson, P. 1994. Crustal movements and relative sea level changes in Iceland. In: *Proceedings of the Hornafjörður International Coastal Symposium, Iceland.* Ed.: Viggósson, G. pp. 24-34.

Greipsson, S. 1993. Soil erosion and land reclamation in Iceland. *European Society for Soil Conservation Newsletter,* 3:13-15.

Greipsson, S. & Davy, A.J. 1994. Germination of *Leymus arenarius* and its significance for land reclamation in Iceland. *Annals of Botany,* 73:393-401.

Halvarson, J.J., Smith, J.L. & Franz, E.H. 1991. Lupine influence on soil carbon, nitrogen and microbial activity in developing ecosystems at Mount St. Helens. *Oecologia,* 87:162-170.

Haraldsson, H. 1981. The Markarfljót sandur area, southern Iceland: sedimentological, petrographical and stratigraphical studies. PhD Thesis. Uppsala, Sweden. 65 pp.

Jónsson, B., 1994. Sea level changes in Iceland in the last 8000 years. In: *Proceedings of the Hornafjörður International Coastal Symposium, Iceland.* Ed.: Viggósson, G. pp. 519-524.

Koske, R.E. & Polson, W.R. 1984. Are VA Mycorrhizae required for sand dune stabilisation? *BioScience,* 34(7):420-424.

Nummedal, D. *et al.* 1974. Recent migrations of the Skeiðarársandur shoreline, southeast Iceland. Final report for NSAP. Coastal Research Division, Department of Geology, University of South Carolina, Columbia, South Carolina, USA.

Palaniappan, V.M., Marrs, R.H. & Bradshaw, A.D. 1979. The effect of *Lupinus arboreus* on the nitrogen status of china clay wastes. *Journal of Applied Ecology,* 16:825-831.

RunÂlfsson, S. 1978. Soil Conservation in Iceland. In: *The Breakdown and Restoration of Ecosystems.* Nato Conference Series 1, Ecology Vol 3. Eds: Holdgate, W. & Woodman, M.J. Plenum Press, New York, USA. pp. 231-240.

Sigurbjörnsson, B. 1960. *Studies on the Icelandic* Elymus. PhD Thesis. Cornell University, Ithaca, New York, USA. 163 pp.

Steindórsson, S. 1954. The coastline vegetation at Gásar in Eyjafjörður in the north of Iceland. *Nytt Magasin for Botanikk*, 3:203-212.

Steindórsson, S. 1976. Some notes on the shore vegetation of Iceland. *Acta Botanica Islandica,* 4:19-35.

Thórarinsson, S. & Sæmundsson, K. 1979. Volcanic activity in historical time. *Jökull,* 29:29-32.

Tómasson, H. 1973. Catastrophic floods in Jökulsá á Fjöllum (English summary). *Náttúrufræðingurinn*, 43:12-34.

Tómasson, H. 1986a. Glacial and volcanic shore interaction. Part I: On land. In: *Iceland Coastal and River Symposium.* Ed.: Sigbjarnarson, G. National Energy Authority, Reykjavík, Iceland. pp. 6-16.

Tómasson, H. 1986b. The effect of man-made reservoirs on sediment load. In: *Iceland Coastal and River Symposium.* Ed.: Sigbjarnarson, G. National Energy Authority, Reykjavík, Iceland. pp. 339-344.

Tómasson, H. 1994. Rate of some geomorphological processes in Iceland. In: *Proceedings of the Hornafjörður International Coastal Symposium, Iceland.* Ed: Viggósson, G. pp. 453-463.

Tüxen, R. 1970. Pflanzensoziologische Beobachtungen an isländischen Dünengesell-schaften. *Vegetatio*, 20:251-278.

Víkingsson, S. 1986. South coast of Iceland. Beach material and coastal changes. In: *Iceland Coastal and River Symposium.* Ed.: Sigbjarnarson, G. National Energy Authority, Reykjavík, Iceland, pp. 231-243.

Studies in European Coastal Management. Jones, Healy and Williams (eds)
1996, Samara Publishing Limited, Cardigan. ISBN 1 873692 07 2

The Role of the SNPO Baltberegozashita in Coastal Defence and Shoreline Protection Along the Baltic Sea Coast of Kaliningrad Region

V.L. Boldyrev, O.I. Ryabkova & I.A. Shelkov

SNPO Baltberegozashita, Svetlogorsk, Kaliningrad Region, Russian Federation

Abstract: The coastal and shoreline protection agency for the Kaliningrad region of Russia is the SNPO Baltberegozashita. This is an integrated Russian State enterprise which conducts both research and engineering activities. The SNPO Baltberegozashita manages 145 km of the Baltic open coast shoreline and 355 km of the Curonian and Vistula Lagoon areas. Coastal management schemes are usually concerned with a coastal band of approximately 1 km in width and water depths which extend from c. 20 m on the open coast to c. 2 m within lagoonal areas. The organisation works closely with other national and international agencies to advance coastal science. Progress in this respect is hampered by limited or absent legislation and regulation.

Introduction

The coastal management and shoreline protection agency in the Kaliningrad region is the Specialised Enterprise for Research and Production (SNPO). This organisation, formed in 1972, is known as the SNPO Baltberegozashita. The activities for which the organisation has responsibility include coastal management, research and surveying. Linked to this is work in the design and engineering of coastal management projects, which includes a construction division. Other activities which are of concern to the SNPO Baltberegozashita include the use of plants to protect and conserve the coastline. As a structural unit, the SNPO Baltberegozashita is affiliated to the Civil Engineering Committee of the Kaliningrad Region Administration.

SNPO Baltberegozashita management sites

Guardianship of the 145 km of Baltic open shoreline, as well as 355 km of the Curonian and Vistula Lagoons, is the responsibility of the SNPO Baltberegozashita. The coastal management zone is a band which is 1 km in width and extends to 20 m water depth on the open coast and 2 m depth within lagoonal areas. Within this band SNPO Baltberegozashita has control over all building and construction work, supervises coastal resource usage by means of permits and prohibitions and has responsibility for shoreline protection and nature conservation.

Table 1   Collaborative agencies currently working with the SNPO Baltberegozashita

Organisation	Location	Main function
SNPO (Specialised Enterprise for Research and Construction), Krasnodarberegozashita	Krasnodar, Russia	Coastal defence and shoreline protection
MP (Marine Enterprise) Enginzashita PNIIS (Civil Engineering Institute for Scientific Surveying)	Moscow, Russia	Design and surveying enterprise for site engineering and coastal defence
Black Sea Department of Coastal Engineering, CNIIS (Central Civil Engineering Institute for Research)	Sochi, Russia	Scientific research and the design of organisation systems in the field of coastal protection
MP (Marine Enterprise) 'Coast' and MP 'Wave'	Sochi, Russia	Scientific research organisations in the fields of coastal defence and coastal evolution
VSEGEI (All-Russia Geological Institute)	St Petersburg, Russia	Scientific research institute for geology, including the monitoring of coastal processes
VNIIGS (All-Russia Research Institute for Hydro-mechanised and Sanitary-technical Works	St Petersburg, Russia	Design and research institute in the field of hydro-mechanised sand deposition and coastal protection
Moscow University, Geographical Faculty	Moscow, Russia	Scientific investigations in the fields of palaeogeography and coastal geomorphology
Kaliningrad University, Geographical Faculty	Kaliningrad	Scientific investigations in the fields of coastal dynamics and environmental conservation
State Geographic Institute of Lithuania	Vilnius, Lithuania	Scientific research in the fields of palaeogeography and coastal geomorphology
NPO Georgeberegozashita	Tbilisi, Georgia	Coastal defence and shoreline protection
Institute of 'Budownictwa wodnego' (Coastal Engineering) of Polish Academy of Sciences	Gdansk, Poland	Research institute in the field of hydrological regime investigations of seas, rivers and reservoirs as applied to coasts and coastal engineering
Marine Institute	Gdansk, Poland	Research institute in the fields of coastal dynamics and marine engineering
Department of Marine Geology, Geologic Institute of Poland	Sopot, Poland	Undertakes research on the palaeogeography and geology of marine coasts

Management activities

The SNPO Baltberegozashita organisation undertakes a variety of research and survey work. This includes coastal monitoring carried out under its own auspices as well as work executed by external bodies. Arising from the results of coastal research, programmes of shoreline management and sea defence projects are instituted. Financial support is provided by the Russian State budget.

Coastal management data

The SNPO Baltberegozashita exchanges coastal information and collaborates with scientific and shoreline protection agencies in Russia and abroad (Table 1). Also a collective member of the European Union for Coastal Conservation (EUCC) and the International Geographical Union (IGU), the organisation is actively involved in international coastal research and management programmes (Board of Russian Academy of Sciences for World Ocean Problems; International Geological Correlation Programme Project (IGCP) 367). Past and current work has generated a sizeable archive of coastal environmental data on the Baltic coast. Other sources of similar data are the Oceanologic Institute of the Russian Academy of Sciences (Moscow and Atlantic departments) and Kaliningrad University. Together, these sources provide a data base on key aspects of the Baltic coastal environment.

Management problems

The central problem facing coastal planners, researchers and managers is the difficulty of providing sustainable coastal conservation regimes in the absence of useful legislation on land utilisation, the development of natural resources and coastal conservation principles. Similar problems confront the management of coastal resource exploitation. Due to the wealth of data now available on some areas of the Baltic coast, valuable progress in coastal management is now possible should appropriate regulatory legislation be introduced.

Conclusion

The SNPO Baltberegozashita has a variety of responsibilities in regard to the management of some areas of the Baltic coast. The organisation works closely with both national and international bodies to advance knowledge about the Baltic coast. Substantial data has been generated which is relevant to coastal planning and management in a variety of fields. However, progress is hampered by limited or non-existent legislation which prevents effective, sustainable management in coastal areas.

Studies in European Coastal Management. Jones, Healy and Williams (eds)
1996, Samara Publishing Limited, Cardigan. ISBN 1 873692 07 2

New Approaches to Shoreline Protection Along the Baltic Sea Coast of Kaliningrad Region

V.L. Boldyrev, A.E. Dimitriev & I.A. Shelkov

SNPO Baltberegozashita, Svetlogorsk, Kaliningrad Region, Russian Federation

Abstract: The Sambian Peninsula on the eastern Baltic Sea coastline of Kaliningrad (Russian Federation) is prone to severe coastal erosion. Traditional methods for coastal defence, such as groynes and sea walls, may fail to prevent erosion and can, in some cases, exacerbate the loss of inter-tidal sediment. Such structures also have a detrimental effect on the quality of various aspects of the coastal environment. In recognition of this, the authority responsible for coastal defence in the region, the SNPO "Baltberegozashita", has taken account of natural processes in the design and implementation of a range of coastal defence projects. These include sand nourishment of the coastal zone, hydraulic methods for the deposition of sediment in the inter-tidal zone, the construction of improved sea defences, the establishment of equilibrium beach arches and the continued use of traditional planting and sand stabilisation methods. New wave-damper structures, which reduce the energy of breaking waves by 80-90%, are also being used to provide immediate protection in some areas.

Introduction

The Sambian Peninsula forms a dominant feature of the Kaliningrad coastline of Russia and comprises a promontory into the Baltic Sea (Figure 1). Exposure to westerly storms causes irreversible abrasion of the coastline and sediment loss. Furthermore, the input of sand from the seabed to the inter–tidal zone of the peninsula is insignificant because extensive areas of sub–tidal block–boulder pavement form the predominant sediment type. Two large spits flank the Sambian Peninsula, the Vistula Spit to the southwest and the Curonian Spit to the northwest. Sediment eroded from the Sambian Peninsula has fed the growth of these two spits.

The protection of the shoreline is a high priority in the region. Whilst it is accepted that the effectiveness of any particular shoreline protection structure is an important consideration, the influence of such structures on the conservation and aesthetic appeal of the natural coastal landscape is now also of the utmost importance.

With this in mind, the authority responsible for coastal defence in the region, the Specialised Enterprise for Research and Production (SNPO Baltberegozashita), has developed a nature conservation approach to shoreline protection (see Boldyrev, Ryabkova & Shelkov, this volume). Key areas which have been investigated include Holocene patterns of coastal evolution, contemporary coastal dynamics, the nature and interaction of different coastal processes and the effectiveness of different shore protection structures in relation to the needs of specific sections of coast. These investigations have allowed the development of a scientifically based approach to shoreline protection over the past decade.

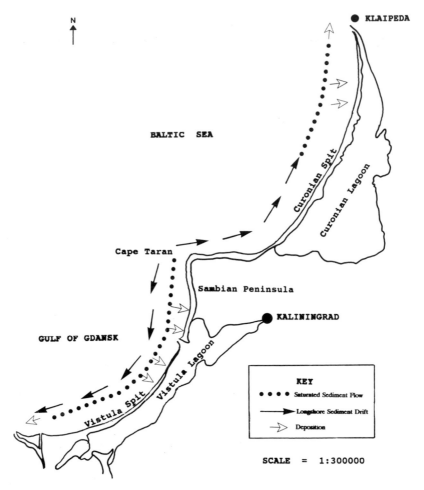

Figure 1   Summary of nearshore sediment movement along the Baltic Sea coast of Kaliningrad Region

This paper will review how such changes of attitude have influenced coastal defence practice along the coastline of the Kaliningrad Region by reference to several recent major coastal engineering projects.

Current and future shoreline defence measures

Sandy shorelines are characterised by high sediment mobility in the nearshore, inter-tidal and supralittoral zones. Intrusions into the coastal zone by man-made shore protection structures (such as sea walls, groynes and jetties) generally have negative consequences for sandy coasts. Typical effects include the obstruction of longshore sediment drift, sediment loss to leeward of protective structures through scouring and the general disturbance which results not only to the sediment budget of protected areas, but also to adjacent unprotected sections of coast. One probable consequence of this on the Kaliningrad coast is that downstream beach erosion zones have now arisen in the centre of the Svetlogorsk embayment, in the Pionersky embayment, to the west of Zelenogradsk and along parts of the Curonian Spit, where the current rate of coastal retreat has been estimated at 1.8 m/year.

Beach nourishment

Experience of a range of techniques has now shown that sand nourishment of the coastal zone, coupled to the hydraulic application of sand on wide beaches which effectively dissipate wave energy, are the most effective methods for shoreline protection. These techniques have been used by the SNPO Baltberegozashita on the sea shore of the Filino-Primorie area (on the northern coast of the Sambian Peninsula) and on parts of the Curonian Spit. Between 1987 and 1991 the SNPO Baltberegozashita removed a 44-47 m high bedrock bluff, comprised mainly of fine-grained sands, from a part of the coast in the Filino-Primorie area near Cape Taran, the tip of the Sambian Peninsula. This exposed location is almost devoid of sand sized beach sediment, although small volumes of material enter the beach system from cliff erosion. As part of the work programme the cliff section was terraced, and the 2.3 million m^3 of sandy material removed from the cliff was used for nourishment of part of the inter-tidal zone. This was achieved using hydraulic methods and resulted in the formation of a new beach up to 140 m wide.

Between 1987 and 1995 there was a high frequency of storms in the eastern Baltic. During this time the Sambian coast experienced eight severe storms with the result that most of the recently deposited beach sediments arising from the nourishment works were lost. Much of the eroded sediment has been redeposited between 1.5 and 3.5 km to the east of Filino where a new 70-100 m wide beach has been formed. This has had the beneficial effect of providing additional protection against storm waves and surges. Smaller volumes of sediment have also been deposited up to 10 km to the east to form a 45-55 m wide beach along the eastern side of the Svetlogorsk embayment. This has also had the effect of reducing the impact of wave action along a substantial length of coastline.

Throughout the post-World War II era, the western coast of the Sambian Peninsula has been subject to the dumping at sea of sand waste arising from land based Amber mines. Over the past 35 years, more than 80 million m^3 of sand pulp has been deposited in this region, resulting in the formation of broad 50-100 m wide sandy beaches up to 50 km south of the dumping grounds. Beach-head foredunes have also developed as a result of this, and in some places front the former cliffed coastline. This situation contrasts sharply with the pre-World War II situation when the western Sambian coast was subject to severe erosion, with retreat rates of 0.5-0.7 m/year being documented in the German literature.

The examples described will have served to demonstrate that large scale sand nourishment programmes can prevent coastal erosion through the formation of wide beaches with an effective wave energy dissipation function. This experience has led to the development of a master plan for the large scale nourishment of the northern Sambian coastal zone. According to this plan, over the next 25 years, the SNPO Baltberegozashita intends to transfer sand overburden sediments through a 12 km long pipeline from the active Yantarny amber plant to the Cape

Taran–Filino holiday resort section of the north Sambian coastal zone. An important step will include the construction of settling tanks for the separation of clay and mud sized particles from the overburden material, as well as pumping stations at intervals along the pipeline. It is hoped that this programme will result in the formation of sandy beaches up to 70 m wide through the action of waves and currents on the freshly deposited material.

Another recent initiative concerns the replenishment of beaches at Morskoe on the lagoon side of the Curonian Spit. During the past 35 years this region has been subject to severe coastal erosion; a coastal strip of land between 110–130 m wide and 25 ha in area has been lost, together with 5 houses. In response to this, a programme of hydraulic beach replenishment was initiated in 1993. For this work sand was obtained by suction dredging from coastal sand banks which were formed by the deposition of eroded coastal sediments and to–date one third of the area of lost land has been reclaimed.

Small peninsulas formed by the planting of reeds (Phragmites australis Trin. ex Steudel) have also been established to help stabilise the seaward fringe of the reinstated land. In the future it is hoped that these peninsulas will aid the deposition of more sand.

Wave energy dissipation structures

Sand nourishment measures are difficult to sustain on a long term basis, but coastal erosion is a permanent phenomenon. Accordingly, over the past 10 years the SNPO Baltberegozashita has been working on the design and construction of new types of wave-breaker or wave-damper structures which reduce the energy of breaking waves by 80-90% whilst not detracting from the natural beauty of the coastal zone (Figures 2a and b, Figure 3). Such structures have already been built at 6 sites over a total distance of 2.4 km and it has been found that the suppression of wave breaking causes sand accretion to seaward and on both beach flanks of the structures. As a result, at some coastal locations an increase in beach thickness of 1-1.2 m has been recorded together with an increase in beach width of up to 40 m. Sand accretion on beaches is also favoured by the development of foredunes over the wave damper structures.

On the Curonian Spit three sites which formerly suffered significant coastal erosion are now being shielded by wave damper structures (Figures 2a and b). Prior to this, foredune loss had progressed to such an extent that storm surges had started to break over the Curonian Spit thus affecting the lagoon and human settlements to landward. Similarly, on the coast of the Sambian Peninsula four sections of coast are now protected with modified wave-damper structures.

During the past decade the SNPO Baltberegozashita has developed five modifications to the basic wave-damper design which have now been incorporated into new structures with a total length of 1.9 km. These structures have been found to work efficiently by reducing the energy of breaking waves by 80-90%.

During the past 20 years more traditional methods such as planting programmes have also been used to encourage the development and stabilisation of dunes along the Kaliningrad coastline.

Figure 2   **A**   **Construction of a wave-damper structure on the beach backshore at Lesnoe on the Curonian Spit, 1993**
                B   **The same structure within a year of its completion**

Figure 3   **Construction of a modified wave-damper structure with a promenade embankment at Pionersky in 1995**

Conclusions

The restoration of an undisturbed sediment regime, together with the re-creation of natural coastal landscapes, forms the basis of the nature conservation approach to coastal protection which has been adopted by the SNPO Baltberegozashita. Through experience the SNPO Baltberegozashita has developed a scientific basis for shoreline protection. This has led to the design and construction of new coast protection structures with optimal performance whilst also showing how particular structures may be especially appropriate for different sections of the coast. Nevertheless, much research and survey work is still required in order to

a)   identify sections of the coast at risk from erosion;

b)   aid the design and selection of shore protection structures which are more efficient; and

c)   provide a basis for the optimal location of coast protection structures.

Studies in European Coastal Management. Jones, Healy and Williams (eds)
1996, Samara Publishing Limited, Cardigan. ISBN 1 873692 07 2

Evaluating Historical Cartography as a Tool for the Study of Coastal Areas

A. Lodovisi & S. Torresani

Istituto di Geografia, University Bologna, Italy

Abstract: Historical maps and their associated documents are linked to the requirements of mapmakers and the resources at their disposal, as well as the particular demands and constraints of their time. This is well illustrated by the historical cartographic resource for the Italian coast, where effort and emphasis in cartography may be traced through discrete historical periods. Care is required in interpreting cartographic documents and a clear methodology is required for their effective use. An historical map, together with any related documents, constitutes a net which filters the past. In this net many elements may have been ignored or overlooked but some remain trapped. These are visible to the researcher, supplying useful indicators for evaluating the performance of socio-economic systems related to the environment.

Introduction

This paper relates the nature of historical maps to their use in the study and planning of coastal areas. Much research on coastal environments recognises the fundamental role of early cartographic sources in establishing past site conditions and in producing historical reconstructions to assist present shoreline management. This approach is enhanced through the analysis of territorial models supported by the application of neural nets, used as a tool for the delineation of shorelines (Ryan *et al.*, 1991).

The hypothesis presented here is that an historical map, together with any related documents, constitutes a 'net' which filters the past. In this net some elements may be ignored or overlooked. Others remain trapped and are therefore visible to the researcher. These elements supply useful indicators for evaluating the performance of socio-economic systems related to the environment.

Historical cartography and GIS

The introduction of computerised mapping and Geographic Information Systems (GIS) in the study of coastal environments raises its own problems. Modern information technology gives faster and easier access than ever before to comparative operations in cartography, quantitative analysis involving linear and surface measurements and procedures involving 'overlay' and 'buffering'. Harley (1993) states:

> There are a number of geographers who make their living by asserting that cartography and GIS deliver a positive knowledge that is value-neutral and culture-independent. It will be argued that the continued acceptance of such beliefs, whether passively or actively, is a matter of cultural authority.

The problems inherent in historical data as a significant element in the theoretical input of GIS and in the actual production of GIS software, remain (Richard, 1994):

> Geographical information is in constant evolution, either under the influence of nature itself or under the influence of mankind. GIS must take into account this special aspect when building up a history of information.

Cartographic resources

If the scale of temporal analysis is wide, information which allows an evaluation of the techniques and cultural contexts which led to the production of maps is necessary. These are essential for evaluating the accuracy of maps and vital in basic research, modelling and simulation. Harley (1968, 1993) suggests that:

> every map ... contains an invisible landscape of ideas in addition to its tangible terrain of distributions, shapes and directions. The meaning of maps is decipherable not just on the basis of their 'factual' content or on that of their measurable accuracy and their tradition of representation ... but also through the cultural and historical milieu in which images were viewed and used.

This is evident in the use of early maps as historical evidence for coastal change. In fact De Boer & Carr (1969) write:

> cartographic evidence from the earliest periods is rarely good enough to stand by itself, but considered together with other kinds of evidence can be suggestive.

Historical and geographical research can generate much information from historical maps through:

a) placing maps in a technical and cultural context in relation to their date of production (descriptive memoirs, essays);

b) pinpointing possible documentation accompanying maps;

c) evaluation of the quality and reliability of maps;

d) developing a hypothesis for a comparative analysis using classification systems; and

e) research in libraries and archives.

These advantages provide a starting point for systematic research aimed at establishing an inventory of historical cartography with reference to European coastal areas. This may be in the form of a 'critical' review, offering useful information for better and wider applications of cartographic information in the context of research and interdisciplinary projects connected to environmental planning. A follow-up project, creating a complementary image bank on video disc for a flexible and multi-media approach, underlining the multi-disciplinary nature of historic map research and taking account of the breadth of cartographic approaches and information would be an added benefit.

Interpreting historical cartography

A feasibility study has been carried out in Italy using the following parameters:

a) analysis of map-making for the period from 1600 to 1870, when the National Cartographic Office (IGM) was established;

b) a listing of the main research centres;

c) an examination of the quantity of documents relating to coastal areas; and

d) provisional formulation of criteria to be taken into account for classifying material.

Research should use a system of classification which allows identification of distinctive elements for each map. Methodologies must consider the maps in terms of 'map series'. In this way connections and differences between maps can be observed, underlined and evaluated. It is not enough to pay attention to "chronology, which is easily representable within a GIS" (Curry, 1994). 'Narrative' must be taken into account, particularly the specific point of view of the narrator/cartographer. Factors which characterise maps are:

a) the expectations of the map-maker and the commissioner;

b) the effectiveness of the representation compared to the expectations;

c) the symbols used; and

d) the technical means used and whether the adopted map-making model is widespread.

Historical cartography in Italy

Within the framework of the approach described, the first systematic examination of maps was conducted on the catalogue in the library of the IGM. The maps used represent historical Italian states which existed prior to their unification and the creation of modern Italy. This library holds material from the Military Topographical Offices and from private collections. Particular attention was paid to maps and city plans showing the historical landscape associated with a description of a settlement or the way of life along the coast. The criterion of scale was used alongside historical–political parameters.

A chronological framework, starting from the 17th century and working through to modern maps, was adopted (Figure 1, Table 1). Particular attention was paid to the period between 1792 and 1815, corresponding with the spread of new philosophies, institutional methods, methods of organisation and cartographic techniques after the French and Napoleonic wars (Figure 2, Table 2). Having compiled a synoptic table for each period of interest, the relative distribution (%) of maps in each scale (based on a total of the maps showing coastal tracts of the single states) was calculated. The same procedure was used on the total number of maps for each period to obtain a preliminary sample. Analysis of city maps was conducted on the basis of four categories:

1. Representations of the cities, their ports, urban structures and important buildings;

2. Relationships between urban cores and surrounding territory (lines of communication, relief, hydrography and agriculture);

3. Presence of military installations (arsenals, forts); and

4. Detailed maps of ports or descriptions of port management.

In every period there is a prevalence of maps referring to the Tyrrhenian coast showing the most important Italian cities (Genoa, Pisa, Leghorn, Naples, Palermo and Rome). During the Napoleonic period and in the 19th century large scale

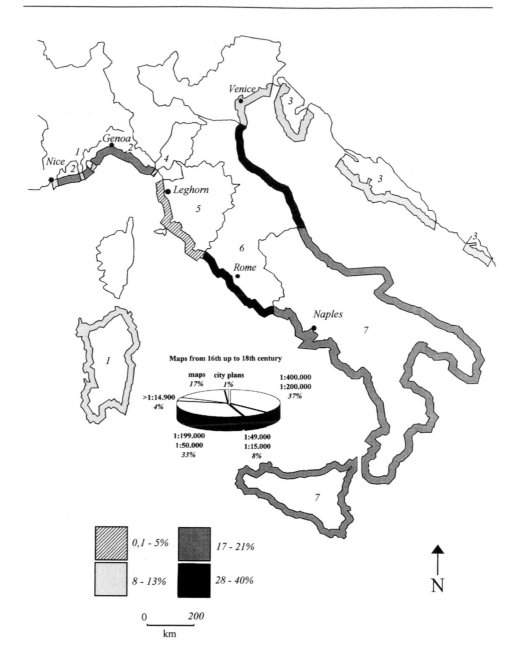

Figure 1 **States of Italy from the 16th to the 18th century with pie charts showing the percentage of maps per scale category**

Numbered areas correspond to the states listed in Table 1

Table 1 **Number and typology of maps produced in the States of Italy from the 16th to the 18th century**

Source: Catalogo ragionato delle carte esistenti nella cartoteca dell'Istituto Geografico Militare, 1932-34

State	Coastline km	1:200.000 - 1:400.000	1:50.000 - 1:199.000	1:15.000 - 1:49.000	>1:14.900	Maps	City plans	Total
1 Kingdom of Sardinia	1,263	2	4	2	1	2		11
2 Republic of Genoa	262	3	4	2	1	5		15
3 Republic of Venice	1,640	3	1			3		7
4 Duchy of Modena	10	1						1
5 Grand Duchy of Tuscany	172		1					1
6 Papal States	532	12	17	2	2	2		35
7 Kingdom of Naples	3,366	9	3	1		4	1	18
Italy	7,409	4	1					

maps are more numerous than in earlier periods and in the 19th century city plans increase in importance. In particular, maps describing the city in relation to its surroundings are more common. Significantly, half of the maps drawn during the 19th century are on a scale between 1:5,000 and 1:10,000 (Figure 3, Table 3). On the one hand maps reach out beyond the limits of the built up areas, while on the other they focus on port areas and port engineering projects, using a scale of less than 1:5,000. Little attention is paid to land reclamation in marshy coastal areas. The presence of coastal marsh and swamp in historical maps highlights the connection between the perception of territory, the perception of the environment and the graphic or written descriptions used.

At the end of the 18th century, and especially during and after the Napoleonic wars, mapmakers who had worked in the fields of art and science in the previous two centuries were absorbed by governmental offices and institutions. The aim of this centralisation was to produce and conserve topographic and geographic information, providing wide accessibility and mass production of maps. This change was not without consequences for the information content of maps, the symbols used, the choice of map scales and geometric parameters. At the same time civil, scientific mapmakers, who had contributed so much from 1750 onwards to improving astronomical, mathematical and geometrical methods for the new cartography, were superseded by military technicians. The change came about due to the financial and human resources available to the military which could

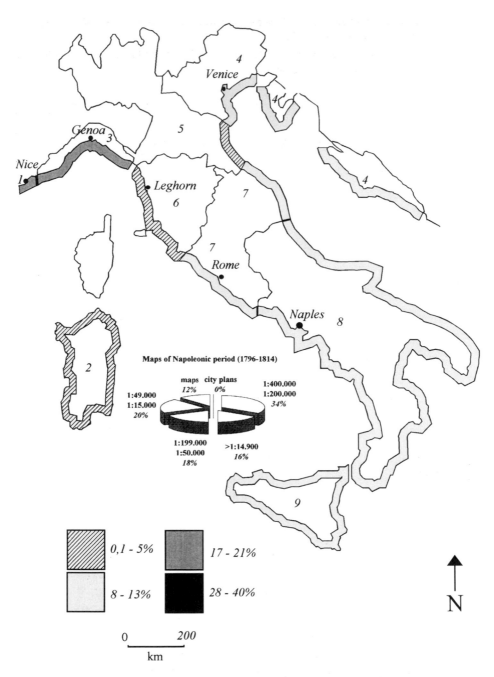

Figure 2   States of Italy in the Napoleonic period (1792 to 1815) with pie charts showing the percentage of maps per scale category

Numbered areas correspond to the states listed in Table 2

Table 2 **Number and typology of maps produced in the States of Italy during the Napoleonic period (1796-1814)**

Source: Catalogo ragionato delle carte esistenti nella cartoteca dell'Istituto Geografico Militare, 1932-34

State	Coastline km	1:200.000 - 1:400.000	1:50.000 - 1:199.000	1:15.000 - 1:49.000	>1:14.900	Maps	City plan	Total
1 Nice	30	1			2	5		8
2 Kingdom of Sardinia	1,200	1						1
3 Ligurian Republic	295	1		1	2	3	3	10
4 Austro-Hungarian Empire	1,640	3		1			1	5
5 Napoleonic Republic of Italy	195	1		1				2
Napoleonic Kingdom of Italy	1,775						1	1
6 Kingdom of Tuscany	248			1			1	2
Principality of Piombino	152			1	1			2
7 Papal States	397	1		2	3			6
8 Kingdom of Naples	1,990	3		1		2		6
9 Kingdom of Sicily	1,300	3		1				4
Italy	7,409	3						3

guarantee the successful completion of expensive geodetic and topographical surveys necessary for the production of scientifically accurate maps. In military cartography effort is concentrated on quantitative and qualitative elements which may influence a war situation; for example mobilisation, mustering, marshalling, manoeuvring, attacking, the possibilities of access and passage and of navigation along the coast. In the case of wetlands which could become traps during the movement of troops, great attention was paid to the use of symbols signifying these marshy zones. On the other hand, little detail on the quality of the vegetation and the presence of human activity was provided. This kind of information, such as the relationship between man and the environment, was left to the 'Mémoires', geographical and statistical monographs which accompany maps (Mezzacapo & Mezzacapo, 1859).

Those who study the evolution of coastal environments can use the information provided by historic maps and memoirs in a selective and effective manner.

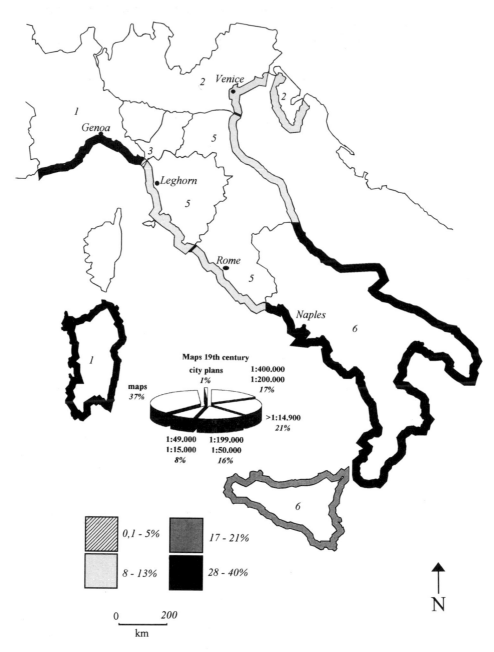

Figure 3   **States of Italy from the 19th century with pie charts showing the percentage of maps per scale category**

Numbered areas correspond to the states listed in Table 3

Table 3 **Number and typology of maps produced in the States of Italy during the 19th century**

Source: Catalogo ragionato delle carte esistenti nella cartoteca dell'Istituto Geografico Militare, 1932-34

State	Coastline km	1:200.000 - 1:400.000	1:50.0000 - 1:199.000	1:15.0000 - 1:49.000	>1:14.900	Maps	City plans	Total	% [1]
1 Kingdom of Sardinia	1,525	11	16	7	11	39		84	57
2 Austro-Hungarian Empire	1,640	4	11	4	4	5		28	25
3 Duchy of Modena	10	1						1	
Lucca	12	1						1	
4 Grand Duchy of Tuscany [2]	324	10	9	4	4	8		35	26
5 Papal States	532	11	8	4		6		29	10
6 Kingdom of the Two Sicilies [3]	3,366	12	18	29	3	48	4	114	65

(1)   percentage of maps produced by the military
(2)   after 1873 three maps were produced by the Instituto Geografico Militare Italiano
(3)   after 1872 six maps were produced by the Instituto Geografico Militare Italiano

Accompanying texts are important for modern-day historians of the environment. For example, the maps from the atlas of William Henry Smyth *The Hydrography of Sicily* (1823) lose part of their impact if they are not read alongside Smyth's writings in the *Memoir Descriptive* which accompanies the cartographic work (Manzi, 1982). Important information may be lost if graphic and textual analysis is not integrated with the study of artistic representations such as views and drawings which often accompany maps.

A further source of information is provided by the cartography of land surveying and reclamation, where particular importance is attached to economic activity and to the nature of property. This alternative focus of attention provides less detail on some aspects of the environment (e.g. bathymetry, coastline dynamics, relief) but a wealth of information on human settlements, types of farming and landuse, activities connected to hunting, fishing and different associations of vegetation. This different focus is also provided in archive documents for some tracts of the Italian coast (the Po delta, Lagoon of Comacchio, the low coasts of the Northern Adriatic) from the 16th century onwards.

The selection of cartographic information is linked to other factors (social, industrial, commercial) which have influenced the evolution of map-making in general and especially the representation of coastal settlements. The prevalence of maps showing coastal towns and their surroundings, and the production of large scale maps illustrating port works and infrastructure in the first decades of the 19th century, illustrates changes taking place in coastal areas. The advent of steam navigation, iron ship building and modern artillery contributed to coastal change. As early as in 1825 the ports of Marseilles, Leghorn and Naples were connected to Great Britain by steam ships. This technological revolution in navigation called for greater knowledge of the coast, the depths and movement of the sea bed and port facilities (piers, wharves, warehouses, cargo systems). Military considerations placed further demands on the coastal resource.

Conclusion

The content of historical maps and their associated documents is closely linked to the requirements of mapmakers and the resources at their disposal, as well as the particular demands and constraints of their time. This is well illustrated by the historical cartographic resource for the Italian coast, where effort and emphasis in cartography may be traced through discrete historical periods. However, extreme care is required in interpreting cartographic documents, and a clear methodology is required for their effective use. Before the unification of Italy, the French Dépot Générale de la Guerre, the Austrian Military Geographical Institute and the British Admiralty carried out work which produced some of the best maps of the coastal regions of Italy. This may suggest the potential benefits of a new collaboration between research institutes of various European countries.

References

Curry, M.R. 1994. Image, practice and the hidden impacts of geographic information systems. *Progress in Human Geography*, 18:441–459.

De Boer, G. & Carr, A.P. 1969. Early maps as historical evidence for coastal change. *Geographical Journal*, 135:17-27.

Harley, J.B. 1968. The evaluation of early maps: towards a methodology. *Imago Mundi*, 22:62-74.

Harley, J.B. 1993. The culture of the map in western history, Abstract of a Paper proposed by J.B. Harley. *Cartographica*, 30:107.

Manzi, E. 1982. William Henry Smyth, l'Atlante Coro-Idrografico siciliano e i rapporti con la cartografia ufficiale delle Due Sicilie. *Bollettino della Società Geografica Italiana*, 11:721-758.

Mezzacapo, L. & Mezzacapo, C., 1859. *Studj topografici e strategici su l'Italia*. Vallardi, Milano, Italia. 350 pp.

Richard, D. 1994. Historique et SIG, *Fifth European Conference and Exhibition on Geographical Information Systems* (EGIS/MARI'94). Mimeo.

Ryan, T.W. *et al.* 1991. Extracting of shoreline features by neural nets and image processing. *Photogrammetric Engineering & Remote Sensing*, 57:947-955.

Studies in European Coastal Management. Jones, Healy and Williams (eds)
1996, Samara Publishing Limited, Cardigan. ISBN 1 873692 07 2

Some Examples of Inappropriate Coastal Management Practice in Northwest Portugal

H.M. Granja

Universidade do Minho, Campus de Gualtar, Portugal

Abstract: The northwest coastal zone of Portugal provides a good example of inappropriate coastal management planning and regulation. This coastal area has intrinsic value and is an important natural resource. There are serious difficulties with the implementation of the National Political Environment Plan. To date, solutions proposed by the decision makers have not solved coastal problems but sometimes introduced others. Some examples of policy are presented to illustrate this. The paradoxes of Protected Areas, and the impotence of those responsible for their management, are illustrated.

Introduction

The coastal zone of Portugal can be subdivided into several sectors based on geology and geomorphology. In the northwest (Figure 1), beach migration and cliff retreat are taking place. In a failed attempt at stabilisation, administrators have favoured the use of a 'protection' model supported by groynes (some hundreds of metres long) and revetments. Beach nourishment is rare, with examples at Ofir (Esposende) and Espinho (Aveiro). At Ofir, the reconstitution of the spit of the Cávado Estuary was executed with sand dredged from the estuary. At Espinho, sediment nourishment favours the presence of a beach between groynes that provides 'coastal protection' for the town. The most worrying consequence of the 'protection' model is the consequential degradation of the coastal landscape through the erosion and destruction of characteristic coastal landforms.

The degradation process promoted by the groynes is characterised by fast downdrift cliff retreat and beaches are becoming narrow with rocky outcrops of bedrock. Examples occur between Caminha and the Ave River; Espinho and Furadouro; and south of the Aveiro inlet. Increased erosion has resulted from the application of the 'protection' model (hundreds of metres in a few years and more than ten metres a day immediately downdrift the groynes during storms). Coastal degradation and destruction also result from footpaths, growth of population centres and roads, fires, tourist facilities and ignorance. In addition, pollution by urban and industrial effluent is a problem. A lack of environmental education leads to random dumping of wastes and litter.

The Portuguese government attempted to reverse the critical situation in the coastal zone by the introduction of European Union directives in Portuguese law concerning the protection of the environment, particularly the coastal zone. Examples are the Natural Reserve of S. Jacinto (Aveiro) and the Protected Area of Esposende. In practice, the effect of the new laws is minimal because the agents of public administration are unable or unwilling to apply them for political and economic reasons. Conservation awareness remains poor. Change requires public and political education and better scientific data. Many Portuguese universities want to develop scientific research for decision makers. However, conflicts based on philosophical and practical preferences in coastal management make this difficult. Further degradation of the coastal zone will bring heavy financial and social penalties in the near future. The decision makers seem only now to begin to fear the consequences.

Planning and regulation

Planning and regulation which deals with environmental policy and management is determined by two main mechanisms. These are the National Political Environment Plan (NPEP) and Coastal Border Management Plans (Planos de Ordenamento da Orla Costeira; POOCs). The NPEP (1994) is a tool of environmental policy. Firstly, it is to be used to address specific environmental problems. Examples of these are questions of water supply and effluent treatment on the European model. Secondly, the plan attempts to define the nature and limits of environmental policy. The successful operation of the plan is limited by the number and variety of interested groups and bodies involved in environmental planning. Coastal Border Management Plans, once completed, will define the conditions, purposes and prevailing uses of sites.

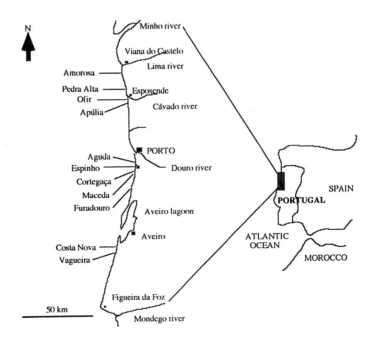

Figure 1   **The northwest coast of Portugal showing the location of sites referred to in the text**

Some examples of inappropriate practice in management

Considering the coastal zone between the Minho River and the Mondego Cape, there are several instances of non-application of basic environmental laws set out in the NPEP. Examples occur at Amorosa, Pedra Alta, Ofir-Aguçadoura, Espinho-Furadouro and south of the Aveiro Inlet. In all of these cases, conflicts are evident between the role of management/mis-management and the landscape. In many instances coastal landforms are under intense pressure from tourism and coastal infrastructure designed to provide an engineered solution to the problem of coastal defence.

The Amorosa case

The Amorosa area is a rich afforested dune ecosystem of medieval age. The area was largely untouched before the proposal for a leisure centre with several residences and condominia in the dune area, which was accepted by the Municipality of Viana do Castelo in 1984. The first residences were erected immediately behind the foredune. In 1987, a proposed second phase of condominia was judicially contested. The court decision allowed the development, which substantially increased the initial number of buildings. The area presently occupied by the Amorosa complex is 300,000 m².

The Pedra Alta case

At Pedra Alta, a small community of fishermen needed easy access to the sea for their boats. In 1992, two groynes and a revetment were built to facilitate this. Erosion increased south of these structures, producing a cliff along the foredune and threatening some houses. After severe storms in December 1993 and January 1994, a system of groynes associated with revetments was built in an attempt to protect the area between Pedra Alta and the mouth of Neiva River. Currently there are five groynes; two in front of the village, one in the Neiva River mouth and two further south. In some areas sand has accumulated, but erosion has generally increased, such as south of the breakwater of the Neiva River. The north to south longshore drift was interrupted by the groynes, leading to cliff retreat at a rate of 30 to 60 m per year during the storms of 1994 and 1995 (Figure 2a).

The sector Ofir-Aguçadoura

This was the first area where stabilisation of sand dunes was attempted on the northwest coast of Portugal (Carvalho *et al.*, 1986). The purpose of the stabilisation work was to protect a hotel built in the foredune at Ofir, which had been threatened by erosion since 1980. The first protective groyne (240 m long) was built at Pedrinhas in 1986, 1,700 m south of the hotel. This groyne, and the others that succeeded it, have been the source of serious environmental problems in a previously stable area (Granja & Carvalho, 1991). During the storms of January and February 1994, the fishing village of Cedobem (south of Pedrinhas), under threat since 1988 and 'protected' by a revetment in 1989, was damaged (Figure 2b). Protests led the Nature Conservation Institute (ICN) to partially destroy the groyne of Pedrinhas. The groyne was shortened by 135 m. This allowed longshore drift to transport sediment south and the beach of Pedrinhas has widened. The

Figure 2   **Examples of coastal erosion and coastal defence on the northwest coast of Portugal**

a   Coastal erosion south of the village of Pedra Alta (Viana do Castelo). The rate of erosion has increased since this photograph was taken (12.1.1994)

b   Coastal erosion now threatens some of the houses in the village of Cedobem. The groyne and revetment at Pedrinhas are located in the background. Photograph taken on 12.7.1994

c   The loss of beach sand at Apúlia (Póvoa de Varzim) has resulted in the exposure of the underlying Paleozoic bedrock. Photograph taken 14.3.1994

d   Breakdown of the root of the groyne at Maceda Beach (Ovar) photographed on 3.2.1994 following the storm of January 1994.

e   The groyne and revetment at Vagueira (Aveiro) were rebuilt after the storms of 1994. Photograph taken on 5.3.1995

previously sharp dune-beach profile has smoothed. Many claim that the entire groyne needs to be removed. However, it is hoped that the building of fences and planting of *Ammophila arenaria*, will contribute to the stabilisation of what remains of the initial dune.

Recent erosion at Apúlia beach has been particularly severe as a consequence of bad management practice in this area. After the storms of 1994 and 1995, Apúlia beach had been stripped of almost all its sand (Figure 2c). Despite warnings about the vulnerability of this coast to storm events, new buildings and urban settlements near the foreshore are planned with the support of the local municipality (a small hotel is already licensed).

Espinho-Furadouro

Espinho is an old settlement set in the coastal dunes. The potential effects of erosion have been known since the last century (Teixeira, 1988). Since 1912, groynes and revetments have been built seaward of the town. The groynes have been subsequently modified in number and shape. In 1988 the present model of protection, with two large and curved groynes 120 m apart, was completed (Valle, 1988). This model of defence protects the seaside avenue but produces a narrowing and thinning of the beach along the seawall and severe erosion problems downdrift of the south groyne. This endangered the beaches and villages at Esmoriz, Cortegaça and Maceda. Cliff retreat in this sector is about 20 m/year. New emergency 'protection' structures were required in 1994 to save endangered houses at Esmoriz and Cortegaça beaches. An unnecessary groyne at Maceda beach was built in 1984, causing the rapid retreat of cliffs to the south. In January 1994, the root of this groyne was broken by the sea (Figure 2d). The groyne was promptly rebuilt, increasing the retreat rate of the cliff during the storms of 1995.

The Aveiro Inlet

The Aveiro Lagoon has an artificial inlet, stabilised by two breakwaters built between 1950 and 1956 (Castanho *et al.*, 1981). Sands transported by north to south longshore drift are deposited updrift of the northern breakwater, causing a sediment deficit downdrift. This has initiated serious erosion problems at Costa Nova and Vagueira to the south of the Aveiro Inlet. Extensions to the breakwaters in later years has caused surplus sand accretion in the northern area of the inlet. The Junta Autónoma do Porto de Aveiro, which is responsible for the management of the area, promoted the sale of excess sand for civil construction.

During the storms of 1994 and 1995, waves broke a revetment at Costa Nova beach and damaged the houses located behind it. Similar problems have been experienced at Vagueira beach. Despite these experiences, beach developments continue, forcing the bodies responsible for coastal management to rebuild revetments and groynes (Figure 2e).

Conclusion

Coastal defence structures appear to stimulate erosion, cliff retreat and beach degradation by the interruption of sand supply, often with serious economic and social implications. It is obvious that in the northwest coastal zone of Portugal, natural resources are exploited for economic reasons. Consequences are not taken into consideration, even when resources which underpin the economy are put in danger. The experiences of this area show that attempts to stabilise the coast must be supported by scientific data about coastal morphodynamics. In Portugal, the natural coastal resources are fundamental for economic and social development, requiring effective solutions to real problems.

The strategy that has been adopted up to now has proved ineffective. What are the alternatives and are they possible? Among the alternatives is artificial beach nourishment using sediments derived from the dredging of estuaries, harbours and other accumulation sites. The problem of inland beach migration and loss of sediment from the beaches and cliffs is a national problem. The solutions must also have a national scope. These solutions must consider:

a) abandoning buildings, if so who will support the social costs?
b) maintaining the present model of protection around big population centres and its financing;
c) forbidding the construction of new buildings and infrastructures such as roads, leisure centres, aquacultures and others in the vicinity of the shoreline; and
d) relocation of buildings at risk behind the set back line.

As a final recommendation, Granja & Carvalho (1995) suggest a national political plan with the following alternatives:

1. The maintenance of the hard 'protection' model applied at present, complementing it with artificial beach nourishment. The costs of this alternative should be borne by users, residents and municipalities of the coast through a coastal protection tax and not exclusively by the state budget. The growth of population centres and leisure centres adjacent to the coastline would be forbidden. This choice can only be made using scientific data and a well documented cost–benefit analysis.

2. Preparation for gradual retreat should be made, conveniently planned and weighted, founded on scientific reasons which prove that coastal dynamics determine the retreat of the coastal zone. This alternative pre-supposes the natural evolution (inland migration of beaches, cliff retreat and thinning of beaches) of the coastal sectors in question. With the choice of this alternative, the 'protection' structures could not be justified. Financial compensation to the inhabitants, especially those with meagre economic resources, must be considered.

In both alternatives the municipalities must be involved in decisions of a national character. The local decision makers profit by the absence of realistic laws and so ensure their immediate benefits. The non–participation of tutelar institutions favours the purposes of some policy makers' private interests. It is hoped that the POOCs can put some order in the development of the coastal zone.

127

Acknowledgements

I am grateful to Professor G. Soares de Carvalho, who has studied the coastal zone for many years, for the lively discussions and suggestions. I also want to thank Mr A. Quadros Silva for the wave data and Drs T. De Groot for improving the English text.

References

Carvalho, G.S., Alves, A.C. & Granja, H.M. 1986. Evolução e ordenamento do litoral do Minho. Publicação do Parque Nacional da Peneda-Gerês, Secretaria de Estado do Ambiente e Recursos naturais, Braga. 33 pp.

Castanho, J.P., Gomes, N.A., Oliveira, I.B.M. & Simoes, J.P. 1981. Coastal erosion caused by harbour works on the Portuguese coast and corrective measures. XXV Congress International Navigation Edinburgh, Section II (5):877-898.

Granja, H.M. & Carvalho, G.S. 1991. The impact of "protection" structures on the Ofir-Apúlia coastal zone (NW Portugal). *Quaternary International*, 9:81-85.

Granja, H.M. & Carvalho, G.S. 1995. Is the coastline "protection" of Portugal by hard engineering structures effective? *Journal of Coastal Research*, 11:1229-1241.

Teixeira, A. 1988. As invasões do mar em Espinho através dos tempos. *Boletim Cultural da Câmara Municipal de Espinho*, 7:209-248; 8:389-407.

Valle, A.S. 1988. As obras de protecção e de reconstituição das praias de Espinho (Tema IV). *Recursos Hídricos*, 9(3):57-67.

Studies in European Coastal Management. Jones, Healy and Williams (eds)
1996, Samara Publishing Limited, Cardigan. ISBN 1 873692 07 2

The Retreat of the Eastern Quarteira Cliffed Coast (Portugal) and its Possible Causes

F. Correia, J.A. Dias, T. Boski & Ó. Ferreira

UCTRA, Universidade do Algarve, Portugal

Abstract: The coastline east of the town of Quarteira (Algarve, Portugal) is characterised by 5-30 m high cliffs cut into poorly consolidated Pliocene-Pleistocene sediments. In this highly urbanised area, rapid coastal retreat has important socio-economic impacts. A time series of aerial photographs (1958, 1969, 1976, 1983 and 1991) enabled the cliff-top position to be used as a measurement reference point to quantify the putative impact of man-made structures upon coastal retreat. Based on photographic evidence, cliff erosion rates at Forte Novo of approximately 0.7 m/year increased to 1.4 m/year after the construction of the Vilamoura jetties and Quarteira groyne fields in 1972/3. At Trafal, some 0.3 km east of Forte Novo, a time lag was observed with an erosion rate of around 0.7 m/year up until 1976 being succeeded by an erosion rate of 1.6 m/year. During the period between 1983 and 1991, the erosion rate increased to 3.0 m/year or more at both sites. At Vale do Lobo the construction of a rip rap seawall seems to have resulted in severe erosion both updrift and downdrift of the structure, with an erosion rate of 1 m/year or less rising to nearly 2 m/year following its construction.

Erosion rate calculations for the entire coastal stretch suggest that jetties induce strong downdrift erosion, groynes transfer the erosion related problems to neighbouring sectors and erosion is enhanced both updrift and downdrift of longitudinal seawall structures.

Introduction

The Algarve coast of southern Portugal is morphologically dominated by cliffs cut into predominantly sandy, heterogeneous Pliocene–Pleistocene sediments (Boski *et al.*, 1993). Numerous joints and faults run through these sediments and the extent of consolidation varies. The low degree of lithification promotes high annual erosion rates.

Wave climate is controlled by winds/waves originating from the south, southeastern and southwestern quadrants, with the latter being the dominant direction. Littoral drift is from east to west or *vice versa* according to the wave direction, but the annual resultant is always from west to east. An intense man–made transformation of the entire area has taken place during the last 25 years due to tourism and urban development. The cliffs to the east of Quarteria (Figure 1) have been severely affected by development. Tourist villages, golf courses, buildings on the beach, fisheries infrastructure, marina jetties and coastal defences (including groynes and seawalls) are all expressions of growing development.

In the last decade, several attempts have been made to determine shoreline retreat rates in the region (Dias, 1984; Granja, 1984; Bettencourt, 1985; Andrade *et al.*, 1989; Marques, 1991; Marques & Romariz, 1991; Dias & Neal, 1992; Correia *et al.*, 1994).

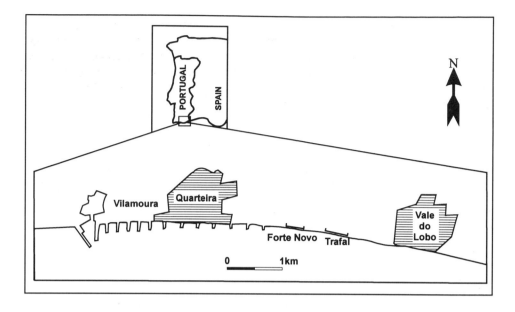

Figure 1   **Location of the study area showing the Vilamoura marine jetties, the Quarteira groyne field and the two study areas (Forte Novo-Trafal and Vale do Lobo)**

Published results vary widely, mainly due to the use of different measurement methods. These include cartographic analyses, cliff profile monitoring in the field and the comparison of aerial photographs taken over time.

A common problem with studies which use aerial photographs to determine shoreline location concerns the lack any quantitative treatment of errors present within the data. In many instances, a best guess estimate is made or errors are ignored altogether (Thieler & Danforth, 1994).

The two main goals of this paper are therefore to:

a) evaluate the impact of man–made structures on coastal development using vertical aerial photographs; and

b) estimate, with photogrammetric techniques, the accuracy of the measurements.

Methods

Two cliff sectors were chosen for this study (Figure 1); Vale do Lobo and the coastline between Forte Novo and Trafal. Five sets of black & white vertical aerial photographs taken in 1958, 1969, 1976, 1983 and 1991 (scale range 1:25,000–1:30,000) were used as a source of data. For each photographic set, the edge of the cliff-top was drawn using an analytical stereo plotter (ZEISS PLANICOMP P3 – floating mark of 36 µm) linked to a computer. A grid of transects 10 m apart and orientated at 90° to the edge of the cliff-top was plotted and mean retreat rates calculated for each time interval between photosets.

The accuracy of maps and digital topographic data depends on the basic operations in conducting a photogrammetric mapping process (American Society of Photo-grammetry, 1980; Ackermann, 1991). Sources of error include relating identifiable points on the ground to the photograph ($\sigma1^2$), aerial photography ($\sigma2^2$), aerial triangulation ($\sigma3^2$), orientation ($\sigma4^2$), stereo compilation ($\sigma5^2$), drafting ($\sigma6^2$) and printing ($\sigma7^2$). The contribution of these elements to the overall accuracy of a map (σ^2) can be expressed as:

$$\text{Total accuracy } \sigma^2 = \sigma1^2 + \sigma2^2 + \sigma3^2 + \sigma4^2 + \sigma5^2 + \sigma6^2 + \sigma7^2$$

Estimates of the total accuracy of plannimetric and altimetric measurements were made. The plannimetric error for erosion rates ranged between 0.40 m and 0.70 m. The error in altimetry is dependant on stereo plotter characteristics together with the height of the plane above ground. In this study, the maximum error was 0.50 m.

Results and discussion

Forte Novo-Trafal case study

Mean cliff retreat rates for the Forte Novo-Trafal and Vale do Lobo study areas are presented in Figure 2. In the period 1958-1969, the entire coastline was subject to a uniform retreat rate of around 0.7 m/year, suggesting a natural erosion trend. Historical records indicate that coastal erosion has been occurring since the 1940s. For example, topographic and hydrographic surveys showed a total retreat of 30 m for the period 1941-1959 at Quarteira beach (Guillemot, 1974).

During 1971, one groyne was built at the eastern end of Quarteira beach to protect the sea front of the town from storm waves. The construction of another ten groynes followed between 1972 and 1973, resulting in the protection of the main extent of the town (Figure 3) (Guillemot, 1974; Bettencourt, 1985). Simultaneously, marina jetties were built at Vilamoura to the west of the Quarteria groyne field. The construction of these structures was marked by a net increase in cliff retreat rates for the 1969-1976 period (Figure 2). This was most pronounced in the Forte Novo sub-sector where cliffs receded by up to 15 m (Table 1). In this period, the mean retreat rate at Forte Novo was 9.5 m, corresponding to 1.4 m/year. During this same period, the mean retreat rate for Trafal was 0.7 m/year, similar to the rate calculated for the period prior to the construction of the jetties and groynes. These data suggest that the construction of jetties and groynes at Quarteira may have resulted in an increase in the rate of shoreline erosion at Forte Novo. However, in the Trafal sub-sector (300 m to the east of Forte Novo), the rate of erosion appears to have remained steady until at least 1976. This effect may have been due to the increased availability of sediment resulting from the erosion of the cliffs at Forte Novo. In the period 1976-1983, mean cliff retreat rates increased, reaching values of 3.1 m/year at Forte Novo and 1.6 m/year at Trafal. Between 1983-1991, these rates increased further, reaching values of 3.5 m/year (Forte Novo) and 3.0 m/year (Trafal). The rate of erosion thus appears to be increasing and extending to the east.

The most likely explanation for the increased erosion rate is that littoral drift may have been interrupted by the construction of groynes and jetties at Quarteria and Vilamoura.

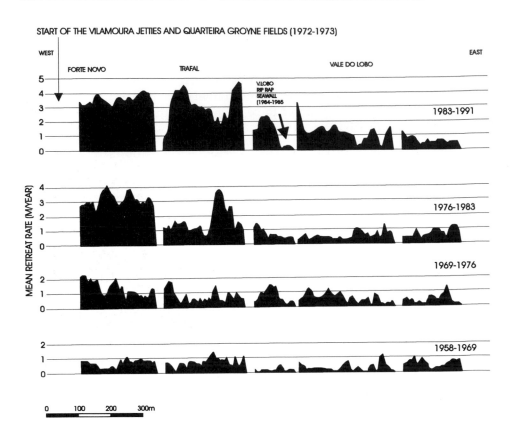

START OF THE VILAMOURA JETTIES AND QUARTEIRA GROYNE FIELDS (1972-1973)

Figure 2 **Variations in the mean rate of cliff retreat over time (m/year) for discrete sections of the coast in the vicinity of Quarteria (southern Portugal)**

Adapted from Correia *et al.*, 1994

Table 1 **Maximum (Max), minimum (Min) and mean extent of cliff-top retreat (metres) over time for the Forte Novo-Trafal study area**

Time period	1958 - 1969			1969 - 1976			1976 - 1983			1983 - 1991		
Study area	Max	Mean	Min	Max	Mean	Min	Max	Mean	Min	Max	Mean	Min
Forte Novo	10.5	8	4	15	9.5	4	28	21.9	15	33	28.3	24.5
Trafal	16	8.1	2	13	5	2	25	11.2	4	36	24.4	5

Figure 3   **View of Forte Novo, showing the Quarteira groyne field and the remains of a house on the beach (photo taken 26 April 1995)**
In the 1970s this house was on the cliff but its remains now lie some 60 m to seaward of the cliff edge

Vale do Lobo case study

Vale do Lobo is a high quality tourist village located 4 km to the east of Quarteira. The construction of the village began in the 1960s and until the 1970s mean cliff retreat rates were relatively small, mostly ranging between 0.6 m/year and 1.0 m/year. However, the sea front swimming pool at Vale do Lobo (Figure 4) was severely affected by coastal erosion in 1976. In the following years, the swimming pool platform and foundations were exposed and water pipes damaged. In the early 1980s the situation became critical. Between 1984 and 1985 a rip rap seawall was built at the base of the cliff in order to protect the swimming pool, restaurants and shops (Figure 5).

By 1986, the effects of wave attack due to wave diffraction caused by the seawall could be seen, especially at the eastern edge of the swimming pool (Dias & Neal, 1992).

For a distance of 100 m to the east and west of the seawall, mean cliff retreat rates doubled between 1983 and 1991 relative to the previous period (1976–1983), reaching values of almost 2 m/year. In the 1983-1991 time period, the measured maximum total cliff retreat was 19 m to the west and 29 m to the east of the seawall (Table 2). In spite of additional protective stone revetments and limited beach replenishment, the situation continues to be critical. For example, field

Figure 4   East facing view of the swimming pool and village at Vale do Lobo (photo taken 21 April 1976)

Figure 5   The same view on 9 January 1995 showing the rip rap seawall in front of the swimming pool
Cliff retreat is especially noticable to the west of the seawall (foreground of photograph)

Table 2   Maximum (Max), minimum (Min) and mean extent of cliff-top retreat (metres) over time for the Vale do Lobo study area

Data is presented for two 100 m sections of cliff coast, one to the east and one to the west of the rip rap seawall

Time period	1958 - 1969			1969 - 1976			1976 - 1983			1983 - 1991		
Study area	Max	Mean	Min	Max	Mean	Min	Max	Mean	Min	Max	Mean	Min
Vale do Lobo West	2.5	1.7	1	10.5	7.2	2.5	10	5.8	2.5	19	15.2	10.5
Vale do Lobo East	8	7.5	2	9.5	5.3	2	5	3.6	2	29	14.2	9

monitoring carried out by the authors in 1994 revealed local cliff retreat of the order of 6 m east of the rip rap. West of this structure, cliffs are still retreating and at least two houses are currently at risk from collapse. At Vale do Lobo the Quarteira and Vilamoura coastal structures are again implicated as the initial causal agents of erosion. In this case, the construction of the protective rip rap seawall appears to have exacerbated this by causing severe erosion on either side of the structure.

Conclusions

Determination of cliff retreat rates using both vertical aerial photographs and photogrammetric techniques for the coastal area between Quarteira and Vale do Lobo enables the following conclusions to be made:

1. The construction of the Vilamoura jetties and Quarteira groyne field appeared to induce an immediate and intense impact upon the cliff coastline to the east. This was probably due to interruption of the littoral drift process.

2. The effect of these structures is apparently continuous and is progressively expanding to the east.

3. The rip rap seawall built in front of the Vale do Lobo swimming pool has resulted in increased erosion on both flanks of the structure.

4. These results confirm the dictum that hard coastal defence structures can be effective for buildings located behind them, but can induce negative impacts on adjacent coastal areas. Quarteira town has been effectively protected by hard coastal defences since the early 1960s. However, downdrift erosion problems have been apparent since this date and several houses have been destroyed. Currently, the situation is critical, especially in the most densely populated section of the coast at Vale do Lobo.

Acknowledgements

The authors which to thank the Instituto Geográfico do Exército (IGeoE), for their collaboration in the photogrammetric restitution and Mr Paolo Ciavola for reviewing and providing comments on the manuscript.

References

Ackermann, R. 1991. *General Aspects of Mapping.* ITC Lecture Notes. ITC, Enschede, Netherlands. 17 pp.

Andrade, C.A.F., Viegas, A.L., Tomé, A.M.B. & Romariz, C. 1989. Erosão do litoral cenozóico do Algarve. *Geolis,* Lisboa 3:261-270.

American Society of Photogrammetry. 1980. *Manual of Photogrammetry.* 4th edition. Falls Church, Va, American Society of Photogrammetry. 1056 pp.

Bettencourt, P. 1985. Géomorphologie et processus d'évolution récente de la Côte Sotavento (Algarve Sud Portugal). Thèse D.E.A., Université de Bordeaux I, Bordeaux, France. 92 pp. (unpublished).

Boski, T., Antão, D.M. & Zazo, C. 1993. Lithostratigraphy of Quaternary deposits in Central Algarve. *INQUA MBSS Newsletter,* 15:16-19.

Correia, F., Dias, J.M. Alveirinho & Boski, T. 1994. The retreat of Eastern Quarteira cliffed coast and its possible causes (preliminary results). *GAIA,* Lisboa, 9:119-122.

Dias, J.M.A. 1984. Evolução geomorfológica das arribas do Algarve. *3º Congresso sobre o Algarve - Textos das Comunicaões,* Vilamoura, 2:705-712.

Dias, J.M.A. & Neal, W.J. 1992. Sea cliff retreat in southern Portugal: Profiles, processes, and problems. *Journal of Coastal Research,* Fort Lauderdale, Florida, 8(3):641-654.

Granja, H. 1984. Etude géomorphologique, sédimentologique et géochimique de la Ria Formosa (Algarve-Portugal). Thèse 3ème cycle, Université de Bordeaux I, Bordeaux. 254 pp. (unpublished).

Guillemot, E. 1974. Le littoral de la région de Faro - Etude de morphologie littorale. Thèse D.E.A., Université de Paris IV, Paris. 131 pp. (unpublished).

Marques, F.M.S.F. 1991. Taxas de recuo das arribas do litoral do Algarve e sua importância na avaliação de riscos geológicos. Seminário "A Zona Costeira e os Problemas Ambientais" (Eurocoast), 18-20 Sept, 1991, Aveiro, 1:100-108.

Marques, F.M.S.F. & Romariz, C. 1991. Nota preliminar sobre a evolução de arribas litorais. 4º Cong. Nac. Geotecnia, 2-4 Out. 1991, LNEC Lisboa 1:57-66.

Thieler, E.R. & Danforth, W.W. 1994. Historical shoreline mapping (I): Improving techniques and reducing positioning errors. *Journal of Coastal Research,* Fort Lauderdale, Florida, 10(3):549-563.

Studies in European Coastal Management. Jones, Healy and Williams (eds)
1996, Samara Publishing Limited, Cardigan. ISBN 1 873692 07 2

Sediment Dynamics of a Coastal Foredune at Schiermonnikoog, The Netherlands

S.M. Arens

Landscape and Environmental Research Group, University of Amsterdam, The Netherlands

Abstract: The sediment dynamics of a coastal foredune was studied between November 1990 and May 1991. Digital Terrain Models (DTMs) of the study area were constructed. The time of construction was chosen after important events. Three time periods can be distinguished, each of which is characterised by the dominance of different processes. In these periods, detailed meteorological measurements and observations of sediment transport rates were performed. This paper presents comparisons between volumetric changes as derived from DTM calculations and calculated sediment transport based on meteorological observations and current transport equations. The main conclusion is that the observed changes in volume correspond reasonably well to predicted transport using standard transport equations and meteorological measurements, but only during part of a yearly cycle.

Introduction

The Dutch foredunes comprise one of the most dynamic geomorphological systems in the Netherlands. Geomorphological processes can operate violently and changes in the landscape may become visible within hours. In order to study the sediment dynamics of foredunes in the Netherlands, field studies and detailed analyses of processes were performed. Meteorological and geomorphological parameters were measured continuously using automated equipment. Changes in the landscape were recorded over a period of months. In this paper, a first comparison is made between these long term observations and the short term measurements for one of the study sites.

Methods

The study area is situated on the Wadden Island of Schiermonnikoog in the north of the Netherlands (Figure 1). The site comprises a wide beach (>500 m) and an exposed, northwest facing, low (<6 m above NAP[1]), gently sloping and well vegetated foredune. The area has been described in detail by Arens (1994) and Arens *et al.* (1995). Four DTMs were constructed after important geomorphic events. In an area of 50 x 250 m², heights were recorded where obvious changes in slope were observed. Heights were transformed into an equidistant grid (provided by the Survey

---

1   NAP - Dutch Ordnance Datum, approximately mean sealevel.

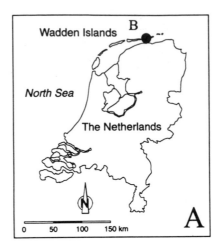

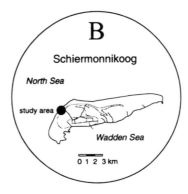

Figure 1   Location of study area

Department, Rijkswaterstaat) with pixels of 5 x 5 m². Meteorologic variables were measured using electronic equipment (Arens, 1994, 1996; Arens *et al.*, 1995). Transport rates were measured using saltation sand traps (Arens & van der Lee, 1995) and saltiphones (Spaan & van den Abeele, 1991; Arens, 1996).

Results

Due to seasonal variations in weather conditions, several time periods can be distinguished. Usually the storm season, with strong winds from southwest to northwest, extends from November to January/February. In the winter season, stormy periods often alternate with cold periods, characterised by temperatures below zero and easterly winds. From March to May, weather conditions can be variable with calm conditions and high temperatures alternating with strong northerly winds and periods of rainfall.

Data collected for the purposes of this study were recorded on the beach as follows: wind speed at 0.87 and 5.15 m height, wind direction at 5.5 m height; dry and wet bulb temperature at 1.15 m height; and saltiphone at 0.11 m height. Rainfall was measured on the foredune, using a tipping bucket rain gauge. Only hourly averages (with respect to rainfall hourly totals) are considered here.

Changes in topography

Figure 2 shows the topographic isolines for the study area at the beginning and the end of the measuring period and Figure 3 shows changes in height following the periods described below.

Period 1: 28 November 1990 – 14 December 1990

This period was mainly characterised by strong winds in combination with high rainfall and marine erosion during one major storm (12th December). The occurrence of a high water level (+3.40 m NAP) resulted in a marine transgression of the foredune, causing a redistribution of sand within the dune system. The output of sand was limited (10 m³ over the total area, 0.2 m³/m). This sand mainly originated from the beach. In the area above +4.00 m NAP, no volume changes were observed. Erosion of the seaward slope of the foredune resulted in a decrease in height, locally of 0.5 m. Most of this sand was deposited on the upper part of the beach (between +2.25 and +2.75 m NAP, giving an increase in height of up to 0.1 m). In this case, marine erosion caused a redistribution of sand within the system without scarp development.

Period 2: 14 December 1990 – 7 March 1991

The second period was characterised by stormy weather alternating with cold conditions. For most of this time the wind was parallel to the foredunes or offshore. Parallel winds have a limited effect on topography, being mainly concentrated in the zone between the dune foot and the upper part of the beach. With offshore winds, some erosion of sand near the dune foot may occur. For this site, the displaced sand was redeposited on a lower, moist part of the beach. Some events with onshore winds and sediment transport occurred, with deposition of sand at the front of the foredune (above +3.25 m NAP). In total, the volume of the study area changed slightly (an increase of 4 m³ or 0.08 m³/m).

Period 3: 7 March 1991 – 22 May 1991

The third period was the main phase of dune building. Onshore winds supplied sand from the beach. First, this sand was deposited near the dune foot. During stronger onshore winds, (when transport on the beach ceases, due to flooding by sea water) most of this sand was eroded and transported up slope. In a period of only a few days, new dunes were constructed on the vegetated slope, with a characteristic gentle windward slope and steep slipface. The height of these dunes extended to 0.5 m above the former surface. The total sediment input in the system was 106 m³, or 2.1 m³/m. Sediment input from the beach declined in May because of the development of algal crusts. From that time, sediment transported inland was derived from aeolian erosion of the dune foot.

a) 28 Nov 1990

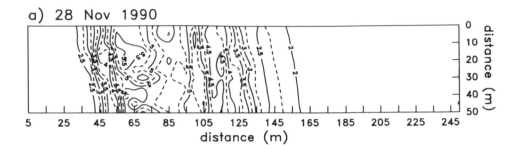

b) 22 May 1991

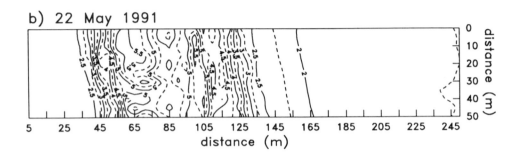

c)

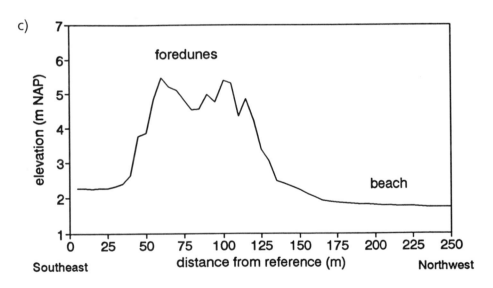

Figure 2   The topography of the study area for two dates

a   28 Nov 1990

b   22 May 1991

c   a simplified transverse profile of the study area

The isolines connect points of equal height (m NAP) have been drawn at 0.25 m height intervals

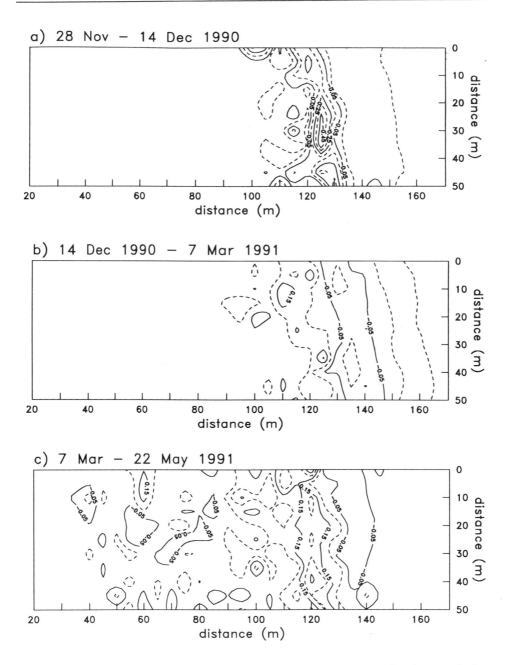

Figure 3   **Plan showing the change in height (m) of the study area for three periods**

a   28 Nov - 14 Dec 1990
b   14 Dec 1990 - 7 Mar 1991
c   7 Mar - 22 May 1991

Negative numbers indicate erosion, positive numbers indicate deposition

Comparison of volume changes and transport rates; calculation procedures

The main changes in topography during period 3 occurred within a few days, with strong onshore winds. Observed changes in topography (long term) are related to measurements of processes (short term). By using meteorological data, the total volume of sediment transported in this period can be calculated and compared to changes in sediment volume as observed by DTMs.

Standard transport equations use friction velocity for the calculation of potential transport. By assuming a logarithmic wind profile in the inner boundary layer,

$$U_z = \frac{U_*}{\kappa} \ln \frac{z}{z_0} \tag{1}$$

it is justified to use the wind speed U_z at the lowest level (0.87 m) and a fixed value of the roughness length z_0 for calculation of the friction velocity U_* near the surface. This method was proposed by Arens et al. (1995) to avoid deviations in the determination of the friction velocity caused by stability effects. Therefore,

$$U_* = \frac{U_{CAM\,1-3}\ \kappa}{\ln \dfrac{z_{CAM\,1-3}}{z_0}} \tag{2}$$

with

$$z_{CAM\,1-3} = 0.87 \text{ m}$$
$$U_{CAM\,1-3} = \text{windspeed at } z_{CAM\,1-3} \text{ m}$$
$$\kappa = 0.41 \text{ (von Karman's constant)}$$

Equation (3) gives the proposed value for the roughness length z_0.

$$z_0 = 10^{-4} \text{ m} \tag{3}$$

Figure 4a represents the wind frequency distribution of hourly wind speeds measured in the period 7 March to 22 May 1991. Onshore winds were dominant during this period, with strongest winds from the north and southwest.

According to the formula published by White (1979) and corrected in Blumberg & Greely (1993), potential transport is calculated by:

$$q = C_W \frac{\rho}{g} (U_*)^3 \left(1 - \frac{U_{*t}}{U_*}\right) \left(1 + \frac{U_{*t}}{U_*}\right)^2 \tag{4}$$

with

$$U_{*t} = 0.22 \ (\text{m/s}) \quad \text{critical friction velocity}$$
$$C_W = 2.61 \ (-) \quad \text{White's constant (2.61)}$$
$$\rho = 1.22 \ (\text{kg/m}^3) \quad \text{density of air}$$
$$g = 9.81 \ (\text{m/s}^2) \quad \text{gravitational constant}$$

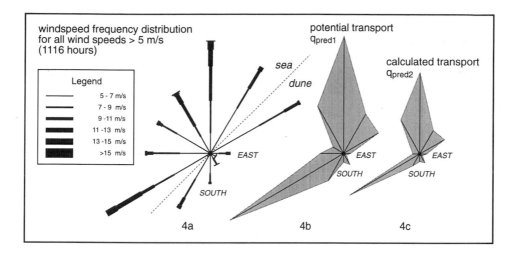

Figure 4   **Wind frequency distribution and potential and calculated sand roses for the study area**

  4a   Wind rose for hourly averaged wind speeds (measured on the beach at 5.15 m above the surface), 7 March - 22 May 1991. Wind speeds <5 m/s are ignored. Length of vectors indicate percentage of occurrence, thickness indicates wind speed

  4b   Sand rose for potential transport q_{pred1}, calculated with the wind frequency distribution and the transport equation (corrected) of White (1979). Vectors indicate importance of sectors relative to total sand transport (vectors are connected for comparison only)

  4c   Sand rose for calculated transport q_{pred2} using the wind frequency distribution of 4a and the transport equation (corrected) of White (1979) adapted with the empirical relationships between transport and humidity, rainfall and wind direction according to Arens (1996)

Combination of the wind frequency distribution and equations (2), (3) and (4) gives the potential sand transport q_{pred1} (Figure 4b). The potential transport is 26.3 m³/m when totalled over all wind directions. When the wind direction is taken into account, the potential sand importation into the foredunes amounts to 8.8 m³/m (with an assumed bulk density of 1,600 kg/m³) which is much higher than the observed volume change of 2.1 m³/m.

Arens (1994, 1996) has shown that actual transport approaches potential transport only during specific conditions. Because of differences in moisture levels, rainfall and fetch, thresholds for sand transport change, and the amounts of sand actually transported are less than predicted. Therefore, Arens proposed empirical relation-ships, relating the changes in threshold velocity U_t to relative humidity, rainfall and wind direction:

$$U_t = U_{tmin} \times \left\{ 1 + 0.17 \, (\, 1 + \cos [\, dd \,] \,) - \frac{2.11}{100} + \frac{2.11}{100 - \% \, RH} \right\} \quad (5)$$

for dry days and

$$U_t = U_{tmin} \times \left\{ 1 + 0.17 \, (\, 1 + \cos [\, dd \,] \,) - \frac{2.11}{100} + \frac{2.11}{100 - \% \, RH} + 0.35 \right\} (6)$$

for wet days,
with

$$U_{tmin} = 5.45 \; \text{m/s} \; (\text{at } 5.15 \text{ m height})$$

Since these relationships were derived for wind speeds measured at 5.15 m height ($CAM1$-1), corrections are necessary:

$$U_{*t} = U_{tCAM1-1} \times \kappa \, \ln \left(z_{CAM1-1} / z_0 \right) \quad (7)$$

$$U_{*tmin} = 0.22 \; \text{m/s} \quad (8)$$

Here a simplification is made, by assuming a constant friction velocity, independent of height. In case of stability effects, this assumption is not valid. It is likely that application of this method has resulted in slight deviations in the predicted critical friction velocities.

Taking these relationships into account (equations 5 and 6) and transforming wind speeds into friction velocities (8), an assumed calculated transport q_{pred2} is computed and presented in Figure 4c. In this case, the total predicted transport is 5.2 m³/m, which is still higher than the observed transport.

The calculated transport rates presented above are theoretical transport rates, based on relationships between transport and meteorological conditions. As Arens (1996) shows, theoretical transport rates often deviate from actual or observed transport. The advantage of a saltiphone is that (despite some instrumental problems) continuous data on actual sand transport are available. Therefore, hours for which the saltiphone has recorded zero transport can be ignored. A new wind frequency distribution for hours with sand transport can be produced, which is visualised in Figure 5a. Figure 5b presents the calculated transport q_{pred3}, using the same equations as above, in combination with the wind frequency distribution of Figure 5a. In this way the 'predicted' total transport amounts 2.8 m³/m, which is of the same order of magnitude as the observed volume change, but still too high. In fact q_{pred3} is not a proper prediction, because measurements of sand transport are used to identify hours without transport. Using current transport equations, it is apparently not possible to accurately predict under which conditions transport is zero.

To compare the predicted transport rates per 30° sector with the saltiphone observations, total recorded saltiphone impacts have been calculated per sector. This gives a relative indication of transport, as it is not yet possible to relate

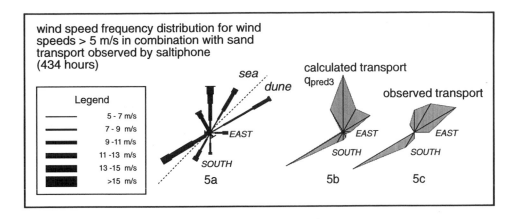

Figure 5   **Wind frequency distribution for sand transport events and calculated and observed sand roses for the study area**

  5a   Wind rose for hourly averaged wind speeds during sand transport events (events without sand transport as observed by saltiphone are ignored)
  5b   Sand rose for calculated transport q_{pred3} as in Figure 4c but using the wind rose of Figure 5a
  5c   Distribution of total number of impacts per sector recorded by the saltiphone

saltiphone grain counts directly to mass transport. Results are shown in Figure 5c. Differences show less important transport in sectors 11 and 12 (300-360°) and more important transport in sectors 1, 2 and 3 (0-90°). The observed differences for sectors 11 and 12 are related to high water levels and reduced fetch. Rainfall events may also be significant: with excessive rainfall, sand transport stops.

Conclusions

The main conclusion is that although prediction of transport for a certain period is of the same order of magnitude as observed changes in volume, it is very difficult to accurately predict when there is no transport. Even for a period during which most of the yearly aeolian events occurred, this causes deviations between observed and calculated transport rates.

This study shows that for this particular site dune building was concentrated in a period of some weeks during spring. In the storm and winter season, hardly any changes in topography due to aeolian events were observed. Changes during these periods were related to marine events.

More research is needed in order to be able to quantify the influence of several factors on aeolian sand transport. Some important factors on which more quantitative information is needed are: the influence of tide/water level; transport during rainfall; the influence of sediment characteristics; moisture effects (surface moisture, groundwater); vegetation effects; topography and interaction with marine processes (either addition or removal of sand to/from the beach).

Acknowledgements

Help from the following people and organisations is acknowledged: W. Gelling and R. Hidding, Rijkswaterstaat, Survey Department, Assen for measuring of DTM's; RIKZ/National Institute for Coastal and Marine Management and directorates Noord-Holland, Friesland and Zeeland of Rijkswaterstaat for financial support; C. Visser, M. Blom and H. Perdok, Rijkswaterstaat, Schiermonnikoog for logistic support during the field work; W. Spaan, Wageningen Agricultural University for providing saltiphones.

References

Arens, S.M. 1994. *Aeolian processes in the Dutch foredunes.* Thesis, University of Amsterdam, The Netherlands. 150 pp.

Arens, S.M. 1996. Rates of aeolian transport on a beach in a temperate humid climate. *Geomorphology*, in press.

Arens, S.M. & Lee, G.E.M. van der. 1995. Saltation sand traps for the measurement of aeolian transport into the foredunes. *Soil Technology*, 8:61-74.

Arens, S.M., Kaam-Peters, H.M.E. van & Boxel, J.H. van. 1995. Air flow over foredunes and implications for sand transport. *Earth Surface Processes and Landforms*, 20:315-332.

Blumberg, D.G. & Greely, R. 1993. Field studies of aerodynamic roughness length. *Journal of Arid Environments*, 25:39-48.

Spaan, W.P. & Abeele, G.D. van den. 1991. Wind borne particle measurements with acoustic sensors. *Soil Technology*, 4:51-63.

White, B.R. 1979. Soil transport by winds on Mars. *Journal of Geophysical Research*, 84(B8): 4643-4651.

Studies in European Coastal Management. Jones, Healy and Williams (eds)
1996, Samara Publishing Limited, Cardigan. ISBN 1 873692 07 2

Metalliferous Mine Waste in West Cornwall: The Implications for Coastal Management

M.G. Healy

Department of Geography, Mary Immaculate College, University of Limerick, Republic of Ireland

Abstract: Metalliferous mining has taken place in Cornwall since the Bronze Age. Copper production in southwest England peaked at 15,255 tonnes of metal in 1860, while c. 12,794 tonnes of tin metal represented its peak production in 1870. Technologies of varied efficiency were employed in the mining industry, which produced large quantities of unwanted material. Waste was frequently disposed of by flushing sediments into local water courses. Much of this material was subsequently transported to the coastal zone. Coastal and river floodplain stratigraphies indicate the presence of mine waste deposits. These are visually distinctive, consisting of finely laminated minerogenic-dominated strata which frequently exhibit a red-brown or grey-green coloration. The structure and texture of these materials corresponds closely with documentary descriptions of mine 'tailings' or 'slimes'. Geochemical analysis of sedimentary cores from selected sites shows that coastal sediment sequences display concentrations of heavy metals in excess of that which may be expected from normal precipitation and weathering. It is concluded that any future large scale disturbance of these deposits may have a significant environmental impact due to heavy metal contamination of sediments, water and biota. A co-ordinated coastal management strategy may help minimise degradation of the coastal resource.

Introduction

Metalliferous minerals have been extracted in parts of west Cornwall since the Bronze Age. Archaeological evidence shows that tin and copper ores were first used to produce weapons and utensils (Dines, 1956). In 1663 the port town of Penzance was appointed a mining town under Royal Charter, becoming a stannary centre in the nineteenth century. The requisites and produce of local mining passed through Penzance until well into the twentieth century.

The main ore minerals found in Cornwall are casserite (SnO_2), wolframite ($[FeMn] WO_4$), arsenopyrite (FeAsS), chalcopyrite ($CuFeS_2$), sphalerite (ZnS) and galena (PbS). Early excavations were in casserite-bearing alluvial sands and gravels. Casserite constitutes the most important ore of tin. Also called 'stream–tin', it is known to have occurred in gravel resting immediately on bedrock and beneath alluvial silt in west Cornwall (Healy, 1993). Where conditions were favourable, it is known that alluvial deposits were repeatedly worked for tin extraction. Marine alluvial tin deposits occur in Mount's Bay and St Ives Bay (Ong, 1966), probably transported by streams flowing through the mining districts. Total production and intensity of tin workings in alluvial deposits is unknown. Copper was obtained from lodes exposed in cliffs. Later, ores of both metals were mined from shallow pits and cliff adits (Ong, 1966). The use of gunpowder and steam engines caused rapid expansion of the mining industry in the 17th and 18th centuries (Hamilton-Jenkin, 1961-1965).

Figure 1 illustrates the production of copper and tin metal in Cornwall and Devon in the period 1200 to 1950 A.D. Copper production peaked at *c.* 15,255 tonnes of metal per annum (tpa) in 1860 but was reduced to almost nil in 1900. Tin production peaked in 1870 (*c.* 12,794 tpa), falling to *c.* 4,000 tpa in 1900 and a few hundred tonnes by 1930. Additionally, a variety of other minerals (including lead and zinc) were brought to the surface as waste. While the graph represents a generalised picture based on documentary sources, it is a useful guide to interpreting the relationship between sedimentation and mining activity through time. It is, however, important to recognise that individual mines may not have conformed precisely to general production patterns.

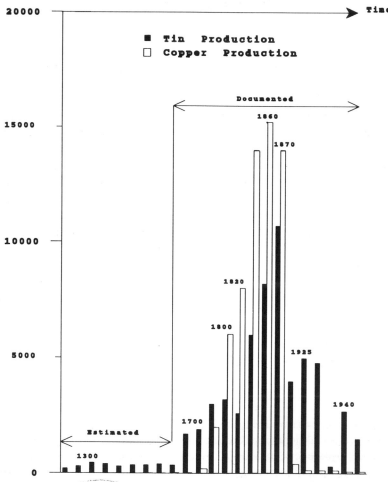

Figure 1   Copper and tin metal production in Devon and Cornwall (thousands of tonnes)

Mine waste materials

In tin and copper mining areas of Cornwall, ores rarely contained mineral grades in excess of 10% (Goode & Taylor, 1988). For this reason mines produced large quantities of waste material. The waste from tin workings, commonly referred to as 'slimes' (Dines, 1956), usually consisted of minerogenic fines (silt and clay size fractions), while other mining debris consisted of randomly assorted and fragmented lithic particles of varied particle size. Primary crushing and sorting (dressing) would produce secondary waste consisting of barren lode material or unwanted (gangue) minerals. In copper mines this often included large quantities of iron or arsenical pyrites, much of which escaped the process of calcination. Metalliferous mine waste has either remained *in situ* in sub-surface dumps or as surface spoil, or has been removed to the coastal lowlands and nearshore area via the fluvial system (National Rivers Authority, 1994). Everard (1962) has demonstrated that the silting of estuaries and bays as a result of mine waste redeposition has been evident on the Cornish coast for many years.

Data sources

Until recently, there has been little collation of documentary evidence relating to the production and disposal of mine waste sediments in Cornwall. While substantial information on the geological and mining background is available, little attention has so far been paid to mine waste redeposition in coastal lowlands. The volume of information on mine waste sedimentation currently available is small and much of what is available is of a generalised and imprecise nature.

The work reported here is based on the findings from a field pilot survey carried out by Healy (1995a). This survey examines the linkages between mine waste materials and the physical and chemical character of sediment sequences at selected sites (Figure 2) in the Cornish coastal lowlands. Field reconnaissance identified sites likely to yield sedimentary records of sufficient quality to satisfy the central aim of the project. A series of sediment cores was retrieved, wrapped and removed to the laboratory for sub-sampling and analysis. The purpose of laboratory work was to establish the concentrations of heavy metals contained within sediment sequences retrieved during field studies. Concentrated nitric acid (HNO_3) was used for sample digestion. Geochemical analysis was performed on a Philips PH7450 Inductively Coupled Plasma Spectrometer (ICP) and a Varian Spectra 250 Plus Atomic Absorption Spectrophotometer (AAS). Procedures and instrumentation used are detailed by Healy (1995a).

Results

A detailed account of site stratigraphies and the results of geochemical analysis for the sites examined is provided by Healy (1995a). The following synopsis of results indicates the physical nature of the sampled substrates and the range of heavy metal concentrations found within sedimentary sequences at the selected study sites.

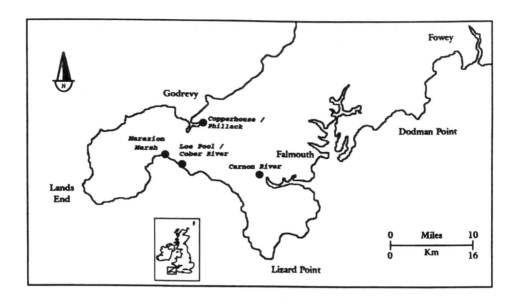

Figure 2   Sites used for the analysis of metalliferous sediments in west Cornwall

Loe Pool

Loe Pool (Figure 2) is a coastal lake located 1 km south of the town of Helston, Cornwall (SW 648 250). The main source of water supply to the lake is the River Cober, which drains approximately 90% of the surrounding catchment (Healy, 1993). At the point where the Cober enters Loe Pool an advanced 'silting up' has taken place. Studies reported by Simola *et al.* (1981), O' Sullivan *et al.* (1982) and Coard *et al.* (1983) show that red-brown/grey sub-laminated sediments occur in Loe Pool. These consist of 'clay-gytta' in the upper sediments underlain by 'red-grey clays'. Coard *et al.* (1983) correlate haematite–rich red-brown layers in the stratigraphy with periods of mining activity in the River Cober catchment.

Samples were taken from two points at this site: a) Loe Pool (from the lake sediment at the mouth of the gorge; and b) Cober River channel (where the river debouches into Loe Pool). The sediment sequence retrieved from the lake bottom extends from +2.27 m to -1.56 m O.D. The stratigraphy is dominated by fine minerogenic material with intermixed biogenic deposits. Concentrations of three metals were measured within the Loe Pool sediment sequence. Iron (Fe) was found to be most abundant within the upper sediment sequence. Concentrations are consistently of the order of 30,000 ppm. The greatest concentrations of copper (Cu) coincide with those of Fe but are generally of a lower order of magnitude, with a peak value of 5,000 ppm. Otherwise, Cu values are of the order of 100 to 1,000 ppm. Tin (Sn) exhibits high concentrations, with a peak of 8,500 ppm and consistently exhibits values of 1,000 ppm to 3,500 ppm. The Cober River channel sequence extends from +4.00 m to +3.26 m O.D. The stratigraphy is dominated by minerogenic material with traces of organic matter, except in the topmost 10 cm where fresh, fibrous, dark brown peat is present. Concentrations of five metals were measured. Cu values are generally less than 600 ppm, though a peak of *c.* 1,300 ppm occurs 10 cm below the present ground surface. Fe values are consistently high throughout, being in the order of 10,000 ppm or above. Concentrations of lead (Pb) range from *c.* 500 ppm to 1,000 ppm in the majority of the sequence, but rise sharply to *c.* 1,700 ppm at the ground surface. Sn concentrations show a distinct peak of c. 1,850 ppm at +3.53 m O.D. but the majority of values fall between 400 and 1,000 ppm. Zinc (Zn) concentrations are generally low throughout but rise towards the sediment surface.

Marazion Marsh

Marazion Marsh (Figure 2) lies west of Marazion village and landward of St. Michael's Mount (SW 515 298). The marsh is protected from direct marine activity by a sand and gravel barrier. The marsh has a long history of alluvial tin workings (Henwood, 1873). Stream banks reveal deposits of red-brown, fine, laminated sediments (Healy, 1993). Considerable quantities of sediment continue to pass through these streams, necessitating occasional dredging of channels to relieve back-marsh flooding. The presence of alluvial deposits in sub-marine channels in Mount's Bay has been confirmed by acoustic sounding (Goode & Taylor, 1988). Healy (1993, 1995b) has provided a detailed environmental history of the Marazion Marsh site.

Sample material was collected from the banks of the Marazion River. The sediment sequence extends from +3.45 m to +1.91 m O.D. The stratigraphy changes from sand dominance in the upper 50 cm to mainly fine minerogenic material with intermixed biogenic and sand deposits with depth. Concentrations of five metals were measured within the sediment sequence. Concentrations of Cu are generally of the order of 400 to 1,000 ppm, with a peak value of *c.* 1,900 ppm recorded. Highest Fe concentrations coincide stratigraphically with those of Cu. Values generally range from 20,000 to 30,000 ppm. Pb concentrations are of a lower order but mirror the patterns described for Cu and Fe, and Pb values rise sharply towards the sediment surface (*c.* 1,000 ppm). Sn values range from 200 to 1,000 ppm through the sequence. Values for Zn are generally lower than those for other metals at Marazion Marsh.

Copperhouse-Phillack

The River Hayle and its tributaries drain a large catchment area of the north Cornwall coast before debouching into St. Ives Bay. The southern margins of the bay are formed by the Hayle Estuary. A semi-fossilised branch of the estuary (Figure 2) lies between Copperhouse and Phillack (SW 567 382). Stratigraphic studies in this area (Healy, 1993) reveal red-brown/grey-green laminated and sub-laminated depositional layers. The sediment sequence retrieved from Copperhouse-Phillack extends from +3.46 m to +2.73 m O.D., with a peaty topsod overlying minerogenic fines at +3.36 m O.D. This gives way to medium-fine sand with an organic component before minerogenic fines dominate the stratigraphy to +2.96 m O.D. Concentrations of five metals were measured within the Copperhouse-Phillack sediment sequence. Cu concentrations generally range between 3,000 and 4,500 ppm between +2.74 m and +3.20 m O.D., with a pronounced peak of 6,300 pm. Values fall sharply within the upper sediment sequence. Fe concentrations are high throughout (*c.* 20,000 to 30,000 ppm) with values reaching c. 70,000 to 80,000 ppm in some horizons. Pb values are generally less than 1,000 ppm but are noticeably higher (2,500 to 3,000 ppm) where silt/clay dominates the stratigraphy. Sn values are generally lower than 1,000 ppm. Values for Zn show a series of peaks and troughs. Peak values exceed 3,000 ppm.

Carnon River

The Carnon River (Figure 2) drains a catchment area which spatially coincides with part of the Gwennap mining district (Dines, 1956). This area has been intensively mined in the past and environmental problems linked to waste water discharge remains a problem in areas adjacent to the river channel and in the Fal Estuary (Carnon Consolidated Ltd, 1992; Dawson, 1993). A sample core was retrieved from the floodplain of the Carnon River in the tidal stretch upstream of Restronguet Creek (SW 786 398). The sediment sequence extends from +6.30 m to +4.76 m O.D. The stratigraphy consists wholly of minerogenic fines with traces of organic debris. Sediment bands are differentiated by colour changes, but these are not indicative of lithological or stratigraphic variations. Concentrations of five metals were measured. Values for Cu generally fall within the range 4,000 to 10,000 ppm, with a prominent peak of 15,000 ppm. Fe values are very high throughout, ranging from *c.* 22,500 to 85,000 ppm in the upper horizons and reaching 127,000 ppm at +5.76 m O.D. Pb values are *c.* 800 to 1,200 ppm through the majority of the sequence, with a notable increase in the surface 10 cm where Pb values reach in excess of 10,000 ppm. Sn concentrations vary from 250 to 1,200 ppm through the sediment sequence, with a single sample demonstrating 2,000 ppm. Zn values are more variable, generally ranging from 800 to 1,800 ppm, with a well defined peak reaching 6,000 ppm between +5.20 m and +5.35 m O.D.

Defining the environmental problem

Heavy metals occur naturally but human activities in mining districts have greatly increased their concentrations, sometimes to a toxic degree. Where more than 1,000 ppm of any metal is present it is usually toxic to plants. Consequently, toxic sediments and soils remain bare and subject to erosion for many years (Thompson *et al.*, 1986). Metalliferous ore extraction results in the production of large quantities of waste material. Such waste may remain *in situ* as 'spoil', or be dispersed in drainage waters to contaminate river and coastal systems far beyond the immediate area of extraction. Metals remaining in wastes are often toxic to animals and humans as well as plants. The presence of high concentrations of heavy metals in sediments and soils gradually leads to available metal uptake by tolerant plants, thus providing a mechanism for entry into food chains/webs. Alterations in coastal wetland geochemistry affects the flora and fauna, but the nature of the problem relates to hydrological transfer routes, reactivities, sedimentation, erosion and bioturbation processes (Viles & Spencer, 1995). Understanding and managing environments in which these problems occur presents a serious challenge for coastal planning and management.

In west Cornwall, the sites studied contain sediment sequences which exhibit physical and chemical characteristics concordant with mining activity and associated redeposition of waste materials. Stratified near-surface sediments display distinctive coloration and sub-lamination. The most common visual characteristic is red-brown mottling (Marazion Marsh, Cober River) and grey-green coloration (Marazion Marsh, Copperhouse-Phillack, Loe Pool). Frequently, colour changes are associated with other physical alterations, in particular particle size (Marazion Marsh, Copperhouse-Phillack). Spatially continuous lamination is rare, possibly suggesting an irregular topography in depositional areas linked to variation in water and sediment throughflow, with 'pulses' of mine waste materials reaching coastal areas through time. Geochemical analysis of samples from sediment sequences with these characteristics reveal that concentrations of heavy metals commonly exceed toxic levels in west Cornwall. Studies published by Abrahams & Thornton (1987), Johnson & Thornton (1987), Brown (1977) and Yim (1976) support this conclusion.

At present, the majority of contaminated sediments remains inactive except in exceptional circumstances, such as the Wheal Jane flood of January 1992 (Dawson, 1993). However, as these deposits occur in potentially high energy coastal, riverine and estuarine locations, there is a considerable likelihood of anthropogenic and/or geomorphological disturbance in the future. Site development, building works, engineering projects and infrastructure improvements have the potential to remobilise mine waste materials. Additionally, geomorphologically induced coastal change, linked to relative sea-level movements (Healy, 1995b), may provide a mechanism for redistribution of contaminated sediments. In the absence of more widespread and detailed surveys the consequences of such disturbance for human health and nature conservation remain unknown.

The coastal management response

At present, there is no comprehensive data on the extent of contaminated land in the UK. While individual organisations are concerned about specific environmental problems linked to land contamination (e.g. the National Rivers Authority initiatives on water quality in Devon and Cornwall), co-ordinated management of areas affected by particular contamination sources remains absent. The evidence presented in this paper suggests that there are significant actual or potential environmental problems linked to land contamination by metalliferous mine waste redeposition in some coastal areas of west Cornwall. This has clear implications for the management of depositional sites at or adjacent to coastal areas. As the majority of such sites take the form of coastal wetlands, marshes, lagoons, estuaries and river floodplains, the potential for contamination of ground and surface water is important. In addition, flora and fauna have limited and specific tolerance thresholds for the uptake of heavy metals, the presence of which will consequently limit biodiversity and constrain the biological resource. Hart & Lake (1987) have summarised several Australian studies which illustrate the risk of heavy metal contamination to human health and wildlife. In a specific study of tin mining and coastal pollution, Chansang (1988) details the environmental consequences of alluvial mining for casserite on the coast of Thailand which has been detrimental to the physical, chemical and biological balance of coastal ecosystems.

While the nature of the problems described may generate serious environmental degradation, solutions which could ameliorate or prevent the most serious consequences of heavy metal contamination have been devised and employed successfully in some mining districts (Bradshaw, 1984). Addressing the problems of the west Cornwall coast remains primarily a question of co-ordinated surveying, data collation and effective environmental management.

The main requirements are:

1. An integrated and comprehensive quantitative survey of sites which are, or may be, affected by heavy metal contamination.

2. An assessment of disturbance risk for individual sites.

3. An evaluation of current technologies for treatment and rehabilitation of sites subject to contamination.

4. A planning and management strategy which takes account of actual and potential risks associated with heavy metal pollution.

5. A forum representing interested organisations and individuals to assess the problem of metalliferous mine waste deposits and to co-ordinate appropriate action.

Conclusions

Geochemical data shows that the sediment sequences from each of the study sites examined demonstrate concentrations of heavy metals of an order in excess of that which may be expected from normal precipitation and weathering processes. These sequences appear to be the product of mine waste release and redeposition, with variations in the concentrations of heavy metals representing distinctive geochemical signatures. It is possible that any future large scale disturbance of these deposits may have a detrimental environmental impact due to heavy metal contamination of substrates as well as groundwater and surface water. Specific conclusions may be summarised as follows:

1. A useful literature which deals with the history of mining in Cornwall is available, though this varies in quantity and quality among sites.

2. Depositional sites in the Cornish coastal lowlands contain sediment sequences which are visually and physically distinctive and correlate well with documented descriptions of metalliferous mine waste materials.

3. Geochemical analysis shows that sediments contain unusually high concentrations of heavy metals (Fe, Cu, Zn, Pb and Sn) which correspond with past mining activity in adjacent areas and mine waste release and redeposition in coastal and riverine areas.

4. Further studies on physiographic conditions in these environments may reveal the potential impact of disturbance of these sediments on the coastal resource.

5. A co-ordinated planning and management response is necessary to respond to the problem of heavy metal contamination.

Acknowledgements

The data presented here are based on a survey carried out by Healy (1995a) which was funded under the Commission of the European Communities Environment Programme DG XII (Proposal PL910049) *The impacts of climate change and relative sea-level rise on the environmental resources of European coasts.*

Thanks are due to:

Dr R.J.N. Devoy, Department of Geography, University College Cork, Republic of Ireland who sponsored this project. Also to Mr S. Patel, Environmental & Geographical Sciences, Manchester Metropolitan University, UK for technical assistance and ICP Spectrometer analysis.

References

Abrahams, P.W. & Thornton, I. 1987. Distribution and extent of land contaminated by arsenic and associated metals in mining regions of south west England. *Transactions of the Institution of Mineralogy and Metallurgy, (Sect. B: Applied Earth Science)*, 96:B1–B8.

Bradshaw, A.D. 1984. Land restoration: now and in the future. *Proceedings of the Royal Society of London*, B223:1–23.

Brown, B.E. 1977. Effects of mine drainage on the River Hayle, Cornwall. A) Factors affecting concentrations of copper, zinc and iron in water, sediments and dominant invertebrate fauna. *Hydrobiologica*, 52:221–233.

Carnon Consolidated Limited. 1992. Information Regarding the Discharge of Mine Water from the Gwennap Mining District into the Carnon River. Carnon Consolidated Limited, P.O. Box 2, Truro TR3 6EH, Cornwall.

Chansang, H. 1988. Coastal tin mining and marine pollution in Thailand. *Ambio*, 17:223–228.

Coard, M.A., Cousen, S.M., Cuttler, A.H., Dean, H.J., Dearing, J.A., Eglinton, T.I., Greaves, A.M., Lacey, K.P., O' Sullivan, P.E., Pickering, D.A., Rhead, M.M., Rodwell, J.K. & Simola, H. 1983. Palaeolimnological studies of annually – laminated sediments in Loe Pool, Cornwall, U.K. *Hydrobiologia*, 103:185–191.

Dawson, T.P. 1993. Using GIS for the classification of contaminated land in association with water quality protection. In: *Proceedings of GIS for Environment Conference, Krakow, 25-27 November.* Geographical Information Systems Laboratory, Institute of Geography, Jagiellonian University, Krakow, Poland. pp. 63-69.

Dines, H.G. 1956. The Metalliferous Mining Regions of South West England. *Memoir of the Geological Society of Great Britain.* HMSO, London.

Everard, C.E. 1962. Mining and shoreline evolution near St. Austell, Cornwall. *Transactions of the Royal Geological Society of Cornwall*, 19(3):199-219.

Goode, A.J.J. & Taylor, R.T. 1988. *Geology of the Country Around Penzance.* Memoir of the Geological Society of Great Britain (for the 1:50 000 Geological Sheets 351 and 358 England and Wales). HMSO, London.

Hamilton-Jenkin, A.K. 1961-1965. *Mines and Miners of Cornwall.* D. Bradford Barton Limited, Truro, Cornwall, UK.

Hart, B.T. & Lake, P.S. 1987. Studies of heavy metal pollution in Australia with particular emphasis on aquatic systems. In: *Lead, Mercury, Cadmium and Arsenic in the Environment.* Eds: Hutchinson, T.C. & Meena, K.M. Wiley, Chichester. pp. 187-216.

Healy, M.G. 1993. Holocene Coastal Evolution and Relative Sea-Level Change in West Cornwall, U.K. Unpublished PhD Thesis. National University of Ireland.

Healy, M.G. 1995a. *Mine Waste Sedimentation on the Cornish Coast*. Report for the Commission of the European Communities Environment Programme (DG XII). The Impacts of Climate Change and Relative Sea-Level Rise on the Environmental Resources of European Coasts.

Healy, M.G. 1995b. The lithostratigraphy and biostratigraphy of a Holocene coastal sediment sequence in Marazion Marsh, west Cornwall, U.K. with reference to relative sea-level movements. *Marine Geology*, 124:237-252.

Henwood, W.J. 1873. On the detrital tin ore of Cornwall. *Journal of the Royal Institute of Cornwall*, 4:191-254.

Johnson, C.A. & Thornton, I. 1987. Hydrological and chemical factors controlling the concentrations of Fe, Cu, Zn, and As in a river system contaminated by acid mine drainage. *Water Resources*, 21(3):359-365.

National Rivers Authority. 1994. *Wheal Jane - A Clear Way Forward*. Public Relations Section, National Rivers Authority South Western Region, Exeter, PR3/94.

Ong, P.M. 1966. Geochemical Investigation in Mount's Bay. Unpublished PhD Thesis, University of London.

O' Sullivan, P.E., Coard, M.A. & Pickering, D.A. 1982. The use of laminated lake sediments in the estimation and calibration of erosion rates. In: *Recent Developments in the Explanation and Prediction of Erosion and Sediment Yield*. Proceedings of the Exeter Symposium, 1992. IAHS Publication Number 137.

Simola, H.L.K., Coard, M.A. and O' Sullivan, P.E. 1981. Annual laminations in the sediments of Loe Pool, Cornwall. *Nature*, 290:238-241.

Thompson, R.D., Mannion, A.M., Mitchell, C.W., Parry, M. & Townshend, J.R.G. 1986. *Processes in Physical Geography*. Longman, Essex, England.

Viles, H. & Spencer, T. 1995. *Coastal Problems: Geomorphology, Ecology and Society at the Coast*. Edward Arnold, London.

Yim, W.W. 1976. Heavy metal accumulation in estuarine sediments in a historical mining (area) of Cornwall. *Marine Pollution Bulletin*, 7(8):147-150.

Studies in European Coastal Management. Jones, Healy and Williams (eds)
1996, Samara Publishing Limited, Cardigan. ISBN 1 873692 07 2

Holocene Coastal Evolution in North Norfolk, UK

R. Jones

School of Environmental Sciences, University of East Anglia, UK

Abstract: Global sea-level rise, local subsidence, sediment supply and human influence are important controls on the evolution of coastlines. A UK National Environment Research Council (NERC) funded interdisciplinary research team based at the University of East Anglia (UEA) has begun a study on how the north Norfolk coast has responded to these influences since the last ice age. The study will also investigate how this knowledge can be used to help coastal managers anticipate and manage future coastal change.

Today, north Norfolk's coast is a broad zone of natural and reclaimed saltmarsh protected from the open sea by a complex of beach barriers. This study combines an understanding of the modern day coast with an investigation of the underlying Holocene sediments which contain vital information about the physical evolution of this coast during the last 8,400 years as relative sea-level rose following the last ice age.

Relative sea-level is still rising and will continue to do so in the future at an increasing rate with significant socio-economic implications. Results of this study will put today's 'snapshot' of coastal evolution into the context of longer term trends and so help anticipate the future response of the coast over the next 50-100 years.

Introduction

The present coastline of north Norfolk from Holme-next-the-Sea in the west to Weybourne in the east (Figure 1) is designated as a Heritage Coast and is part of a larger Area of Outstanding Natural Beauty (AONB) in recognition of its landscape and wildlife value. Its national and international importance for wildlife is further reflected in its status as a Special Protection Area (SPA) under the European Communities Bird Directive (Council Directive 79/409/EEC for the conservation of wild birds) and Wetland of International Importance under the 1971 Ramsar Convention.

Despite these designations, the coast is under mounting pressure from recreational use and localised marine erosion. The Norfolk Coast Project, funded by the UK Countryside Commission and local authorities, is producing management strategies to deal with these issues, initially aimed at managing conflicts that arise between wildlife, landscape, recreation and socio-economic interests in the AONB (Hayes, 1995).

Characteristics of the Norfolk coast

Norfolk's coastline is one of contrasting geomorphological features between north and east. In the north, the land slopes gently into the sea across a broad inter-tidal zone (Figure 1) with mud flats, tidal creeks and saltmarshes fronted by sand flats,

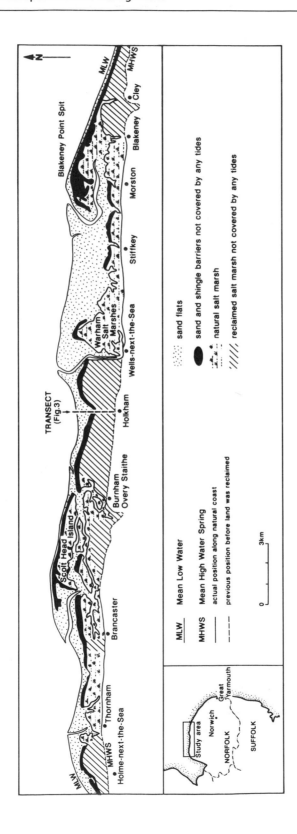

Figure 1   Map of the north Norfolk coast showing the width of the inter-tidal zone and the distribution of modern day depositional environments

sand dunes, a gravel spit (Blakeney Point) and a barrier island (Scolt Head). The width of the inter-tidal zone ranges from 1-4 km. During high spring tides the whole of the unreclaimed coastal zone is under water apart from the barriers of Scolt Head Island, Blakeney Point and the northern tip of the Warham Saltmarsh. Important geomorphological and botanical data from these sites is summarised in Allison & Morley (1989).

This is Norfolk's soft coastline and is highly dynamic, characterised by localised erosion and accretion in the present day. The physical coastal features observed in north Norfolk are mainly the result of natural processes. Human influence has been relatively minor and includes building earth sea walls, draining saltmarshes, stabilising beach barriers and dredging navigation channels. In contrast, to the east beyond Weybourne the coastline is defined by steep cliffs of chalk and Quaternary glacial deposits fringed by a sand/shingle beach. This 'hard' coastline is undergoing cliff erosion and loss of sediment at present, requiring coast protection measures in some areas. Coastal accretion in the study area has been possible due to an abundant supply of sediment during the Holocene. Today, the coast is dominated by wave and tidal processes and almost all sediment is of marine origin. Sediment comes from three main sources:

1. It is eroded from the poorly consolidated sea cliffs between Weybourne and Sheringham (Figure 2) and subsequently transported west by longshore currents (Clayton et al., 1983). East of Cromer, longshore currents transport sediment southeast towards Great Yarmouth (Figure 2). Erosion is occurring in the region between Sheringham and Cromer consequent on wave refraction controls.

2. Gravel from this local source travels no further west than the western tip of the Blakeney Point spit, so the source of gravel for Scolt Head Island is not entirely clear. It is most likely that both sand and gravel was supplied to this western area from the Burnham Flats, an extensive offshore sheet of gravely sand north of the coast, by waves and tidal currents (Clayton, 1989; Shih–Chiao & Evans, 1992). The paths of tidal currents are complex in this part of the North Sea (Figure 2) with the net effect being onshore currents in the Hunstanton to Sheringham area and offshore currents east of Cromer (Shih–Chiao & Evans, 1992).

3. The large volume of mud and silt that is accumulating on the saltmarshes of north Norfolk is transported in suspension from other sources (Eisma, 1981). At present, sediment supply is more or less balancing relative sea-level rise along the north Norfolk coast. The implications of an increasing rate of rise in relative sea-level are discussed later.

The Holocene sedimentary record

Stratigraphies containing inter-tidal sediments which represent Holocene coastal evolution (c. 11,000 years) are preserved in this area. A variety of techniques have been employed to elucidate the sedimentary record.

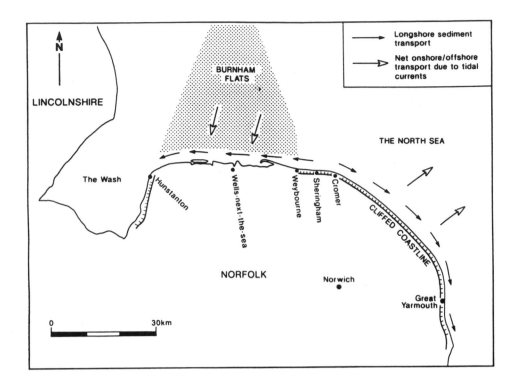

Figure 2 Transport of sediment off the coast of north Norfolk, adapted from Shih-Chiao & Evans (1992)

Building on a study by Funnell & Pearson (1989), new onshore and offshore seismic surveys reveal that Holocene sedimentation infills an underlying glaciated landscape and 'pinches out' onto rising topography of glacial sediments and chalk bedrock 1-4 km inland of the mean low water mark (Figures 1 and 3). Moving seawards, the succession typically thickens to around 10 m and then gradually thins across the subtidal zone to a patchy veneer over the sea floor which extends several kilometres offshore.

Sediment samples have been obtained by coring and augering through the Holocene stratigraphy to the bedrock. Past depositional environments are then determined by analysing the nature of these sediments and their microfossil assemblages. The sediments consist of peat (generally freshwater marsh), mud (upper saltmarsh, lower saltmarsh, inter-tidal mud flat), sand (beach, inter-tidal sand flat, channel fill) and gravel (spit, barrier island, channel fill, inter-tidal flat). The coastal stratigraphy from the central portion of the area at Holkham (Figure 1) is presented in Figure 3, drawn by correlating between sample points. In the more landward position, the section comprises saltmarsh and inter-tidal flat muds, a small proportion of minor channel sands and gravels and two peats, one at the base and one in the middle of the section.

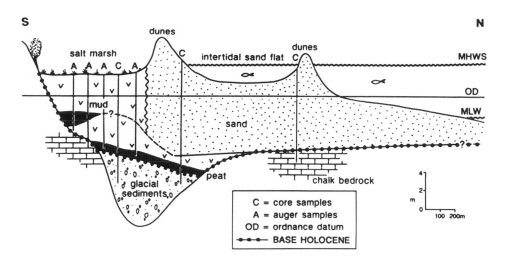

Figure 3   Transect at Holkham (see Figure 1 for transect location) showing depositional environments in the modern day coastal zone and underlying Holocene sediments. Note vertical exaggeration of scale

Seaward, the section is sandier and the peats are often missing. In the most seaward location, the Holocene stratigraphy is comprised entirely of sand directly overlying chalk bedrock. The lateral and vertical variations that are apparent in the stratigraphy record significant events in the evolution of the coastal zone which are discussed later. To assess the timing of these changes, a variety of dating techniques are being applied according to sediment type. These include radiometric techniques (lead, caesium, uranium and thorium isotopes, used in muddy sections), secular magnetic variation measurements (muddy sections), radiocarbon dating (in peats) and optical luminescence (in sands). Dating will enable correlations to be made between boreholes, ultimately resulting in a three-dimensional picture of the Holocene sedimentary record and a fuller understanding of how the coastal zone has evolved through time.

Holocene evolution

As global relative sea-level rose following the last ice age, the southern North Sea was gradually flooded. This led to impeded drainage, waterlogged conditions and consequent peat formation in fresh water marshes which developed along the margin of the chalk hinterland of north Norfolk. Radiocarbon dating of these peats reveal that they began forming around 8,400 years ago (Funnell & Pearson, 1989) when relative sea-level was around 35 m lower than it is today (Arthurton et al., 1994). As relative sea-level rose to around 10 m lower than present, the sea flooded the freshwater environments for the first time, leading to the earliest cessation of peat accumulation around 6,600 years ago (Funnell & Pearson, 1989). The coastal zone developed into a form broadly similar to that of the present, with marine muds accumulating in saltmarsh and inter-tidal flat environments, pro-tected from the open sea by wave-formed sandy barriers or extensive inter-tidal sand flats. Evidence suggests that the coastal zone has maintained its configuration during the Holocene but has narrowed significantly. In the more landward portion of the area, saltmarsh muds have continued to accumulate throughout the Holocene. In unreclaimed areas of saltmarsh the most landward extent of the early Holocene deposits is only a few hundred metres north of the present day mean high water spring tide (MHWST) mark and hence present depositional limit. This strongly suggests that the MHWST mark had reached approximately its present position by the early Holocene, and despite rising relative sea-level has been prevented from shifting significantly landward since then by the rising hills to the south. In the subsurface, Holocene saltmarsh and peat deposits extend seaward to positions beneath and beyond present day barriers. These deposits have been cored around the Holkham area (Figure 3) and are exposed at low tide on sections of the beaches at Holme, Titchwell, Brancaster and Scolt Head Island. Since these deposits would also have accumulated behind a barrier system, this strongly indicates that the position of the barrier has shifted landwards to its present position during the Holocene. Supporting this evidence, seismic data off the coast of Great Yarmouth to the east suggests the existence of an early Holocene shoreline about 8 km offshore (Arthurton et al., 1994).

These observations reveal that as relative sea-level rose the last 10 m to its present level during the Holocene, the coastal zone narrowed from its seaward side, squeezed against the fixed edge of the rising chalk hills to the south. The landward shift in the position of the barrier is probably related to a rise in relative sea-level which may be contemporaneous with a major flooding phase identified within the Breydon Formation in the Yare River valley and beneath the shoreface off Great Yarmouth (Arthurton et al., 1994), although a reduction in sediment supply may also have played a part. The timing of the shift is thought to have occurred after the formation of the younger peat deposit encountered in some boreholes (Figure 3). This hypothesis will be tested through dating of flooding horizons in the saltmarsh sediments, defined by microfossil analysis and by comparing the timing and nature of events in the Holocene stratigraphy in adjacent areas.

Future changes on the Norfolk coast

Given that around 10 m of inter-tidal sediments have accumulated in north Norfolk since marine conditions began to replace freshwater conditions around 6,000 years ago, then the rate of relative sea-level rise averages at just over 1.5 mm/yr. Although this obviously obscures any long term or short term trends within the Holocene, and periods of erosion, it enables a comparison of total relative sea-level rise to be made with adjacent areas. In the Broadland area of east Norfolk, close to Great Yarmouth, around 20.4 m of inter-tidal sediments accumulated over the last 7,500 years, following the deposition of a basal peat, from which an average rate of relative sea-level rise of approximately 2.7 mm/yr can be estimated (Coles & Funnell, 1981). The discrepancy suggests that overall, the Broadland area underwent more substantial subsidence than north Norfolk during the Holocene.

Global (eustatic) sea-level is estimated to have risen between 1.0 and 2.0 mm/yr over the last 100 years (Warrick & Oerlemans, 1990). Within the next 100 years, the rate of global sea-level rise is predicted to increase to a rate 4 to 5 times faster than in the last century (Wigley & Raper, 1992). If the position of the barrier system along the north Norfolk coast is to remain stable in the future, then sediment supply must keep up with this increased rate. If sediment supply is insufficient, marine erosion will probably shift the barrier landward again, while the MHWST mark would continue to remain relatively fixed against the rising chalk landscape behind, although very low lying areas such as river valleys would be flooded if left unprotected.

There are several reasons why future sediment supply may not be sufficient to keep up with accelerated relative sea-level rise. If the shallow and extensive Burnham Flats off the north coast are providing a large proportion of the current supply of sediment to the coast, rising relative sea-level would increase the water depth, possibly leaving the surface of the sand flats below wave base. This could render the sediment inaccessible to marine processes which currently transport sand and gravel to the shore. Human influence may also affect future sediment supply. Placing groynes beneath cliffs around Sheringham to the east aims to stem cliff erosion and may also reduce longshore transportation of sediment to the barrier coast to the west.

Conclusion

Marine flooding of the north Norfolk coast in the early Holocene established a coastal system of sand and gravel barriers protecting saltmarsh and mud flat environments on their landward side. The coastal zone as a whole has narrowed during the Holocene, probably in response to continued relative sea-level rise. The landward side of the zone has been fairly fixed in its position adjacent to the rising topography to the south, whereas the position of the barriers has shifted significantly landward.

Under the likely future scenario of accelerated global sea-level rise, the coastal zone of north Norfolk is predicted to narrow further by continued landward shifting of the position of the sand and gravel barriers. This would reduce the effectiveness of the coastal zone in protecting coastal communities from exceptional flooding and storm surges.

Given the seemingly inevitable future changes, anticipation and early planning for relative sea-level rise within the constraints of finances, technology and manpower appears wise (Carter, 1988). Preliminary strategies are beginning to take this approach (Brown et al., 1994).

Acknowledgements

This project is funded by the NERC and is a contribution to the LOIS (Land-Ocean Interaction Study) Community Research Project (Publication Number 35). Thanks to co-workers Brian Funnell, Ian Boomer and Neil Chroston for useful discussions during work on this manuscript.

References

Allison, H. & Morley, J. (Eds). 1989. *Blakeney Point and Scolt Head Island*. The National Trust, Norfolk, UK. 116 pp.

Arthurton, R.S., Booth, S.J., Abbott, M.A.W. & Wood, C.J. 1994. *Geology of the Country Around Great Yarmouth*, Memoir for 1:50,000 geological sheet 162 (England and Wales). British Geological Survey, HMSO, London. 138 pp.

Brown, A.F., Grice, P.V., Radley, G.P., Leafe, R.N. & Lambley, P. 1994. *Towards a strategy for the conservation of coastal habitats in north Norfolk*: A discussion paper. *English Nature Research Reports*, No. 74. English Nature, Peterborough, UK.

Carter, R.W.G. 1988. *Coastal Environments: An Introduction to the Physical, Ecological and Cultural Systems of Coastlines*. Academic Press, Harcourt Brace Jovanovich Publishers. 617 pp.

Clayton, K. 1989. Sediment input from the Norfolk cliffs, eastern England - a century of protection and its effect. *Journal of Coastal Research*, 5:33-442.

Clayton, K.M., McCave, I.N. & Vincent, C.E. 1983. The establishment of a sand budget for the East Anglian coast and its implications for coastal stability. In: *Shoreline Protection*. Institute of Civil Engineers, London, UK. pp. 91-96.

Coles, B.P.L. & Funnell, B.M. 1981. Holocene palaeoenvironments of Broadland, England. In: *Holocene Marine Sedimentation in the North Sea Basin*. Eds: Nio, S.D., Shuttenhelm, R.T.E. & van Weering, Tj.C.E. Special Publication of the International Association of Sedimentologists, Number 5, Blackwell, London, UK. pp. 123-131.

Eisma, D. 1981. Supply and deposition of suspended matter in the North Sea. In: *Holocene Marine Sedimentation in the North Sea Basin*. Eds: Nio, S.D., Shuttenhelm, R.T.E. & van Weering, Tj.C.E. Special Publication of the International Association of Sedimentologists, Number 5, Blackwell, London, UK. pp. 415-428.

Funnell, B.M. & Pearson, I. 1989. Holocene sedimentation on the North Norfolk barrier coast in relation to relative sea-level change. *Journal of Quaternary Science*, 4:25-36.

Hayes, G. 1995. *A Visitor Management Strategy for the Norfolk Coast - An Area of Outstanding Natural Beauty*. The Norfolk Coast Project, Norfolk County Council, Norfolk, UK. 82 pp.

Shih-Chiao, C. & Evans, G. 1992. Source of sediment and sediment transport on the east coast of England: Significant or coincidental phenomena? *Marine Geology*, 107:283-288.

Warrick, R.A. & Oerlemans, J. 1990. Sea-level rise. In: *Climate Change: The IPCC Scientific Assessment*. Eds: Houghton, J.T., Jenkins, G.J. & Ephraums, J.J. Cambridge University Press, Cambridge. pp. 257-281.

Wigley, T.M.L. & Raper, S.C.B. 1992. Implications for climate and sea level of revised IPCC emission scenarios. *Nature*, 357:293-300.

Studies in European Coastal Management. Jones, Healy and Williams (eds)
1996, Samara Publishing Limited, Cardigan. ISBN 1 873692 07 2

Monitoring Environmental Change in Chichester Harbour

S. Edwards

Centre for Coastal Zone Management, Department of Geography, University of Portsmouth, UK

Abstract: Chichester Harbour is a natural harbour system in West Sussex, UK. The harbour is managed by the Chichester Harbour Conservancy (CHC). The CHC aims to improve the amenity area for the conservation of wildlife, which requires the monitoring of existing sites. In order to establish the degree of change in the harbour habitat, an environmental study using aerial photography was undertaken. The use of photogrammetric techniques reduced the need for extensive field measurements and provides a permanent site record for future reference. This paper reviews techniques, interpretation and the significance of the results of the study in the context of coastal management. The initial results highlight the importance of having good scientific information with which to inform the management process.

Introduction

Chichester Harbour (Figure 1) is one of three linked natural harbour systems in West Sussex, UK, the others being Portsmouth and Langstone. The harbour has a water area of *c.* 28.5 km² and *c.* 27 km of navigable channels. It is of national importance for its landscape and international importance for its ecology. It is designated an Area of Outstanding Natural Beauty (AONB) with a variety of habitats, including saltmarsh, sand, shingle and a mix of wooded shores and creeks (CHC, 1992). The ecological importance of the harbour is recognised in its designation as a Site of Special Scientific Interest (SSSI) under the UK Wildlife and Countryside Act (1981). It is a Wetland of International Importance under the Ramsar Convention (1971) and a Special Protection Area (SPA) under the EC Birds Directive (Council Directive 79/409/EEC for the conservation of wild birds). Within Chichester Harbour there is a substantial Local Nature Reserve at Nutbourne Marshes, with a Royal Society for the Protection of Birds (RSPB) Reserve at Pilsey Island. The National Trust owns and manages East Head spit sand dune system in West Sussex.

Prior to 1971, the administration of the Harbour was divided between the two separate harbours of Emsworth and Chichester. The CHC was created in 1971. It has statutory powers over the water area of the harbour and an advisory role over the land included within the conservancy (CHC, 1992). The CHC actively seeks to buy land within the AONB to allow management through ownership. Management activity is designed for the benefit of recreation, conservation and natural beauty. The CHC was identified as a model for coastal zone management by the House of Commons Environment Select Committee Report on *Coastal Zone Protection and Planning* (HMSO, 1992).

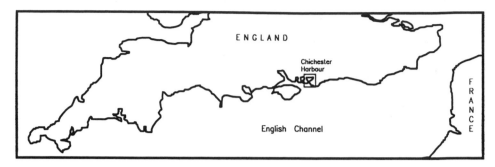

Figure 1   Location of Chichester Harbour, West Sussex, UK

One of the CHC's policy objectives is the improvement of the amenity area for the conservation of wildlife (CHC, 1993). This requires monitoring of existing habitat types. A significant concern has been the loss of saltmarsh habitat. Around 1920-1930 it is estimated that there was some 81 ha of prime saltmarsh within the harbour. Current estimates suggest that there is now only about 16 ha. One of the main purposes of the study reported here is to attempt to quantify the extent and rate of loss of saltmarsh in the harbour using aerial photography.

Techniques

A set of 1:10,000 scale, colour, infra red, diapositive photographs taken in 1978 was used to provide the baseline data for this study. This set was chosen for its completeness, the quality of the photographs and its previous use in an earlier vegetation study (Budd, 1985). New photography was produced at 1:5,000 scale, again as colour, infra red, diapositive images. The change in scale was to enhance clarity of detail for possible future use in vegetation mapping. The new photographs were taken in August 1994, at low tide, to ensure compatibility with the 1978 photographs. August is also the best time of year for the capture of infra red reflectance from vegetation and low tide minimised errors made possible by the presence of water.

A section of saltmarsh at West Itchenor (*c.* 700 m long from west to east and varying in cross section from 150 m to 50 m) was chosen for a pilot study due to its being an area of saltmarsh loss (Figure 2). An impression of this terrain is provided in Figure 3. Photographic information was simultaneously plotted from stereo pairs of photographs using plotting devices which were linked using Kork photogrammetric data capture and plotting software. Care was taken to eliminate potential distortions and a 3D image of ground features was obtained. Vegetation maps produced by Budd (1985) were digitised and used to confirm the presence of various vegetation types. The advantages of using this system were that direct comparisons between the two surveys were possible and the results could be verified immediately. The accuracy of mapping was improved as distortions were eliminated. The main problem confronted was the lack of ground control points in both sets of photographs. However, enough such points were eventually identified to allow the first model to be created.

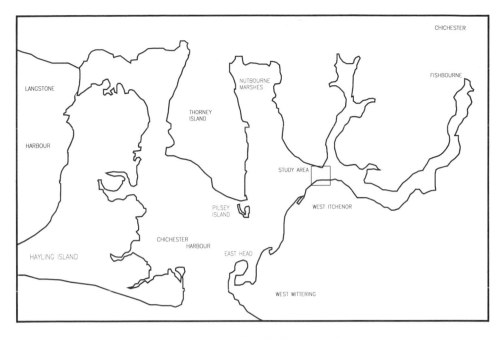

Figure 2   Location of the study site within Chichester Harbour

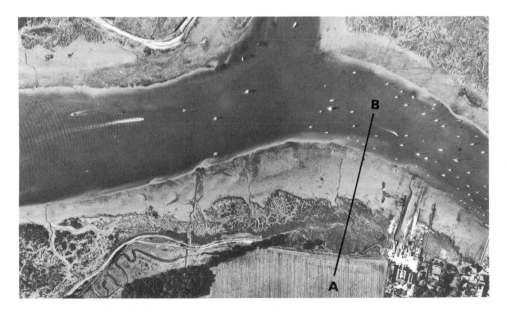

Figure 3   Aerial photograph of the study area at West Itchenor, West Sussex

The line from A to B shows (in sequence) agricultural land, vegetated saltmarsh, inter-tidal mudflat and open water. The photograph was taken at low tide and north lies at the top of the figure

167

Analysis

Figure 4 shows the final map produced for the initial study area. The most significant observation is the loss of saltmarsh at the seaward margin. The extent of loss is relatively uniform, ranging between 7-10 m for the 1978-1994 period. This approximates to an erosion rate of 60 cm/yr, but it is not possible to establish whether the rate of loss has been uniform. Saltmarsh protected from the sea has not been greatly affected, remaining stable throughout the 16 years. The cover of *Spartina anglica* in this section of saltmarsh is not uniform, being present mainly in the western part of the study area, but its presence does not appear to have reduced the rate of loss of saltmarsh as might be expected. It is also clear that the saltmarsh has not retreated, as its landward boundary remained unchanged in 1994. In some areas it has not been possible to monitor the situation on the ground from photographic analysis.

The loss of saltmarsh is locally significant, having an impact on both the landscape and ecological value of the harbour. The uniform extent of loss along the seaward edge would support the suggestion that relative sealevel rise and associated processes are the primary causes of saltmarsh erosion in the south of England, mainly due to isostatic re-adjustment (Burd, 1992). Temporal variations in rates of erosion can only be guessed at in the absence of more frequent measurements than are employed in this study, such as those used in Morecambe Bay (northwest England) between 1983 and 1992, where monthly measurements of marsh edge erosion were made (Pringle, 1995).

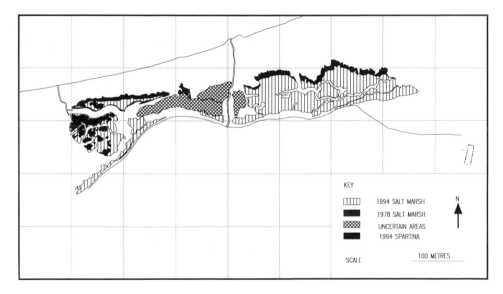

KEY

[IIIII]	1994 SALT MARSH
■	1978 SALT MARSH
▨	UNCERTAIN AREAS
■	1994 SPARTINA

N

SCALE   100 METRES

Figure 4   Map showing the extent of saltmarsh loss between 1978 and 1994 at the West Itchenor study site

Each grid square defines an area of 1 ha. North lies at the top of the figure

Conclusion

It is not yet possible to establish whether saltmarsh loss is uniform across Chichester Harbour. It has been suggested by some with local knowledge that areas of accreting saltmarsh occur in the Nutbourne Marshes. Even so, the initial results still pose some interesting questions for management of the harbour. If sediments are being eroded and released into the harbour, where are they going? If the released sediments are entering the navigable channels, will there be a need for dredging and if so when?

What exactly is causing the change and why? Can it be controlled or reversed, or is it part of a long term trend or relatively recent phenomenon? Can the lost marsh be recreated, and what are the possibilities of managed retreat? (see Pethick, this volume).

The CHC has always recognised the need for good scientific information on which to base management decisions and it is now directing more resources to this end than has been possible in the past. Research themes include sediment tracing within the harbour and monitoring environmental degradation such as saltmarsh loss. This work would ensure that new research initiatives are designed to be easily repeatable and that comparative data would become available. Perhaps more than anything else the initial results of this study highlight the importance of having good scientific information with which to inform the management process.

References

Budd, J. 1985. An Investigation into the Utility of Remote Sensing in the Study of the Ecology of Some South Coast Harbours. PhD Thesis, Department of Geography, Portsmouth Polytechnic, UK.

Burd, F. 1992. *Erosion and Vegetation Change on the Saltmarshes of Essex and North Kent Between 1973 and 1988*. Research and Survey in Nature Conservation 42, Nature Conservancy Council, Peterborough, UK.

Chichester Harbour Conservancy. 1992. Managing Chichester Harbour. G&B Printers, Middlesex, UK.

Chichester Harbour Conservancy. 1993. Chichester Harbour Management Plan (Draft copy). CHC, UK.

House of Commons Environment Committee, Second Report. 1992. *Coastal Zone Protection and Planning*. HMSO, London.

Pringle, A.W. 1995. Erosion of a cyclic saltmarsh in Morecambe Bay, north west England. *Earth Surface Processes and Landforms*, 20:387-405.

Management and Conservation
of Coastal Habitats

Studies in European Coastal Management. Jones, Healy and Williams (eds)
1996, Samara Publishing Limited, Cardigan. ISBN 1 873692 07 2

The National Trust: 100 Years of Coastal Habitat and Species Conservation in Britain

H.J. Harvey

National Trust Estate Advisors' Office, Cirencester, UK

Abstract: The National Trust is a major British charity which owns and protects 250,000 ha of land in the United Kingdom, including over 800 km of undeveloped coastline. This paper briefly summarises, with particular reference to the coast, the Trust's growth and activities over the past 100 years. Special attention is paid to the nature of the organisation and its aims, to key developments over the past century and to a selective examination of some of the Trust's present responsibilities and problems. The paper concludes with a review of some valuable lessons which have been learnt from the Trust's role as a major coastal conservation agency in Britain.

Introduction

The National Trust is a registered British charity which is independent from the UK government. In the UK the Trust operates in England, Wales and Northern Ireland, but not in Scotland where a separate but similar organisation carries out many of the same functions. Whilst many people associate the Trust with the preservation of historic buildings and gardens, the Trust also owns, manages and protects over 250,000 ha of land, including some of the most beautiful and natural landscapes in Britain. This holding includes over 800 km of coast and 39,000 ha of mostly undeveloped coastal land, approximately 18% of the combined coastline of England, Wales and Northern Ireland. The Trust does not routinely receive state funding and meets its yearly expenditure of £100,000,000 from various sources. Of key importance is a membership of over 2.25 million which generates 40% of the Trust's annual expenditure through subscription.

The activities of the National Trust, which was formed in 1895, are governed by Acts of Parliament and its key objectives are laid down in the 1907 National Trust Act. This not only requires the Trust to promote the "permanent preservation for the benefit of the Nation of lands and tenements (including buildings) of beauty or historic interest" but also to preserve "(so far as practicable) their natural aspect features and animal and plant life".

It is important to stress that the Trust functions "for the benefit of the nation" and not solely for the benefit of its members. Although not specified in the 1907 Act the provision of access is a major objective of the Trust, indeed one of the reasons for its foundation was to provide access to the countryside for residents of urban areas.

173

With its emphasis on preserving the best of the past and its commitment to meeting the perceived need of society for quiet recreational space, the National Trust is often viewed as a typical product of late-Victorian Britain. These ideals may indeed encapsulate enlightened thinking of the last century, but the support which the Trust has achieved in recent years suggests that they continue to represent, or perhaps reflect even more now than they did in 1895, the genuine and deeply held feelings of a significant proportion of the population of the United Kingdom. The founders of the National Trust saw the ownership of land as the most effective way of preventing damage to valued landscapes and of protecting historical features and nature conservation interests. The acquisition of land has always been at the core of the Trust's work.

As with many conservation organisations, the Trust had to learn that conservation is a process that frequently involves active management. In consequence the Trust now devotes considerable resources to the management of its land and the habitats or features which occur there. Whilst the National Trust is not concerned solely with the conservation of the coast, almost one sixth of its land holding is on or close to the coast. This makes the organisation a key player in the conservation of the physical and biological features of the coast of the United Kingdom, a role which will be examined in this paper.

Milestones in the acquisition of coastal sites by the National Trust

The coast has always been integral to the Trust's activities and to its growth (National Trust, 1992). The first property to be acquired, in 1895, was a site overlooking the sea at Barmouth (Gwynedd, Wales) and another early coastal acquisition was Blakeney Point (Norfolk) in eastern England in 1912. The 1920s in particular saw the acquisition of a suite of important coastal sites, including Scolt Head (Norfolk) in 1923 and the Farne Islands (Northumberland) in 1925. Chalk cliffs came to the Trust with the acquisition of Tennyson Down (Isle of Wight) in 1927 and a part of the Seven Sisters (East Sussex) between 1928 and 1931. A major acquisition in the west of England was of Gurnard's Head (Cornwall) in 1928. By 1965 some 269 km of coast had been acquired by the National Trust.

The Trust's involvement with the coast increased significantly after the launch of Operation Neptune in 1965. This initiative had three purposes:

a) to acquire unspoilt coast line for permanent preservation and public access;

b) to alert people to the increasing pressures and threats to the coasts of England, Wales and Northern Ireland; and

c) to raise an initial £2 million for the purchase of unspoilt coastline.

In 1965 it was calculated that the combined coastline of England, Wales and Northern Ireland amounted to approximately 4,960 km, of which about 1,600 km had already been developed, with another 1,600 km partly spoilt. Of the remainder, about 300 km was already in Trust ownership and 1,450 km were judged to be unspoilt, of high quality and requiring protection. In the 30 years since 1965 considerable progress has been made in acquiring these high quality areas for permanent protection. There have been some changes of perception and emphasis since 1965, in particular low lying coasts are now more highly rated than they were at the start of Operation Neptune, when the emphasis was on the acquisition of hard coast sites. Recent examples of coastal acquisitions include Orfordness (Suffolk) and lengths of the Durham coast heavily contaminated with mining waste. The impact of Operation Neptune on the acquisition of coastal land by the Trust is illustrated in Table 1, while Figure 1 shows the growth in the total land holding, length of coastline and number of members since the formation of the Trust.

Table 1 **Variations in the length of coastline acquired by the National Trust since its formation in 1895**

Decade	Length of coast acquired in decade (km)
1895-1904	1.2
1905-1914	18.6
1915-1924	12.3
1925-1934	59.2
1935-1944	75.9
1945-1954	37.7
1955-1964	92.0
1965-1974	381.4
1975-1984	153.4
1985-1994	133.1

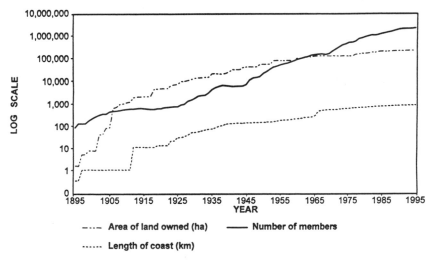

Figure 1 The increase over time in the number of National Trust members and the area of land and length of coast owned by the Trust

As a result of its programme of coastal acquisition, the National Trust is now a major owner of the coastline in certain parts of the UK. In some areas, such as Durham, it owns over 30% of the coast but in Devon and Cornwall the figure approaches 50%. There are certain areas, of which the County of Hampshire is an example, where the Trust currently owns no coastline. Included with the ownership of many coastal sites are a variety of human heritage features which range from important archaeological sites, through historic monuments (such as Lindasfarne Castle) to more recent constructions such as Lighthouses.

Operation Neptune has become the model for coastal acquisition strategies in some other countries. In particular it was the basis for the development of the Conservatoire du Littoral in France, although that organisation is closely related to the state and operates in a different manner from the National Trust.

Nature and geological conservation features on coastal lands owned by the National Trust

As the owner of almost 20% of the combined coastline of England, Wales and Northern Ireland, the Trust is responsible for many important geological and nature conservation sites.

Indeed the Trust is almost certainly responsible for more coastal geological and geomorphological conservation sites than any other single organisation in the UK.

Included within coastal land owned by the National Trust are examples of most of the geological formations represented in the United Kingdom (National Trust, 1993). These range from the serpentine rocks of the Lizard Peninsula at the southern–western extremity of England, through the basaltic formations of the Giant's Causeway in Northern Ireland to the sedimentary and glacial deposits of north Norfolk and Dunwich (Suffolk). In some cases the National Trust is the largest single owner of a particular geological formation. For example, the Trust owns approximately 17% of the UK and 5% of the European resource of chalk sea cliffs (Fowler & Tittley, 1993). Some of the soft coast sites owned by the Trust, for example, Blakeney Point (Norfolk) and Orfordness (Suffolk), are important as geomorphological features. The former has been the object of considerable scientific study (e.g. Hill & Hanley, 1914; Pethick, 1974), whilst the latter is probably the best developed example of a shingle spit in the United Kingdom (Randall & Doody, 1995). Sedimentary cliffs in the south of England, notably those on the Isle of Wight and in the vicinity of Lyme Regis (Dorset), are important for their fossil assemblages (Melville & Freshney, 1982).

The National Trust has recently agreed a policy which favours allowing natural processes to operate on coasts and discourages artificial protection and stabilisation. This policy has already been put into operation in a number of situations, notably the chalk cliffs at Birling Gap (East Sussex) and the shingle bank at Porlock (Somerset). Furthermore, the first experimental investigation in the UK of managed coastal retreat involving former agricultural land was carried out on Trust property at Northey Island on the Blackwater Estuary in Essex (Turner & Dagley, 1993; Radley, 1995).

Almost all of the maritime plant communities recognised in the British Isles can be found on Trust property (Hearn, 1994). On the exposed rocky cliffs of the west of England (especially Devon and Cornwall) and Wales, extreme maritime communities, including crevice communities, are very well represented. These often grade into maritime heaths, particularly in Pembrokeshire (South Wales), on the Lleyn Peninsula (North Wales) and in Cornwall. Uncommon or rare community types include the dwarf woodland composed of *Quercus petraea, Sorbus torminalis* and *Ilex aquifolium* of the Dizzard in Cornwall (Ratcliffe, 1977) and the ultra-nitrophilous plant communities associated with the seabird colonies of the Farne Islands in Northumberland (Mitchley & Malloch, 1991). Despite the impression that Trust ownership is normally associated with hard rock coasts, the Trust also owns extensive areas of sand dune, saltmarsh and shingle (e.g. Randall & Doody, 1995). Major shingle sites owned by the Trust are listed in Table 2, while Figure 2 shows the location of all major sand dune and saltmarsh holdings.

Many coastal sites owned by the National Trust are important not only for their flora, but also for their fauna. Examples include the natterjack toad (*Bufo calamita*) populations of the west coast dune sites of Formby Point (a component part of the Sefton Coast dune system on Merseyside) and Sandscale Haws (Cumbria). Large colonies of breeding seabirds occur at sites such as Blakeney Point (Norfolk) and Orfordness (Suffolk). The Farne Islands are especially important, supporting (in 1989/90) 6,150 pairs of kittiwake (*Rissa tridactlya*), 12,975 pairs of guillemot (*Uria aalge*) over 26,330 pairs of puffin (*Fratercula arctica*), nearly 2,846 pairs of sandwich tern (*Sterna sandvicensis*) and more than 3,228 pairs of arctic tern (*Sterna paradisaea*) (Hawkey, 1991; Pritchard et al., 1992). One scarce bird species which breeds at a number of Trust properties is the chough (*Pyrrhocorax pyrrhocorax*), which has an essentially western coastal distribution in the United Kingdom. The species is particularly abundant on Trust owned properties on the Lleyn Peninsula and in Pembrokeshire and Ceredigion (all in Wales).

The Farne Islands also support the largest breeding colony of grey seals (*Halichoerus grypus*) in England, with around 1,000 pups born each year.

Table 2 Inventory of coastal sites in England, Wales and Northern Ireland where the National Trust owns more than 0.5 km of shingle habitat. In each case the site name is followed by the administrative county in which it occurs

England	Wales	Northern Ireland
Blakeney Point, Norfolk	Aber Mawr, Dyfed	Mourne Coast, Co. Down
Chesil Beach, Dorset	Bishopston, West Glamorgan	
Dunwich, Suffolk	Cemlyn, Anglesey	
The Duver, Isle of Wight	Criccieth, Gwynedd	
East Head, West Sussex	Pennard Burrows, West Glamorgan	
Loe Bar, Cornwall	Pwll Du, West Glamorgan	
Orfordness, Suffolk		
Porlock, Somerset		
Scolt Head Island, Norfolk		

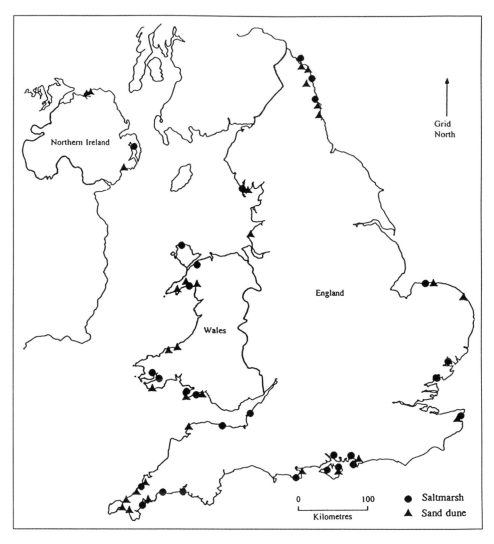

Figure 2   The location of major sand dune and saltmarsh sites owned by the National Trust

The Farne Islands typify some of the management dilemmas which may face a land-owning organisation with an interest in nature conservation. The large colony of seals can, through animal induced erosion of the thin mineral soils which cap the islands, cause very considerable damage to the breeding habitat of puffins. Indeed, if the seals were allowed free access to the islands it is almost certain that the soil caps would be destroyed with the concomitant loss of nesting burrows. For the past 20 years, Trust wardens have remained on the important bird islands during the autumn period to act as a deterrent to seals. This limited disturbance is very effective in protecting the sensitive habitat. The wardens also make detailed observations on seal breeding.

The Farne Islands are also important as an educational resource. Approximately 50,000 people visit the islands by boat each year and are able to come within close range of breeding seabirds. This provision is one of the ways in which the Trust can fulfil its requirement to provide access to the countryside. Nevertheless, visitors must be carefully managed to avoid undue disturbance to breeding birds. Furthermore, in many places it has proved necessary to provide board-walks to minimise damage to vegetation.

Management for nature conservation

The provision of board-walks and the conservation of soil profiles on the Farne Islands are just two examples of the extensive management carried out by the Trust to safeguard features of nature conservation interest. One of the chief management initiatives in recent years has been the reintroduction of grazing by domestic livestock on ungrazed cliff-top sites. In many coastal areas in the UK the grazing of cliff-top vegetation was formerly common, as evidenced by the provision of (now disused) gaps and gates in boundary fences and walls to link agricultural land to unimproved cliff-top vegetation. The Trust has now reintro-duced grazing to a range of different plant communities across a wide geographical area and has also used a variety of different grazing animals including cattle, ponies, sheep and goats. Sites subject to the reintroduction of grazing occur throughout the UK and include coastal grassland, heathland, calcareous grassland and sand dune habitats. The Trust's work in this area has been innovative and is probably unmatched by any other nature conservation organisation in the UK.

In addition to management for nature conservation, the Trust has carried out many access improvement works. Examples include the creation of car parks, the provision or improvement of footpaths, the clearing of litter and, at popular sites such as Studland Beach (Dorset), the development of extensive visitor facilities. The Trust has also carried out major works to safeguard or improve landscapes of high value, examples include the relocation of farm buildings and even the demolition of buildings at some sites (e.g. Kynance Cove in Cornwall).

Over the past 100 years the Trust has effectively fulfilled its obligations as laid down by Act of Parliament. It has been successful in preserving the coast both as a landscape and as a zone with important geological, geomorphological and nature conservation features. It has combined these responsibilities with the provision of free access for the whole of society.

Lessons learnt from 100 years of coastal conservation

The experience of the Trust over the past 100 years makes it possible to identify certain principles which can contribute to successful conservation. Amongst these are the value of ownership, the importance of public support, the necessity for professional expertise, the need to balance specialist interests and the necessity of being innovative.

Ownership gives management control. It means that unsatisfactory situations can be changed and it permits the implementation of effective policies for conservation. If ownership is combined with the Trust's ability to declare its land inalienable, a provision which is almost a veto on adverse developments, then land ownership may be a very considerable strength, albeit a costly option.

Public support is vital to the Trust, both because it provides income and because it increases the Trust's influence when it is forced to confront those wishing to damage coastal features. The Trust's experience is that the public has a very positive attitude to coastal conservation and can be recruited in large numbers to support conservation activities on the coast.

Public support and land ownership may be insufficient in themselves to ensure appropriate conservation. It is vital that a land-owning organisation has access to the professional skills which allow the appropriate policies to be developed and has in place a suitable staff structure which ensures that day to day management of sites is carried out. The Trust has both structures in place.

It is well known (e.g. Sidaway, 1995) that problems can arise when a special interest group seeks to impose a narrow set of management objectives on a site. The Trust's responsibility to safeguard a wide variety of features on the coast, including landscape, nature conservation, archaeology and access, ensures that no single interest becomes dominant. Few formal mechanisms have been developed to ensure that these multiple interests are balanced, but the Trust's general experience is that conflicts can be minimised.

The coast is a dynamic and ever changing environment. The same is true of the social, political and economic frameworks within which conservationists operate. Similarly biological communities are in a continual state of flux, as species invade or become extinct, or as ecosystems respond to changing environmental conditions. No organisation can succeed in this dynamic situation if it adopts a static approach. Organisations like the National Trust must always be willing to be innovative and to change their methods of working. In the case of the Trust this was well demonstrated by the introduction of Operation Neptune and by the recent emphasis on the reintroduction of grazing to coastal areas. The same willingness to change is necessary in all aspects of an organisation.

Conclusion

The first 100 years of the National Trust's work has led to it becoming a major organisation involved in the conservation of the coast of the United Kingdom. Its work on the coast has been a stimulus to those in other countries. The present indications are that the Trust is sufficiently dynamic to continue to play a vital role in this area for the next 100 years.

References

Fowler, S.L. & Tittley, I. 1993. *The Marine Nature Conservation Importance of British Coastal Chalk Cliff Habitats. English Nature Research Reports 32.* English Nature, Peterborough, UK.

Hawkey, P. 1991. The birds of the Farne Islands. *Transactions of the Natural History Society of Northumbria,* 55:155-193.

Hearn, K. 1994. The "Natural Aspect" of the National Trust. *British Wildlife,* 5:367-379.

Hill, T.G. & Hanley, J.A. 1914. The structure and water content of shingle beaches. *Journal of Ecology,* 2:21-38.

Melville, R.V. & Freshney, E.C. 1982. *British Regional Geology: The Hampshire Basin and Adjoining Areas. 4th Edition.* HMSO, London, UK.

Mitchley, J. & Malloch, A.J.C. 1991. *Sea Cliff Management Handbook for Great Britain.* Joint Nature Conservation Committee, Peterborough, UK.

The National Trust. 1992. *Properties of The National Trust.* The National Trust, London, UK.

The National Trust, 1993. *The National Trust Countryside Handbook.* The National Trust, London, UK.

Pethick, J.S. 1974. The distribution of salt pans on tidal salt marshes. *Journal of Biogeography,* 1:57-62.

Pritchard, D.E., Housden, S.D., Mudge, G.P., Galbraith, C.A. & Pienkowski, M.W. (Eds). 1992. *Important Bird Areas in the UK Including the Channel Islands and the Isle of Man.* Royal Society for the Protection of Birds, Bedfordshire, UK. 540 pp.

Radley, G.P. 1995. English Nature's campaign for a living coast. In: *Coastal Management and Habitat Conservation.* Eds: Salman, A.H.P.M., Berends, H. & Bonazountas, M. European Union for Coastal Conservation, Leiden, The Netherlands. pp. 289-297.

Randall, R.E. & Doody, J.P. 1995. Habitats inventories and the European Habitats Directive: The example of shingle beaches. In: *Directions in European Coastal Management.* Eds: Healy, M.G. & Doody, J.P. Samara Publishing Limited, Cardigan, UK. pp. 19-36.

Ratcliffe, D.A. (Ed.). 1977. *A Nature Conservation Review. Volume 2. Site Accounts.* Cambridge University Press, Cambridge, UK.

Sidaway, R. 1995. Recreation and tourism on the coast: managing impacts and resolving conflicts. In: *Directions in European Coastal Management.* Eds: Healy, M.G. & Doody, J.P. Samara Publishing Limited, Cardigan, UK. pp. 71-78.

Turner, K. & Dagley, J. 1993. What price sea walls? *Enact,* 1:8-9. English Nature, Peterborough, UK.

Studies in European Coastal Management. Jones, Healy and Williams (eds)
1996, Samara Publishing Limited, Cardigan. ISBN 1 873692 07 2

Habitat Diversity in the Veleka River Mouth and Silistar Protected Areas in Bulgaria

I. Apostolova, T. Meshinev & A. Petrova

Institute of Botany, 1113 Sofia, Bulgaria

Abstract: The southeastern sector of the Bulgarian Black Sea Coast is a region of great beauty which also supports a wide range of important biotopes. In recognition of this, two new protected areas, Silistar and the Veleka River Mouth, have recently been established in this region. This paper provides the first ecological description of these areas by discussing the principle characteristics of 12 main habitat types which were identified during a recent survey. The description of each habitat type also includes a brief discussion of future conservation needs.

Introduction

The southernmost part of the Bulgarian Black Sea Coast is a national boundary zone which was subject to restricted public access until 1990. Prior to this, human disturbance was insignificant with just two villages in the zone (Sinemoretz and Rezovo) with less than 400 inhabitants.

The two new protected areas of the Veleka River Mouth and Silistar were established in the region in 1991 (Figure 1). Through financial support from the government of Monaco, the Bulgarian Ministry of the Environment has recently provided an ecological evaluation of the area and is now preparing management plans for the two protected areas.

No detailed ecological appraisal of the territory was available until 1994 when a detailed floristic and phytosociological survey of an area of 2,284.5 ha was carried out to identify the main characteristics of the established habitats. This information will be used in the preparation of management plans for the two protected areas. Twelve major habitat types have been identified on the basis of the conventions established for the CORINE system of habitat classification (Devillers & Devillers-Teruschen, 1994), and the essential characteristics of these are presented in this paper. Attention is also drawn to rare plant species occurring in the region which are listed in the Bulgarian Red Data Book (Velchev, 1984) and the List of Rare, Endemic and Threatened Plants of Europe (Lucas, 1983). Vascular plant nomenclature follows Andreev (1992).

Description of habitats

Sand beaches

The southern part of the Bulgarian Black Sea Coast is predominantly composed of rocky sea cliffs. Within the two protected areas there are four small sand beaches.

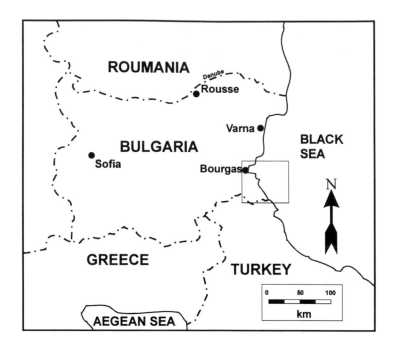

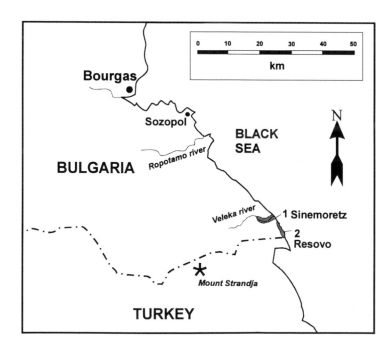

Figure 1   The Black Sea Coast of Bulgaria showing the location of the Veleka River Mouth (1) and Silistar (2) protected areas

These occupy small bays and are popular tourist destinations. The largest sand beach system is approximately 1.5 km long and several dozens of metres wide and occurs at the Veleka River Mouth. A similar system is also present at Silistar Bay. The species diversity of the duneland vegetation is not high (only 43 species were recorded), although many rare and endangered plants are present, including *Euphorbia paralias, E. peplis, Otanthus maritimum, Stachys maritima, Hypecoum ponticum, Silene euxina* and *Lactuca tartarica*. In comparison with other beaches in Bulgaria, most of these species are represented by small populations only and several endangered species (including *Pancratium maritimum, Imperata cylindrica* and *Argusia sibirica*) were represented by just a few individuals.

Both sites are vulnerable to damage through trampling of psammophytic vegetation by tourists. Vehicle access is also currently unrestricted. In the future some provision will have to be made for organised car-parking and litter collection. These sand beach systems are considered to be the most fragile and threatened habitats in the region, and interpretation is required to inform the public of the high nature conservation value of the area.

Cliffs

Within the survey area, the Black Sea Coast is rocky and jagged with numerous bays and promontories (Figure 2). Much of the stony ground is bare and open, and approximately 20 vascular plant species were recorded in such areas. Characteristic species of the cliff slopes include *Crithmum maritimum, Ficus carica* and *Limonium gmelinii*. On the elevated and less steep cliff sections species diversity is higher with *Silene compacta, Achillea clypeolata, Anthemis tinctoria, Sedum album, Echinops ritro, Silene italica, Sonchus asper* var. *glaucescens* and *Parietaria diffusa* occurring as typical components of the vegetation.

Rare plant species in these habitats include *Scorpiurus subvillosus, Hymenocarpus circinatus, Lophochloa cristata* and *Lolium ridgidum*.

The cliffs are not under any immediate threat, partly because of their inaccessibility to tourists, and exposure to sea borne pollution is the only readily identifiable factor which could harm this habitat.

Open grass communities of cliff terraces

This habitat type occupies the area between the cliff and forest zones and varies in width from 10-150 m. The terraces are flat, covered by eroded soils and support vegetation of secondary origin in areas formerly under forest or arable cultivation. Most of the herbaceous communities have also been subject to grazing in the past. The specific environmental conditions of this habitat are determined by high humidity, a favourable light regime, a range of soil depths and the influence of strong northeasterly winds, and this habitat was the most floristically rich of those studied. Many typical Mediterranean elements are present, including *Cistus salvifolius* and *Asparagus acutifolius,* and *Romulea bulbocodium, Agrostis capillaris, Festuca valesiaca, Chrysopogon gryllus* and *Lolium perenne* may occur as dominant species. In the southernmost parts of the Silistar protected area the cliff terrace habitat provides the only Bulgarian station for the orchid *Serapias vomeracea*.

Figure 2   The coastline of the Silistar protected area

The floriferous appearance of this habitat type makes it attractive to tourists interested in nature. Future management of this habitat type should include grazing to prevent forest expansion, but not arable cultivation.

Ridges and slopes covered by *Quercus frainetto* dominated forest vegetation

This habitat type occupies large territories over the Silistar protected area and to the north of the Veleka River. It also occurs as a narrow belt along the southern boundary of the Veleka River Mouth protected area. Most of the *Quercus frainetto* forests are outliers of a once more extensive forest cover, and areas which have been felled and grazed in the past can be identified. The economic value of these forests is now low, but they play an extremely important role as a component of the environment.

The presence of species with a southern Black Sea Coast (Euxinian Province) distribution (*sensu* Tahtadjyan, 1974) under the forest canopy is very typical, and the highest number of rare plants recorded during the survey (16) was found in this habitat. Some, such as *Celsia bugilifolia* and *Cicer montbretii,* are rare in Bulgaria as a whole and are otherwise restricted to Mount Strandja which has been subject to large scale conifer afforestation in recent decades. The management plan should argue very strongly against this form of landuse. Afforestation would result in massive habitat change and the concomitant loss of many characteristic and important floral and faunal elements. Tree felling would also be extremely harmful, not least because of the changed hydrological regime which would follow.

Wet valleys dominated by *Fagus orientalis* communities

This habitat type is confined to the Veleka River Mouth protected area and is restricted to this region in Bulgaria. The relict communities composed of *Fagus orientalis* and *Rhododendron ponticum* have survived since the Tertiary, chiefly because of the unique geomorphological composition, high humidity and warm climate of the area, and the communities which are present are typical of the vegetation of the eastern Black Sea Coast Colhyda region.

The dominant species is *Fagus orientalis* which, together with *Rhododendron ponticum* and *Daphne pontica,* forms very attractive communities.

This community type, which reaches its easternmost European limit here, must be regarded as vulnerable and any human activity which results in a decrease in air or soil humidity could cause irreversible damage.

Hydrophillous and freshwater vegetation

This habitat type occurs in the basins of both the Veleka and Silistar Rivers. Slow water flow encourages the sedimentation of organic material on the stream bed and thus ensures favourable conditions for hydrophillous species such as *Nuphar luteum.* Communities dominated by *Najas marina* and *Myriophyllum spicatum* can also be found, whilst a dense population of *Ruppia maritima* is present at the mouth of the Silistar River.

Currently these habitats are undisturbed, but the management plan should take into account their sensitivity by ensuring the preservation of the current water regime of both rivers.

Longos type communities dominated by *Fagus oxycarpa*

The periodically flooded forests which occur along the lower reaches of some Bulgarian rivers are referred to as Longos communities (Stojanov, 1950). Within the study area, this habitat was found to occur in a number of regions along the banks of the Veleka and (less commonly) Silistar Rivers, as well as in some valley bottoms with a high soil moisture content. The habitat is rare on a European scale (Devillers & Devillers-Teruschen, 1994) and was probably once more widely distributed in the area, but high soil fertility has inevitably led to the development of arable cultivation.

The floristic composition of these woodlands is extremely interesting. Although lianas are scarce in the riverbank forests (as distinct from typical Longos vegetation), species such as *Smilax excelsa, Tamus communis, Hedera helix* and *Clematis vitalba* are abundant in the valley bottom. High soil moisture allows the presence of montane species such as *Aremonia agrimonoides, Circea lutetiana* and *Impatiens noli-tangere* which are otherwise absent from the dry, low altitude parts of Strandja Mountain. Rare species which occur in this habitat type include *Primula acaulis* ssp. *sibthorpii, Symphytum tauricum, Fritillaria pontica, Scilla bithynica* and *Leucojum aestivum.*

Suitable sites for camping at the mouth of the Veleka River have already been occupied by tourists and this has led to the indiscriminate cutting of young trees and lianas and the development, in places, of a ruderal flora. There is now an urgent need for the regularisation of this form of recreation.

Floodplain habitats with hydrophytic vegetation

This habitat type occupies large territories at the Veleka River Mouth, but also occurs less commonly along the lower reaches of the Silistar river. A high water table level ensures wet soil conditions throughout the year, and flooding is common during the spring months. Dominant species include *Agrostis stolonifera, Poa sylvicola, Juncus articulatus, J. effusus, Schoenoplectus triqueter, Typha latifolia* and *Carex remota.* Threats to this ecosystem include an increase in soil salinity and the development of ruderal communities through overgrazing. The management plan should prescribe the protection of this habitat because of the presence of many notable taxa, and further botanical investigations are required to determine the actual diversity of species.

Floodplain habitats with vegetation dominated by species of *Populus*, *Salix* and ruderal taxa

Communities dominated by *Salix alba, S. triandra, Populus nigra, Alnus glutinosa, Fraxinus oxyphylla* and *Ulmus minor* occur as a narrow belt along parts of both the Veleka and Silistar Rivers. Beneath the open canopy a dense shrub layer commonly develops composed of species such as *Crataegus monogyna, Corylus avellana, Cornus sanguinea, Ligustrum vulgare* and *Rubus* spp. *Viscum album* occurs commonly as a parasite of *Populus nigra,* whilst lianas such as *Clematis vitalba, Tamus communis, Vitis sylvestris, Calystegia sepium* and *Hedera helix* are also typical of the habitat. The soils are typically nitrogen rich, a factor indicated by the presence of *Urtica dioica, Conium maculatum* and *Sambucus ebulus,* indeed the herb layer can become impenetrable. This habitat is of especial value for feeding and breeding birds.

Northern slopes covered with *Quercus polycarpa* dominated vegetation

Quercus polycarpa is a typical species of Mount Strandja and also has a restricted distribution in the East Balkan mountains. A surviving fragment of this habitat also occurs over an area of between 1 and 2 ha in the Veleka River Mouth protected area, where it supports the locally endemic species *Quercus hartwissiana.* Mesotrophic herbaceous plants which occur in this habitat include *Trachystemon orientale, Cyclamen coum* and *Primula acaulis* ssp. *sibthorpii.* High anthropogenic pressure has resulted in the presence of ruderal species such as *Galium aparine* and *Physocaulis nodosa.* In the future visitor pressure should be reduced because of the risk to rare species from the spread of aggressive ruderals.

Bare rock habitats in the forest zone

This habitat type is confined to the Veleka River Mouth protected area and has developed because of soil erosion following episodes of clear felling. Herbaceous plant cover in these areas is now complete and xerophytes, such as *Chrysopogon gryllus* and *Cistus incanus,* occur as dominant components. The management plan should not recommend tree planting in this habitat type because this would reduce species diversity in the area as a whole and also result in the extinction of the only rare species which was recorded in this habitat type (*Echium plantagineum*).

Agricultural lands

Agricultural lands occur around the village of Sinemoretz and on the terraces of the Veleka River. Much of this land is no longer cultivated and is dominated by ruderal vegetation with a high density of species such as *Echinochloa crus-gali, Sorghum halepense, Cirsium arvense, C. creticum, Conium maculatum* and *Arctium lappa.*

The future of these habitats requires careful consideration as the intensive use of pesticides could prove harmful, not only to these lands but to neighbouring areas as well. One option would be to harmonize these formerly cultivated landscapes with their natural or semi-natural ecosystems, either through management as meadows, or through the cultivation of medicinal plants such as *Althaea officinalis* and *Leucojum aestivum.*

Although not specifically included in this study, the vegetation of the nearby Strandja Mountain deserves a brief mention. An overview of the vegetation and flora of those parts of the mountain lying within Bulgaria was provided many years ago by Jordanov (1939), and the area is of great phytogeographic interest because of the presence of floristic elements from the Mediterranean, Asia Minor and Pontic regions. The mountain was also free of ice during the last glaciation, and this has contributed to the continuing presence of many relict species.

Conclusion

The study area has survived to the present day in a highly natural form and repesents an extremely important nature conservation resource. A management plan for the area for use by local authorities and decision makers is thus urgently required to guide future development in a sustainable manner. Whilst the two protected areas have been established for the primary purpose of nature conservation, it is important to recognise that human activities within these areas, such as agriculture and recreation, are of great economic importance to local people. The management plan should acknowledge these other forms of landuse by making provision for the use of forests, pastures and agricultural lands in a sustainable manner which avoids over-exploitation. Key issues which will require consideration include the regulation of pasture management regimes, control over tree felling to ensure that it does not proceed at a rate which exceeds replacement through natural recruitment, the gradual restocking of conifer plantations with native species, and the prevention or control of pesticide and fertilizer use on agricultural lands.

Vegetation establishes the main characteristics of the environment and plays an active role as a trophic base and biotope for the rich local flora. It is thus hoped that this description of the vegetation of the region will aid the formulation of the management plan.

References

Andreev, N. 1992. *Guide to Bulgarian Vascular Plants*. Sofia, Bulgaria. 788 pp.

Devillers, P.J & Devillers-Teruschen, J. 1994. *Habitats of the Palearctic Region*. Council of Europe, Strasbourg.

Jordanov, D. 1939. The vegetation of Strandja Mountain. *Annuaire de l'Université de Sofia, Faculté de Physique et Mathématique*, 34, 3:409-476 and 35, 3:1-90 Sofia, Bulgaria.

Lucas, G. 1983. *List of Rare, Threatened and Endemic Plants of Europe*. Council of Europe, Strasbourg.

Stojanov, N. 1950. *Phytogeography*. Sofia, Bulgaria. 529 pp.

Tahtadjyan, A. 1974. Floristic Regions of the Earth. In: *Life of the Plants*, Volume 1. Eds: Fedorov, A. & Moskwa, A. pp. 123-125.

Velchev, V. 1984. *Red Data Book of Bulgaria, Volume 1 Plants*. Sofia, Bulgaria. 447 pp.

Studies in European Coastal Management. Jones, Healy and Williams (eds)
1996, Samara Publishing Limited, Cardigan. ISBN 1 873692 07 2

Coastal Management by the French National Forestry Service in Aquitaine, France

J. Favennec

Service ONF-Littoral, Bordeaux, France

Abstract: The French National Forestry Service (ONF) manages a large coastal area. Much of this consists of sand dunes stretching from Noirmoutier (Vendée) in the north to the Adour Estuary (southern Landes) in the south. During the last century the majority of this area was afforested with maritime pine (*Pinus pinaster*), but unplanted foredune and forest fringe habitats still comprise a large part of the current coastal ecosystem. The area is subject to specific management and protection measures. Regular maintenance and management of the dune area in Aquitainian demonstrates how sand drift and vegetation cover can be effectively regulated.

Introduction

The French National Forestry Service (ONF) manages 500 km of the French shoreline of which 360 km consist primarily of sand dune coast (mainly along the English Channel/Atlantic seaboard). Some 78% of this 101,000 ha area is afforested. Along the Aquitaine coast of the Bay of Biscay (Aquitainian), the ONF manages 64,000 ha of dune forest and open dunes stretching for 263 km from the island of Oléron in the north to the Adour Estuary in the south (Figure 1). This large area has many physical and biological similarities but there are also strong phyto-geographical variations evident which are linked to geology and climate. This paper will briefly examine some aspects of the history of sand dune stabilisation on the Aquitainian coast, before going on to consider current approaches to management.

Vascular plant nomenclature follows Auger & Lapoafe (1985).

History of the coastal dunes

During the latter half of the Holocene period two generations of coastal sand dunes were formed: old parabolic dunes (3 - 5 ka B.P.) and modern crescentic or Barchan dunes (developing through to the Middle Ages). Dune formation has resulted in the evolution of a chain of lakes and marshes as a result of impeded drainage to the rear of the dune belt (Figure 2).

At the beginning of the 19th century, the first attempts were made to control dune movement using afforestation with maritime pine (*Pinus pinaster*). A 'Dune Commission' was established in 1801 which led to the afforestation of 4,374 ha between 1802 and 1814. This work was continued after 1817 by the French Highways Department. In 1862 responsibility passed to the Forestry Department, with 'dune fixing' activities continuing until 1876. In all, 80,000 ha of coastal dunes were planted.

191

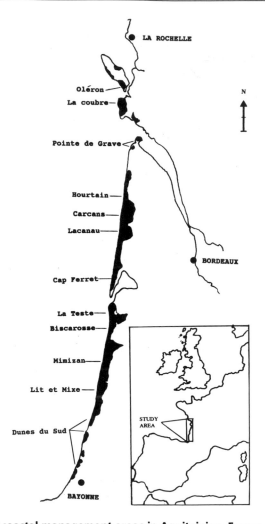

Figure 1   Map of coastal management areas in Aquitainian, France

Areas under the management of the French National Forestry Service (ONF) are shaded

During the past century, planting involved sowing a series of large (500–1,500 ha) polygonal plots along the shoreline. These were protected by palisades of boards driven through the dune surface which were subsequently raised as they were covered by sand. Seed mixtures were typically composed of 20–30 kg/ha of maritime pine seeds mixed with 8 kg of broom (*Cytisus scoparius*) and gorse (*Ulex europaeus*) and 5 kg of marram grass (*Ammophila arenaria*). Branches were used to cover the plots to prevent sand loss following sowing. The resultant forest produced wood and pine resin, supporting a thriving local industry. Traditional landuse was substituted by tourism as the resin trade declined, and the current management of the area centres around the importance of the beaches and lakes, as well as the coastal forest, as a tourist resource. As a result of tourism, urban development on the coast has been stimulated.

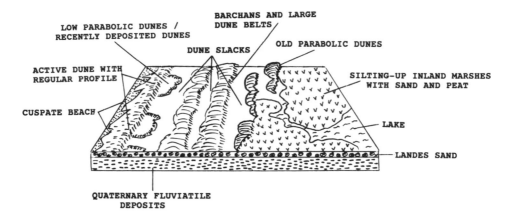

LOW PARABOLIC DUNES /
RECENTLY DEPOSITED DUNES

BARCHANS AND LARGE
DUNE BELTS

DUNE SLACKS

OLD PARABOLIC DUNES

ACTIVE DUNE WITH
REGULAR PROFILE

SILTING-UP INLAND MARSHES
WITH SAND AND PEAT

CUSPATE BEACH

LAKE

LANDES SAND

QUATERNARY FLUVIATILE
DEPOSITS

Figure 2   Schematic diagram showing the succession of land forms on passing inland from the coast to the Plain of Landes

Regional development

Regional development is regulated by a 'Coastal Decree' (1986), which allows limited urban development near the coast but requires the protection of natural habitats of ecological or scenic significance. These include active sand dunes, dune slacks and the forest fringe within a 500 m coastal strip. This is in keeping with the management philosophy of the ONF which aims to reconcile forestry activities with sand dune conservation and recreation (Figure 3).

Coastal foredune management

Coastal foredunes are active boundaries between land, sea and air. In Aquitainian the dominant sea swells are from the northwest, giving a north to south longshore sediment drift. The conjunction of storms and high tides cause erosion and scarping of the dune foot, facilitating subsequent wind erosion in the foredunes. Currently, the dunes recede at c. 0.5-1.5 m/year, with some very rapid erosion phases, and the prevailing westerly winds transport inland an estimated 10-30 m³ of sand per metre length of coastline each year. As the dunes serve no sea defence function, erosion is not controlled. Management emphasis is placed on the control of sand blow and conserving the geomorphological and ecological resource which the dunes represent. These objectives are achieved through the use of sand traps (branches) within foredune gullies/blowouts and trapping of sand drift in depressions within the dune belt. The use of vegetation to repair and secure the dune surface following erosion is common practice. This is achieved through seeding deflation areas and blowouts with typical sand dune taxa (Figure 4).

Particular management problems arise where buildings occur adjacent to eroding areas of sand dune. Sea defence structures are necessary in these cases. This will often require remodelling of dune ridges to mimic naturally occurring dune forms. Subsequent to remodelling, a variety of established techniques are used to secure the dune surface and stimulate the development of vegetation.

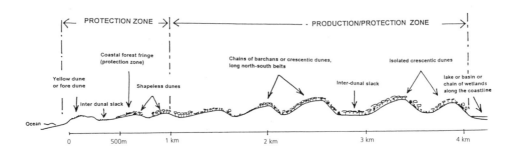

Figure 3   Zonal dune management practised by the French National Forestry Service (ONF) in Aquitainian

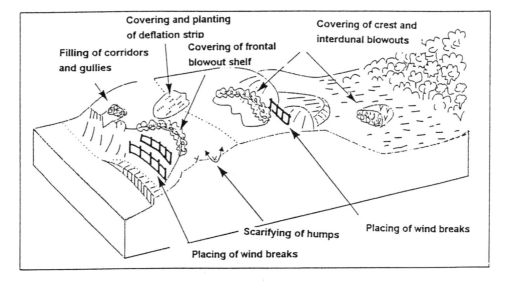

Figure 4   Sand dune management and maintenance techniques practised by the French National Forestry Service (ONF) on the Aquitainian coast

Sand dune vegetation

Dune vegetation is a biological indicator which reflects the quality and status of the dune habitat. In Aquitainian, several endemic vascular plant taxa occur due to the specific geographical position and habitat conditions of the area. Taxa confined to the region include *Alyssum arenarium* (southern Landes), *Solidago virgaurea* ssp. *macrorhiza* (southern Landes), *Hieracium eriophorum* (Landes and southern Gironde) and *Linaria thymifolia*. On the Atlantic coast notable taxa include *Artemisia campestris* ssp. *lloydii* (up to southern Brittany), *Astragalus baionensis* (south of the Loire), *Dianthus gallicus* (southern Cotentin), *Galium arenarium* (up to Brittany), *Linea arenaria* (from the Gironde to Cotentin) and *Silene thorei* (up to the Vendée). There are also endemic plant communities such as *Galium arenarium* with *Hieracium eriophorum* and *Alyssum arenarium* with *Helychrisum stoechas* in southern Landes.

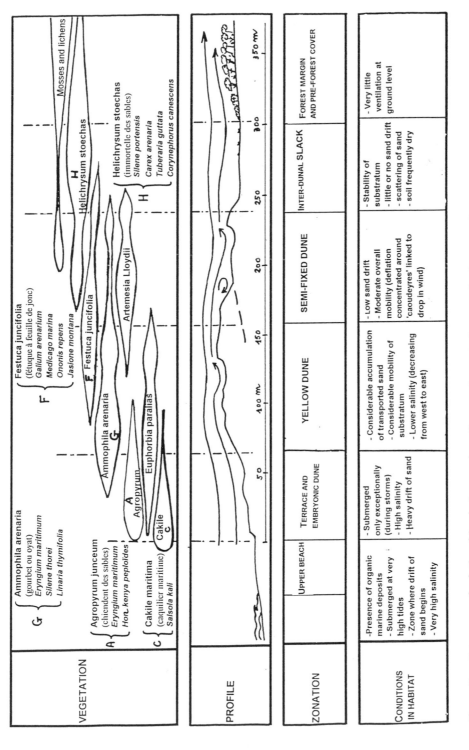

Figure 5   Summary of relationships between dune form and vegetation type in the central Aquitaine area

The relationships between dune form and vegetation type in the central Aquitaine area are summarised in Figure 5.

Dune management techniques

A single standard method of dune management is not suitable for a complex ecological system. Effective management requires the compilation of an inventory of techniques which can be adapted to particular circumstances. The ONF uses cartographic techniques, developed in association with the University of Bordeaux, to produce computer generated colour maps at a scale of 1:5000 which show the relationships between relief, sand dune processes and vegetation. Maps are created from stereoscopic analyses of 1:5000 scale aerial photographs linked to ground reconnaissance. Aerial photography is repeated at five year intervals and SPOT satellite images are also employed.

In 1990 a 1:25000 scale atlas of sand dunes on the coast of Aquitaine was published, providing information on vegetation cover as well as the distribution of 11 major homogeneous vegetation types. This facilitates dune management and assessment programmes. Further development of this atlas, with reference to coastal and sand dune processes as well as vegetation patterns, is planned. Several avenues of research remain to be explored. These include the relationship between dune shape and resistance to erosion; the nature of dune bio-indicators; flora and fauna diversity studies and the forecasting of marine erosion impacts. Fulfilment of these will require improved and expanded links between researchers and practitioners in sand dune management. The research programme is incorporated in a European Commission LIFE project entitled 'Biodiversity and Dune Protection' which is co-ordinated by the Coastal Service of the ONF. Several French national organisations, as well as international bodies, are involved in this project which operates pilot schemes along the Atlantic coast of France. Initial results will be available in 1996.

Conclusion

Coastal dunes are buffer areas where natural processes, habitat conservation, leisure and research can co-exist where dune areas are sufficiently large. Intact sand dune ecosystems can effectively resist sudden change. Resistance depends substantially on the response of dune vegetation, particularly in exposed frontal ridges and foredune areas. Regular maintenance and management of the dune area in Aquitainian demonstrates how sand drift and vegetation cover can be effectively regulated.

References

Auger, R. & Lapoafe, J. 1985. *Flore du domaine Atlantique du Sud Ouest de la France et de gironde plaine.* 3rd edition.

Studies in European Coastal Management. Jones, Healy and Williams (eds)
1996, Samara Publishing Limited, Cardigan. ISBN 1 873692 07 2

Changes in the Vegetation and Management of Saltmarsh Communities in Southern Norway

A. Lundberg

Department of Geography, University of Bergen, Norway

Abstract: Phytosociological methods and vegetation mapping have been used to analyse vegetation change over a 20 year period at a saltmarsh site in SE Norway. Statistical data which document changes in agricultural practice have also been used to trace possible reasons for vegetation change during this period. The main change after 20 years has been the development of dense stands dominated by, among other species, *Phragmites australis*. This has had a detrimental effect on a number of rare species and has resulted in a general decrease in diversity. The cessation of cattle grazing and mowing as arable farming has expanded in this region appears to be the main cause for this vegetation overgrowth problem and is one symptom of the increasing trend towards the regional specialisation of farming practice in Norway. The government is now seeking ways to relax this extreme specialisation. Field experiments have shown that the reintroduction of cattle grazing can be a very effective management tool for the restoration of species-rich saltmarsh vegetation.

Introduction

Extensive analyses of coastal vegetation have been carried out in western and southeastern Norway by Lundberg (1989, 1992) and Lundberg & Rydgren (1994a,b). In these studies phytosociological methods have been used to describe most of the littoral zone vegetation types and this has allowed a detailed assessment of the current status of rocky cliff, stony beach, sand dune and saltmarsh community types in the area. For some locations it has been possible to compare the present status of coastal vegetation types with data from former surveys conducted in this and the 19th century. This paper provides a model example for this type of investigation by analysing vegetation change for an area of saltmarsh vegetation in southeastern Norway at Tomb, Østfold County (Figure 1). This area, which was first mapped over twenty years ago (Marker, 1973), was resurveyed in 1993 (Lundberg & Rydgren, 1994b) and a comparison of these two data sets permits an assessment of the rate and type of change which has occurred together with an assessment of the causal agents of change. This paper will discuss these three aspects and will consider how this information can be used to formulate habitat management objectives.

Vascular plant nomenclature follows Tutin *et al.* (1964-1980) and syntaxonomical units are named in accordance with Vevle (1985) and Fremstad & Elven (1987).

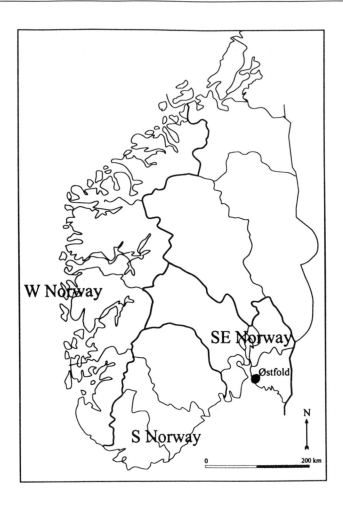

Figure 1   Map showing the location of the Tomb (Østfold County) study site in SE Norway (solid circle)

Thin lines denote county boundaries and thick lines are used to separate regions

Changes in vegetation, 1973-1993

The vegetation map of the study area by Marker (1973) is shown in Figure 2a. This map indicates the existence of a diverse landscape supporting eight major natural and semi-natural community types in an area surrounded by land under pasture and cultivation. The dominant vegetation types in 1973 were the Puccinellietum maritimae (map code 2), Scirpetum maritimae (4) and Juncetum gerardii and *Festuca rubra* (3) community types. The Juncetum gerardii and *Festuca rubra* community types are especially significant as they are often species-rich and support some of the rarest saltmarsh species in Norway, including elements with oceanic, southern-thermophilous and northern distributions.

In analysing the complex of vegetation types present at the site in 1973, useful reference can be made to the definition of landscape elements. Forman & Godron (1986) characterise a landscape by its structure which is defined by basic homogeneous ecological elements or units of land. The lack of any distinction between a natural or anthropogenic origin in this common definition seems to be particularly appropriate when dealing with cultural landscapes or landscapes affected by man. Landscape elements may take the form of patches (a non-linear area of land differing from its surroundings), corridors (a strip of land which differs from the matrix on either side) and matrices. The matrix is generally the most extensive and interconnected type (Forman & Godron, 1986) and usually plays the dominant role in the functioning of landscapes by allowing the flow of energy, materials and species. The patches in Figure 2a are vegetation types 1-12, the corridor is the tidal inlet and the most connective landscape element in 1973 (vegetation unit 4, Scirpetum maritimae) is the matrix.

The vegetation map for the same area in 1993 is shown in Figure 2b. All of the vegetation types recorded in 1973 were still present, but reference to Figure 2c demonstrates marked changes in the area of each vegetation type. In explaining these changes one important factor concerns the decline of grazing at the site. In 1973 two fields on the northern side of the marsh and a large area to the south of the site were grazed by cattle, but by 1993 this latter area was under cultivation with grazing restricted to the southwestern corner of the site only.

The most striking difference in the mosaic of vegetation types after 20 years concerns the distinct increase in the area dominated by the Scirpetum maritimae and *Phragmites australis* community types. In 1973 this latter community had a rather restricted distribution, being limited to small areas along the inner eastern part of the saltmarsh area and near the bridge at the western end of the site. Over the last 20 years *Phragmites* has colonised many new areas and in 1993 was represented by 13 separate populations of variable size (compare with 2 in 1973). During the 1993 survey the largest populations were recorded along the inner parts of the site, bordering both sides of the tidal inlet, but small populations were also found at the centre of the site. The convex boundaries of these populations indicate that they are expanding landscape elements (or tesserae; Forman & Godron, 1986) and they seem to represent the advancing front of a westward expansion of the species. From observations of other marshes in SE Norway it seems likely that *Phragmites* will become the dominant species across the entire site at the expense of a diverse range of saltmarsh communities.

In 1973 the Scirpetum maritimae played a major role in the hydrolittoral zone. With the exception of two small areas near the bridge this was the dominant marsh bank community type. Grazing effectively ceased in 1975 when pastures to the south of the site came under arable cultivation. Since this time the Scirpetum maritimae community type has expanded, even into parts of the geolittoral zone (Figure 2b).

In summary, both the *Phragmites australis* and Scirpetum maritimae community types have spread over the open marsh since the cessation of grazing. By 1993, the optimum distribution of the two types was reflected in the abundance of *Phragmites australis* towards the eastern (inner) part of the marsh and the Scirpetum maritimae community type towards the west where the influence of freshwater

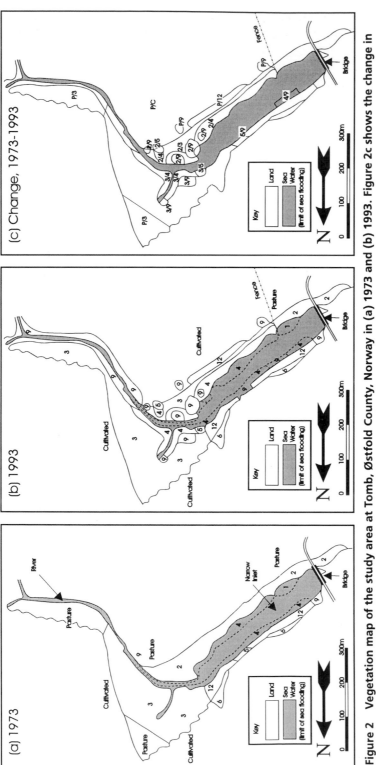

Figure 2   Vegetation map of the study area at Tomb, Østfold County, Norway in (a) 1973 and (b) 1993. Figure 2c shows the change in the distribution of vegetation types between 1973 and 1993

Figure 2a has been redrawn from Marker (1973) and Figure 2b is after Lundberg & Rydgren (1994b)

Key to numbers and letters: 1, Salicornietum europaeae; 2, Puccinellietum maritimae; 3, Juncetum gerardii and *Festuca rubra*; 4, Scirpetum maritimae; 5, Caricetum paleaceae; 6, Lycopo-Alnetum glutinosae; 9, *Phragmites australis* community; 12, *Filipendula ulmaria* community; P, Pasture; C, Cultivated lands. Codes 7, 8,10 and 11 are absent because the corresponding vegetation types were not recorded at the study site is less. Nevertheless, *Phragmites australis* has expanded at the expense of the Scirpetum maritimae, and by 1993 formed the matrix community type at the site.

The success of *Phragmites australis* at the study site is due to its life history and ecology. *Phragmites* can grow in both fresh and saline water, and once dominant is able to spread rhizomatously to form dense, almost monospecific, stands. In this part of Europe few other species function as effective competitors. As the new (1993) matrix element of the landscape, *Phragmites australis* has become dominant in both a physiognomic and interspecific sense.

The Puccinellietum maritimae has declined considerably since 1973 when it used to dominate the southern banks of the site. By 1993 it was restricted to the grazed southwestern corner, and the sharp boundary between this type and the Scirpetum maritimae of the ungrazed marsh illustrates the potency of this form of landuse.

The northern species *Carex paleacea* has spread since the cessation of grazing and by 1993 had become established in two new areas. However, the original population which was mapped in 1973 has apparently been lost to the more aggressive *Phragmites australis*.

Other ecological changes are summarised in Figure 2c and Table 1 which show the increase or decrease in the number of stands of each vegetation type between 1973 and 1993. The most stable vegetation types are the Salicornietum europaeae (1) and the Lycopo-Alnetum glutinosae (6) which occur at the margins of the study area in the pioneer and mature stages of saltmarsh succession respectively. These two community types have changed little in the areas they occupy. Conversely, the Puccinellietum maritimae shows the biggest reduction in area with eight patches being succeeded by other vegetation types between 1973 and 1993. Five stands of vegetation type 3 (Juncetum gerardii & *Festuca rubra*) were also lost between 1973 and 1993. *Phragmites australis* has undergone the largest expansion in the area with 11 new stands becoming established since 1973. It is significant that all of the stands which were present in 1973 remained in 1993.

Table 1   Changes in the number of stands of 8 vegetation types at the Tomb saltmarsh site (Østfold County) in SE Norway between 1973 and 1993

Vegetation type code (Figure 2)	Vegetation type name	Number of stands lost, 1973-1993	Number of stands gained, 1973-1993
1	Salicornietum europaeae	0	0
2	Puccinellietum maritimae	8	0
3	Juncetum gerardii and *Festuca rubra*	5	3
4	Scirpetum maritimae	1	4
5	Caricetum paleaceae	1	2
6	Lycopo-Alnetum glutinosae	0	0
9	*Phragmites australis* community	0	11
12	*Filipendula ulmaria* community	0	1

Factors influencing vegetation change between 1973 and 1993

The changes in vegetation structure documented above are thought to have arisen because of changes in the intensity of grazing. During the period 1955-1970 the area to the south of the marsh was grazed by between 60 and 80 cattle. After this period the practice of keeping and feeding cattle under cover for much of the year was introduced and the number of grazing animals adjacent to the site dropped to about 30 from 1972 until 1976 when the number was further reduced to between 10 and 15 animals. Another factor which has affected the marsh concerns the advent of arable cultivation and land drainage to the south of the site in 1975. Some drainage pipes cross parts of the marsh and are thought to have resulted in a lowering of the water table and a decrease in soil salinity. Such factors may well have reduced the competitiveness of species such as *Puccinellia maritima* in areas subsequently occupied by *Phragmites australis*, but observations both at Tomb and other Norwegian sites suggest very strongly that the key factor leading to the spread of *Phragmites* has been a reduction in the number of grazing animals. Soil enrichment, through the heavy application of manure on the neighbouring corn fields, is another factor which may have contributed to the spread of *Phragmites australis*. This was not specifically examined in this study, but the absence of vegetation change at the southwestern (grazed) part of the site suggests that even if nutrient enrichment has occurred, the cessation of grazing remains as the main reason for vegetation change.

Lundberg & Rydgren (1994a,b) have shown that the expansion of *Phragmites australis* in such situations is very widespread in south and southeastern Norway. To analyse whether such regional changes are also due to the factors discussed in the case of the site at Tomb, it is necessary to consider wider scale changes in Norwegian agricultural practice which have followed the increasing trend towards regional specialisation since 1950.

Table 2 shows how the number of grazing cattle has changed in three coastal districts of south Norway since 1969.

The three regions considered in the table have been chosen because they include areas of coastline supporting saltmarsh habitat. The data for each region have also been collected from districts with similar patterns of agriculture. Unfortunately, detailed information for stocking rates on saltmarshes is not known, and a proportion of the animals would also have been kept indoors for much of the time. The table nevertheless shows a clear decrease in the number of cattle in SE Norway amounting to a reduction in the total national percentage from 14.8% to 8.1%. The region of S Norway (Sörlandet) has never been particularly important for milk production and the decline here is less evident. However, in W Norway, the most important dairy region, a rise in cattle numbers from 35.4% to 40.6% of the total national stock is shown. Even though present day practice does not utilise saltmarshes as grazing lands to the same extent as in the past, the increase in the number of cattle in W Norway has been instrumental in preventing the type of vegetation overgrowth problems described here (Lundberg, 1989, 1992).

Another indication of the change in grazing pressure on saltmarshes is demon-strated in Table 3 which shows the decline in the area of surface cultivated grazing pasture and other related uncultivated permanent grasslands in the same three regions of Norway. The contraction in the area of these grasslands partly reflects the decline in grazing and partly the increasing shift towards indoor cattle management. To illustrate this, even though the number of cattle has risen in the region of W Norway (Table 2) the area of surface cultivated pasture and permanent grassland has still declined, although by only a small amount. The same trend is also shown by the decline in the area of surface cultivated meadows mown for forage and other related uncultivated permanent grassland types over the same three regions (Table 4). Some areas of saltmarsh vegetation are included by these definitions, even though they only constitute a relatively small total area compared to the other grassland types.

These changes are mirrored by the increase in corn production which is shown for the three regions of SE, S and W Norway in Table 5. As in the case study site at Tomb, former pastures are now used for corn production in many areas, and in SE Norway as a whole the area of land farmed in this way has risen by 48% since 1969. This trend is less in W Norway, the Norwegian dairy farming stronghold.

These analyses demonstrate profound changes in agricultural practice in recent years and it is necessary to consider how these influence landscape structure and biological diversity.

Lundberg (1989, 1992) and Lundberg & Rydgren (1994a,b) have investigated 377 coastal sites in southern Norway, some of which had been studied by botanists between 20 and 70 or more years ago. For the Oslofiord region of SE Norway one especially useful source of archive data originates from the studies of the late Professor Rolf Nordhagen (1920) who provided detailed descriptions of saltmarsh vegetation in the region. During 1990-1991 six of these sites were resurveyed and comparisons with the earlier surveys of Nordhagen revealed distinct changes in:

a)   the types of vegetation;

b)   the relative importance of each type; and

c)   the number of species present.

These changes will be illustrated by considering a site at Holtekilen, close to the national airport of Fornebu. The flora and vegetation of this site was described by Nordhagen (1918,1920) who found a very diverse range of species and vegetation types including rare taxa such as *Eleocharis parvula*. A resurvey of this site almost 70 years later in 1990-91 revealed an almost complete cover of *Phragmites australis* and a low diversity of species. Similar comparisons at other formerly grazed sites show a similar picture, with a general reduction in the number of vegetation types and species. The extent of change seems to be determined by the length of time elapsed since the cessation of grazing. At the Tomb study site, grazing practically ceased 18 years prior to the time of resurvey (1993) and although *Phragmites australis* does not yet dominate the whole marsh, it is currently a prominent component of the landscape.

Table 2 Changes in the number of cattle in three coastal regions of Norway between 1969 and 1989

Region	1969		1979		1989	
SE Norway	144,411	(14.8%)	102,303	(10.5%)	77,049	(8.1%)
S Norway	50,683	(5.2%)	46,075	(4.7%)	44,903	(4.7%)
W Norway	344,388	(35.4%)	385,834	(40.6%)	385,144	(40.6%)
Norway (total)	973,425	(100.0%)	970,700	(100.0%)	949,369	(100.0%)

Table 3 Changes in the area (hectares) of surface cultivated grazing pastures and other related uncultivated permanent grasslands in three coastal regions of Norway between 1969 and 1989

Region	1969		1979		1989	
SE Norway	13,191	(11.3%)	9,230	(9.8%)	6,408	(7.3%)
S Norway	6,548	(5.6%)	5,011	(5.3%)	4,222	(4.8%)
W Norway	56,422	(48.5%)	5,188	(58.7%)	55,771	(63.7%)
Norway (total)	116,174	(100.0%)	94,035	(100.0%)	87,554	(100.0%)

Table 4 Changes in the area (hectares) of surface cultivated meadows mown for forage and other related uncultivated permanent grasslands in three coastal regions of Norway between 1969 and 1989

Region	1969		1979		1989	
SE Norway	3,928	(9.3%)	2,729	(9.4%)	1,979	(9.1%)
S Norway	2,381	(5.6%)	2,571	(8.8%)	2,143	(9.8%)
W Norway	19,325	(45.6%)	12,998	(44.6%)	11,587	(53.2%)
Norway (total)	42,368	(100.0%)	29,135	(100.0%)	21,769	(100.0%)

Table 5 Changes in the area of corn production (hectares) in three coastal districts of Norway between 1969 and 1989

Region	1969		1979		1989	
SE Norway	131,240	(52.0%)	178,379	(54.8%)	194,578	(55.1%)
S Norway	8,266	(3.3%)	12,547	(3.9%)	13,394	(9.8%)
W Norway	5,823	(2.3%)	4,977	(1.5%)	7,337	(2.1%)
Norway (total)	252,421	(100.0%)	325,479	(100.0%)	352,980	(100.0%)

Numbers in brackets refer to the percentage of the national total. Data obtained from the Central Bureau of Statistics (1971a,b; 1982a,b; 1992a,b)

The development of dense stands of *Phragmites australis* also has an undesirable effect upon some bird species and in some areas has been linked to the loss of breeding populations of the yellow wagtail (*Montacilla flava*) and redshank (*Tringa totanus*).

The specialisation of agricultural practice between regions in Norway clearly represents a threat to the biological diversity of saltmarshes, particularly with respect to grazing patterns. Other problems related to these changes in practice have now forced the Norwegian government to investigate ways in which this regional specialisation can be relaxed. In some areas of SE Norway cattle grazing has now been reintroduced, and the final part of this paper will consider the effects of this upon landscapes and vegetation types.

Suggestions for future management

Cattle have recently been reintroduced at a site near the Ramsar reserve of Kurefjorden (Østfold County) where saltmarsh and wet pasture communities have become overgrown by *Phragmites australis* and *Filipendula ulmaria*. An area of 10 ha has been stocked with 15 sheep and between 10 and 12 Hereford cattle, and within the first year of grazing (1993) both *Phragmites* and *Filipendula* were heavily cropped. This reduction in biomass may eventually favour less competitive species and the choice of Hereford cattle was particularly appropriate in this case because they grazed unselectively. In contrast, Norwegian breeds are much more selective in terms of their grazing preferences.

Whilst the value of grazing as a tool for nature conservation has been amply demonstrated in this paper, the risk of overgrazing also deserves consideration. Overgrazing can lead to loss of vegetation cover and subsequent soil erosion and can also result in the development of a ruderal flora, especially when in conjunction with the use of manure as a fertiliser.

Investigations in both Sweden and Norway (Johansson et al., 1986; Lundberg & Rydgren, 1994a,b) have shown that a moderate grazing pressure of 1-1.5 cattle/ha over a period of 130-140 days serves as an ideal moderate grazing regime. Studies from saltmarshes in south Norway demonstrate that such a regime serves to maintain or even increase species diversity. Therefore, the reintroduction of cattle grazing can serve as an extremely valuable tool for ecological management in areas which are currently strongly biased towards arable farming.

Conclusions

Cessation of grazing can lead to a decline in species richness and structural diversity in saltmarsh vegetation. The rapid spread of competitive species such as *Phragmites australis* may be an important causal agent in this decline. The reintroduction of grazing on saltmarshes has been successful in combating vegetation overgrowth and indicates the importance of maintaining a diverse agricultural system rather than one which is heavily specialised between regions.

References

Central Bureau of Statistics. 1971a. Census of Agriculture 1969. Vol. II. *Norwegian Official Statistics, A 427.* 213 pp.

Central Bureau of Statistics. 1971b. Census of Agriculture 1969. Vol. III. *Norwegian Official Statistics, A 446.* 149 pp.

Central Bureau of Statistics. 1982a. Census of Agriculture and Forestry 1979. Vol. IV. Agriculture - area utilisation. *Norwegian Official Statistics, B 296.* 205 pp.

Central Bureau of Statistics. 1982b. Census of Agriculture and Forestry 1979. Vol. V. Livestock and Poultry. *Norwegian Official Statistics, B 328.* 140 pp.

Central Bureau of Statistics. 1992a. Census of Agriculture and Forestry 1989. Vol. V. Agriculture - area utilisation. *Norwegian Official Statistics, C 24.* 143 pp.

Central Bureau of Statistics. 1992b. Census of Agriculture and Forestry 1989. Vol. V. Livestock. *Norwegian Official Statistics, C 30.* 95 pp.

Forman, R.T.T. & Godron, M. 1986. *Landscape Ecology.* John Wiley & Sons, New York. 619 pp.

Fremstad, E. & Elvan, R. (Eds). 1987. *Enheter for vegetasjonskartlegging i Norge.* Okoforsk Utredn. 1987, 1.

Johansson, O., Ekstam, U. & Forshed, N. 1986. *Havvsstrandsängar.* LTs förlag, Stockholm. 96 pp.

Lundberg, A. 1989. Havstrand i Hordaland. Flora og Vegetasjon. *Direktoratet for naturforvaltning, Rapp.* 1989, 9, 286 pp. (with English summary).

Lundberg, A. 1992. Havstrand i Hordaland. Regionale trekk og verneverdiar. *Direktoratet for naturforvaltning, Rapp.* 1992, 2, 181 pp. (with English summary).

Lundberg, A. & Rydgren, K. 1994a. Havstrand pa Sörlandet. Regionale trekk og botaniske verdier. *NINA, Forskningsrapp,* 59, 127 pp. (with English summary).

Lundberg, A. & Rydgren, K. 1994b. Havstrand pa Söröstlandet. Regionale trekk og botaniske verdier. NINA, *Forskningsrapp,* 47, 222 pp. (with English summary).

Marker, E. 1973. Verneverdige strandenger i Östfold. Botanisk rapport. University of Oslo. Unpublished Report.

Nordhagen, R. 1918. *Scirpus parvulus* ved Kristiania. Et nyt fund og en gammel etiket. *Svensk bot. Tidsskr.* 12, 127-128.

Nordhagen, R. 1920. Vegetationsstudier i Kristianiafjorden. I. Strandvegetatioen. University of Oslo, Botanical Garden and Museum. Unpublished Manuscript.

Tutin, T.G., Heywood, V.H., Burges, N.A., Valentine, D.H., Walters, S.M. & Webb, D.A. (Eds). 1964-1980. *Flora Europaea.* Volumes 1-5. Cambridge University Press, Cambridge, UK.

Vevle, O. 1985. Norske vegetasjonstypar. 2. utg. Nistås forlag, Bö i Telemark. 42 pp.

Studies in European Coastal Management. Jones, Healy and Williams (eds)
1996, Samara Publishing Limited, Cardigan. ISBN 1 873692 07 2

Dune Heath on the Sefton Coast Sand Dune System, Merseyside, UK

S.E. Edmondson

Department of Environmental and Biological Studies, Liverpool Hope University College, Liverpool, UK

P.S. Gateley

Groundwork St. Helens, Knowsley and Sefton, St. Helens, UK

Abstract: The ecology of British dune heath habitats has received little attention. This paper presents the results of a detailed survey of the vegetation and substrates of dune heath habitats on the Sefton Coast, a major dune system on the west coast of Britain. Most dune heath sites are located on the landward fringe of the dune system, where habitat loss has been most pronounced and the surviving resource is highly fragmented.

Much of the Sefton Coast dune heath appears to be of secondary origin, having developed as a successional stage in the recovery of vegetation on areas formerly subject to disturbance. Primary dune heath, developing as a stage in the succession of vegetation types on old dunes, is also present and is floristically similar to secondary heath. In both cases stands dominated by *Calluna vulgaris* closely match the National Vegetation Classification H1d *Calluna vulgaris* - *Festuca ovina* heath *Carex arenaria* sub-community type, a community which is considered to have a predominantly eastern distribution in Britain.

Whether of primary or secondary origin, the substrate of heathland sites has a low pH (mean value 4.2) suggesting that a considerable timescale is required for the development of suitable substrate conditions from sand which is initially highly calcareous.

The successional development of *Calluna* dominated dune heath from acid dune grassland communities has not been commonly observed. The development of scrub on dune heath sites is widespread and there is currently very little management in hand to prevent this.

Dune heath is included as a priority habitat type under the EC Habitats and Species Directive. This, together with its national rarity and locally fragmented and threatened status, indicates that further statutory protection of sites in conjunction with active conservation management is now required.

Introduction

Although there is a considerable body of published literature on British lowland heaths (e.g. Bunce, 1989; Gimmingham, 1992; Farrell, 1993), much less attention has been focused upon dune heaths, especially those developing upon formerly calcareous dune sand substrates.

Farrell (1993) reports an estimated total of 60,000 ha of lowland heath vegetation in Britain, of which less than 50% is found in England. Lowland heath community types as defined by Rodwell (1991) occupy an area of 197 ha on English dunes (Radley, 1994), just 0.6% and 1.6% respectively of the total English resource of lowland heath and sand dune. Dune heath vegetation has much in common with the vegetation of inland lowland heaths developed on sandy acid soils and the widespread dominance of the dwarf shrub *Calluna vulgaris* imparts a basic physiognomic similarity. Gimmingham (1992) however, recognises *Carex arenaria* as a distinctive and widespread component of dune heaths in contrast to most lowland heaths. Nevertheless, the UK National Vegetation Classification (NVC) does not recognise a specific heathland community type for sand dunes, although NVC community H11 (*Calluna vulgaris - Carex arenaria* heath) is considered to correspond with dune heath (Rodwell, 1991). Various other heathland plant communities have also been recorded from coastal dunes (Radley, 1994).

Away from the coast, lowland heath has mostly developed following episodes of forest clearance; the resultant increase in the precipitation:evapo-transpiration ratio promoting leaching and the subsequent development of acidic soil conditions favourable for the development of heath. Long term management (grazing and burning) has also played an important role by preventing the secondary successional development of scrub and woodland. Dune heath differs in being either a seral stage in the primary succession of plant communities on sand dunes (primary heath) or a stage in the secondary succession of plant communities which follow disturbance (secondary heath). Although the former process was noted by Tansley (1939) and Salisbury (1952), little direct evidence has so far been collected to document the spread of *Calluna vulgaris* onto older acidic grasslands (Gimmingham, 1992). Indeed, the processes and stages involved in the successional development of dune heath vegetation are poorly understood. In the specific case of the Sefton Coast for example, Edmondson *et al.* (1993) noted difficulty in understanding the nature of successional transitions between heathland and dune grassland community types, although the seral development of scrub (chiefly *Ulex europaeus* and *Betula* spp.) was widely observed on acidic dune substrates.

The general lack of information concerning the development and composition of dune heath, coupled with the inclusion of dune heath as a habitat type within Annex I of the EC Habitats and Species Directive (Council Directive 92/43/EEC on the conservation of natural habitats and of wild fauna and flora), prompted Sefton Metropolitan Borough Council to commission a survey of heathland sites within the extensive Sefton Coast sand dune system in 1993. A previous coast-wide survey of sand dune vegetation in the area (Edmondson *et al.*, 1989), conducted as part of the National Sand Dune Survey of Great Britain (Radley, 1994), placed dune heath vegetation within the NVC H11 (*Calluna vulgaris - Carex arenaria* heath) community type. The present survey, completed in 1994, has provided a more comprehensive appraisal of dune heath vegetation and substrates in the area.

The Sefton Coast

The Sefton Coast is a large, calcareous, hindshore type dune system situated on the northwest coast of England (Figure 1). Despite extensive habitat loss due to housing development, changes in agricultural practice and afforestation (with conifers) the Sefton Coast dune complex is still listed as the largest dune system in England (Doody, 1991).

Freshly deposited sand in the region is highly alkaline with a pH which approaches 9.0 (James, 1993). Over time, leaching leads to decalcification and acidification but the time-scale required for the development of substrate conditions suitable for the establishment of dune heath is unknown. The highly calcareous nature of freshly deposited sand suggests that a considerable period of time may be required, although Salisbury (1925) proposed a time-scale of just 300 years. More recent work, summarised by Plater *et al.* (1993) and Innes & Tooley (1993), has shown that the dunes of the Sefton coast originated at least 2,000-2,500 years ago and many surfaces are therefore likely to exceed this 300 year threshold. However, James (1993) reports that there is very little information concerning the chemistry of dune heath substrates in the region.

History, extent and distribution of dune heath sites on the Sefton Coast

The dune heath sites are located along the landward (eastern) edge of the sand dune system (Figure 2). The former distribution of dune heath is poorly documented, although Blanchard (1952) refers to the development of housing estates on extensive areas of 'dune heath' around 1930. It thus seems likely that the area of heathland was once more extensive.

The surviving areas of dune heath are located on golf courses, abandoned agricultural land, a military airfield and in a church-yard. The remainder of the landward dune fringe now consists of coniferous woodland, housing estates and agricultural land. An inventory of dune heathland sites for the area is provided in Table 1.

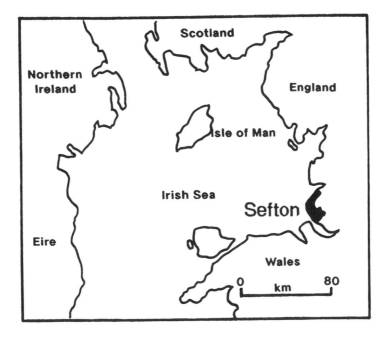

Figure 1   **The location of the Sefton Coast dune system**

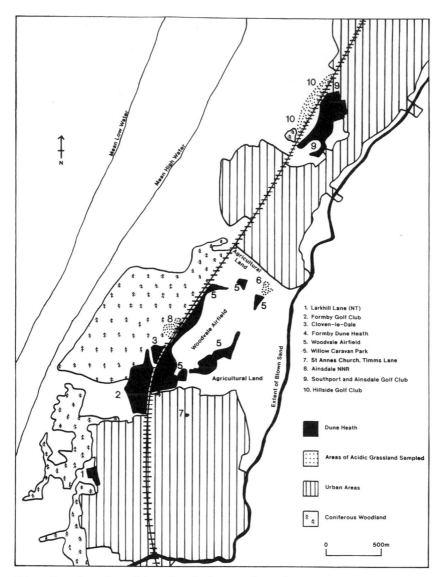

Figure 2   Location of dune heath sites on the Sefton Coast

The extent of primary dune heath is uncertain; the only extensive areas, as evidenced by the surviving topography, occur in old dry slacks on the Southport and Ainsdale Golf Course (Figure 2). Further south, Blanchard (1952) recorded the colonisation of some old slacks in the Formby area by *Calluna vulgaris* and this process may still be observed. It is thus likely that at least some of the dune heath on Formby Golf Course (Figure 2) is also of primary origin. Unfortunately, golf course management has resulted in the widespread fragmentation of dune heath in this area (Figure 3). Secondary heath is apparently more common than primary heath (Table 1). For example at Freshfield, dune heath has developed on land

Table 1   **Inventory showing the area and history of all major dune heath sites on the Sefton Coast dune system. Sites which support areas of acid grassland and scrub, as well as heath dominated by *Calluna vulgaris*, are included**

Site	Area (ha)	Origin/Comments
Ainsdale Sand Dunes NNR	5.25	Mostly acid grassland developed on abandoned asparagus fields
Hillside Golf Course	15.70	Acid grassland
Cloven-le-Dale	4.23	Former agricultural land
Freshfield Dune Heath	3.78	Former golf course and agricultural land
Formby Golf Course	29.06	Probable mixture of primary dune heath and disturbed areas
Larkhill	3.96	Former agricultural land
Southport and Ainsdale Golf Course	35.78	Primary heath in old dune slacks
St Annes Church	0.22	Churchyard with probable history of disturbance
Willow Farm	2.22	Former agricultural land
Woodvale Airfield	53.95	Site disturbed during construction of airfield
Total area of dune heath	154.15	
Total dune area of Sefton Coast	2,109.00	Based on Doody (1991)
Proportion of total dune area occupied by dune heath	7.30%	

formerly subject to agricultural and golf course management and on land which was levelled to provide an airfield. In such cases it is possible that the removal of vegetation on older dune areas has promoted leaching and the loss of nutrients in the surface sediments to create an open impoverished substrate surface suitable for the establishment of *Calluna* seedlings.

Vegetation and soil survey methods

As part of the 1993/4 survey of dune heathland sites, vegetation data were recorded from a total of 305 quadrats partitioned between 9 sites. Quadrats were located within representative stands of heathland vegetation at each site, and quadrat sizes were chosen to conform with those recommended by the NVC (Rodwell, 1991) with quadrats of 4 x 4 m being used for sub-shrub communities and 2 x 2 m for grass/herb vegetation. The percentage cover of each species was recorded on the 10 point Domin scale of cover abundance. Vegetation height was also recorded as a mean of 5 measurements, one at each corner of the quadrat and one at the centre. At 128 quadrat sites, sediment samples were collected from the surface and from a depth of 10 cm for pH measurement. Sediment pH was measured with a glass electrode and calomel reference in a 2.5 : 1 de-ionized water : sediment slurry.

Survey effort was concentrated on areas dominated by *Calluna vulgaris* although associated vegetation types, including acid dune grassland and gorse scrub, were also sampled and mapped.

Data analysis

Vegetation data were analysed using Two Way Indicator Species Analysis (TWINSPAN) and Detrended Correspondence Analysis (DECORANA; Hill, 1979a,b). Four levels of division were used for the TWINSPAN analysis, and the 12 end groups produced were assigned to NVC community types using the MATCH computer programme of Malloch (1990). Detrended Correspondence Analysis of the data set was performed using a default run of the programme as implemented on the Vespan II software package (Malloch, 1988).

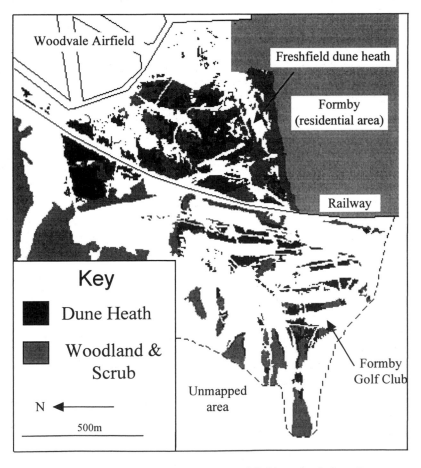

Figure 3   **Fragmented areas of dune heath at Freshfield on the Sefton Coast**

Pearsons Product Moment Correlation Coefficient has been used to examine, by means of 2 x 2 matrices, the relationships between vegetation data (in the form of DECORANA quadrat scores) and selected edaphic and biotic variables. Although the ordination utilised all 305 quadrats, the above analysis has been confined to the subset of 128 quadrats with accompanying substrate pH measurements.

Results

Variations in substrate pH between nine of the dune heathland sites are presented in Figure 4. Although substrate pH ranges from 3.3 to 7.2, the mean value for the surface of the substrate and sediments at a depth of 10.0 cm is the same (4.2). This is surprising in view of the very different appearance of the two horizons. The surface sediments under *Calluna vulgaris* were generally composed of very dark *Calluna vulgaris* litter and dark-stained sand, whereas most samples collected from below the surface were composed more or less entirely of unstructured sand.

The most frequent species recorded during the survey (occurring at a constancy level of V, i.e. present in 81-100% of quadrats) were *Agrostis capillaris*, *Calluna vulgaris*, *Carex arenaria*, *Festuca ovina*, *Holcus lanatus*, *Hypnum cupressiforme*, *Hypochaeris radicata*, *Luzula* sp. and *Rumex acetosella*.

Calluna vulgaris was the only ericoid sub-shrub recorded. This is in contrast to the North Walney dune system, 65 km further north on the west coast of England, where Radley (1988) recorded *Erica cinerea* and *E. tetralix* as typical components of dry and wet heath respectively.

Other species which were frequently recorded during the study are listed in Table 2.

Quadrat groups in which *Calluna vulgaris* was present as the dominant species have all been identified as the H1d *Calluna vulgaris* - *Festuca ovina* heath, *Carex arenaria* sub-community. However, during the 1988 survey (Edmondson et al., 1989) these areas were identified as being comparable to the H11c *Calluna vulgaris* - *Carex arenaria* heath, species-poor sub-community. This difference may have arisen because the latter classification was performed without the aid of computer matching and prior to the publication of the NVC Heaths volume (Rodwell, 1991). During the Sand Dune Survey of Great Britain, Radley (1994) states that the H11c community type was recorded only from Merseyside, whilst H1d was the only heathland community type recorded from the Norfolk dunes on the east coast of Britain. Radley (1994) does, however, consider that the two sub-communities are almost indistinguishable and that stands could possibly have been assigned to either vegetation type during mapping. The identification in this study of a large number of the Sefton dune heath samples as H1d is noteworthy as H11 is supposed to be the typical dune heath vegetation type, whilst H1 is generally considered to be confined to the lowlands of eastern England (Rodwell, 1991).

A significant finding is that the floristic composition of *Calluna vulgaris* dominated dune heath differs little between sites which are believed to have a primary successional origin and sites where secondary dune heath has developed (Table 3).

The remaining seven end groups of quadrats produced by TWINSPAN were matched with the following NVC community types: SD12 *Carex arenaria* - *Festuca*

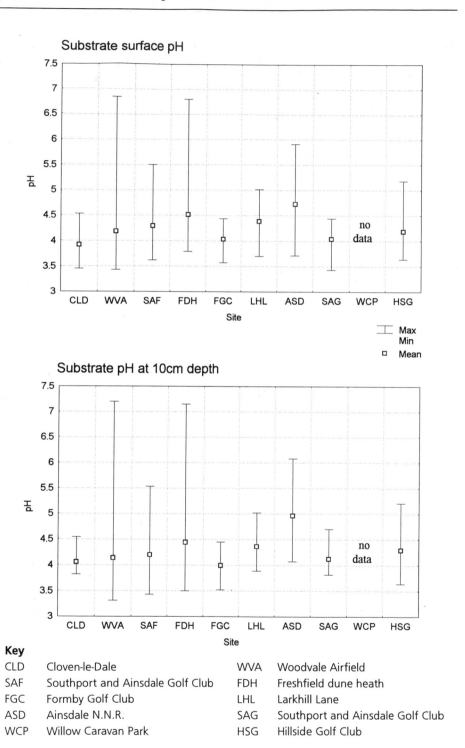

Key

CLD	Cloven-le-Dale	WVA	Woodvale Airfield
SAF	Southport and Ainsdale Golf Club	FDH	Freshfield dune heath
FGC	Formby Golf Club	LHL	Larkhill Lane
ASD	Ainsdale N.N.R.	SAG	Southport and Ainsdale Golf Club
WCP	Willow Caravan Park	HSG	Hillside Golf Club

Figure 4   **Variations in substrate pH at the surface and at a depth of 10.0 cm for nine dune heath sites on the Sefton Coast**

ovina - Agrostis capillaris dune grassland; U1f *Festuca ovina - Agrostis capillaris - Rumex acetosella* grassland, *Hypochaeris radicata* sub–community; U4b *Festuca ovina - Agrostis capillaris - Galium saxatile* grassland, *Holcus lanatus - Trifolium repens* sub–community; MG1a *Arrhenatherum elatius* grassland, *Festuca rubra* sub–community; MG7e *Lolio - Plaginetum* grassland and W23c *Ulex europaeus - Rubus fruticosus* scrub, *Teucrium scorodonia* sub–community.

A scatter plot of quadrat scores on the first two axes of the DECORANA ordination is shown in Figure 5 together with the location of quadrat groups conforming to the eight NVC community types.

Heathland quadrats classified as NVC community type H1d have the lowest axis 1 scores and are succeeded on axis 1 by calcifugous grassland types U1f and U4b and the acid sand dune grassland type SD12. Quadrats with the highest axis 1 scores are variously classified as *Carex arenaria* dune grassland, two mesotrophic grassland community types and scrub community type W23c and these are well separated on axis 2. The close proximity on axis one of the calcifugous grassland and *Calluna* heath quadrats is interesting, especially as *Calluna* shows little sign of spreading into these former areas. This might have been expected in view of the relaxation of grazing which followed the arrival of myxamatosis on the Sefton Coast (Edmondson *et al.*, 1993). That axis 1 does not apparently represent variations in stand composition in relation to age or successional history is

Table 2   **Summary table of species constancy for all sampled dune heathland sites on the Sefton Coast dune system**

Numerals refer to the presence of a species in 41-60% (III), 61-80% (IV) and 81-100% (V) of samples

Constancy class		
V	**IV**	**III**
Agrostis capillaris	*Aira praecox*	*Cerastium fontanum*
Calluna vulgaris	*Ammophila arenaria*	*Cladonia* spp.
Carex arenaria	*Betula pendula*	*Crataegus monogyna*
Festuca ovina	*Chamerion angustifolium*	*Cytisus scoparius*
Holcus lanatus	*Dicranum scoparium*	*Dactylis glomerata*
Hypnum cupressiforme	*Festuca rubra*	*Deschampsia flexuosa*
Hypochaeris radicata	*Hieracium* sp.	*Eurhynchium praelongum*
Luzula sp.	*Juncus conglomeratus*	*Galium saxatile*
Rumex acetosella	*Nardus stricta*	*Hypogymnia physodes*
	Pinus nigra	*Juncus squarrosus*
	Polytrichum juniperinum	*Juncus tenuis*
	Rubus sp. sec. *Glandulosi*	*Ornithopus perpusillus*
	Salix repens	*Plantago lanceolata*
	Ulex europaeus	*Populus* sp.
		Quercus robur
		Rubus caesius
		Senecio jacobaea
		Trifolium repens

Table 3   **Summary table showing variations in the constancy and cover of selected taxa between primary and secondary dune heath sites**

All primary dune heath samples were collected from the Southport and Ainsdale golf course, and all secondary heath samples from Woodvale Airfield. In each case data is firstly given for all samples and secondly for samples collected from stands in which *Calluna vulgaris* was dominant. For each site all taxa occurring at a constancy level of III or more in at least one of the sample catagories are included. Numerals refer to the presence of a species in 21-40% (II), 41-60% (III), 61-80% (IV) and 81-100% (V) of samples. The range of cover values (Domin) is shown in parentheses

Species	Primary dune heath		Secondary dune heath	
	All samples	*Calluna* heath	All samples	*Calluna* heath
Calluna vulgaris	V (1-10)	V (7-10)	IV (0-10)	V (5-10)
Carex arenaria	V (2-10)	V (2-4)	IV (0-9)	V (2-5)
Hypnum cupressiforme	V (2-7)	V (2-7)	III (2-8)	IV (2-7)
Dicranum scoparium	IV (1-7)	V (2-7)	II (0-5)	III (0-5)
Cladonia spp.	II (1-3)	III (1-3)	III (0-5)	IV (1-5)
Nardus stricta	III (1-8)	IV (1-8)	-	-
Festuca ovina	III (0-8)	II (0-2)	-	-
Holcus lanatus	-	-	III (0-10)	II (1-4)
Lophocolea spp.	-	-	II (0-3)	III (0-3)

indicated by the high axis 1 scores shared by seral communities which might be expected to precede (*Carex arenaria* dune) and follow (*Ulex europaeus* - *Rubus fruticosus* scrub) *Calluna* dominated heath. Quadrats classified as mesotrophic grassland also have high axis 1 scores; the establishment of *Calluna* in these relatively productive communities is probably unlikely.

Axis 1 of the ordination does appear to represent variation in quadrat composition in relation to a pH linked gradient; axis 1 quadrat scores are significantly and positively correlated with both surface pH and sediment pH at a depth of 10 cm (Table 4). *Calluna vulgaris* cover is significantly and negatively correlated with the quadrat scores on axis 1 and with substrate pH both at the surface and at a depth of 10.0 cm. Quadrat scores on ordination axis 2 are not significantly correlated with any of the measured variables.

Current management of the dune heaths

Only a small part of the dune heath area is currently subject to practical management. The Cloven-le-Dale site is grazed by horses and much of the heathland area at Formby Golf Club is closely mown. Many areas however, are free from intervention and the development of scrub, particularly *Betula* spp., is occurring on most sites.

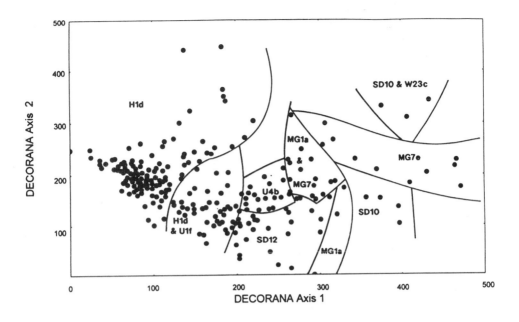

N.V.C. community types

H1d   *Calluna vulgaris - Festuca ovina* heath, *Carex arenaria* sub-community

MG7e *Lolio - Plaginetum* grassland

SD12 *Carex arenaria - Festuca ovina - Agrostis capillaris* dune grassland

U1f   *Festuca ovina - Agrostis capillaris - Rumex acetosella* grassland, *Hypochaeris radicata* sub-community

U4b   *Festuca ovina - Agrostis capillaris - Galium saxatile* grassland, *Holcus lanatus - Trifolium repens* sub-community

W23c *Ulex europaeus - Rubus fruticosus* scrub, *Teucrium scorodonia* sub-community

MG1a *Arrhenatherum elatius* grassland, *Festuca rubra* sub-community

SD10 *Carex arenaria* dune

Figure 5   **Scatter plot showing the distribution of 305 dune heath vegetation samples (quadrats) on axes 1 and 2 of the DECORANA ordination**

Samples were collected from 9 sites and numerous samples are obscured by overlap. Also shown are the location of the eight quadrat groups identified by TWINSPAN and subsequently matched with community types of the National Vegetation Classification. Note the use of different scales for axes 1 and 2 of the ordination

Table 4   **Pearson Product Moment Correlation Coefficient matrix defining the relationships between vegetational and environmental variables for the Sefton Coast dune heath sites**

These figures are the product of a 2 x 2 correlation between quadrat scores on DECORANA axes 1 and 2 generated by a default run of the programme and selected edaphic and vegetation variables. The data relate to 128 vegetation samples collected between 1993 and 1994. Significant correlations (at $p < 0.05$) are given in bold type

	DECORANA Axis 2	Surface pH	pH - 10cm depth	Mean vegetation height	*Calluna vulgaris* cover
DECORANA Axis 1	0.02	**0.69**	**0.65**	- 0.17	**- 0.45**
	DECORANA Axis 2	0.04	- 0.09	- 0.05	0.11
		Surface pH	**0.84**	- 0.05	**- 0.23**
			pH - 10cm depth	- 0.04	**- 0.27**
				Mean vegetation height	0.05

Conclusions

These results represent the first comprehensive description of dune heath vegetation on the large calcareous Sefton Coast dune system.

James (1993) notes the lowest previously reported dune sediment pH on the Sefton Coast as 5.5, but acknowledges that the maximum extent of decalcification and acidification of unafforested duneland sediments would occur below heathland vegetation for which he could find no available data. The results reported here show this to be the case, with very low sediment pH values recorded from all dune heath sites.

All areas of *Calluna vulgaris* dune heath closely matched community H1d (*Calluna vulgaris - Festuca ovina* heath, Carex arenaria sub-community) of the National Vegetation Classification, irrespective of the age, successional origin and management status of individual sites. On the basis of floristic attributes alone therefore, heath developing as part of a secondary succession appears to be of similar quality to primary heath.

The process by which heath develops from acid dune and grassland communities is poorly understood and does not appear to be occurring on the Sefton Coast. The development of heath in dune slacks, although not widespread, does appear to be more common. In the future this transition may cease because the currently low intensity grazing regime seems to promote the development of mesotrophic sub-shrub communities dominated by *Salix repens* with tall grass-herb vegetation

(Edmondson *et al.*, 1993). Further north, Radley (1988) records similar patterns for the dune heath areas at North Walney.

The inclusion of dune heath as a priority habitat in the EC Habitats Directive, and the proportionately small quantity of dune heath remaining in the UK, makes the protection of existing areas highly desirable. That much of the present area of dune heath is of secondary successional origin suggests that the creation of heathland may be possible at suitable sites on the coast. Furthermore, the floristic similarity of primary and secondary dune heath indicates that locally typical dune heath vegetation of high nature conservation value may develop on previously disturbed areas of the dune system. Such opportunities exist, for example, on old abandoned fields formerly used for the cultivation of asparagus (*Asparagus officinalis* ssp. *officinalis*) where substrates are acidic and nutrient deficient.

Ideally, in an active, dynamic dune system, the development of new areas of dune heath would roughly balance those lost to scrub encroachment. This is not occurring on the Sefton Coast. Such a dynamic balance is only likely on a natural, actively accreting dune system rather than on one where the development of late successional stage vegetation types to landward has been constrained by urbanisation. Succession to scrub can be widely observed on the Sefton Coast, but the development of dune heath from acid dune vegetation types is rare. Intervention management to maintain and extend the current status of the fragmented dune heaths is therefore an important conservation priority.

Only a very small proportion of the Sefton Coast dune heath resource is currently protected by Site of Special Scientific Interest designation under the 1981 Wildlife and Countryside Act. Similarly, very little is included in the proposed Sefton Coast Special Area of Conservation. Further statutory protection for these dune heath sites is therefore desirable.

References

Blanchard, B. 1952. An Ecological Survey of the Sand Dune System of the South West Lancashire Coast, with Special Reference to an Associated Marsh Flora. Unpublished PhD thesis, University of Liverpool, UK.

Bunce, R.G.H. (Ed). 1989. *Heather in England and Wales*: Institute of Terrestrial Ecology Research Publication No. 3. HMSO, London, UK.

Dobson, F. 1981. *Lichens: an Illustrated Guide*. Richmond Publishing Company, London, UK.

Doody, J.P. (Ed). 1991. *Sand Dune Inventory of Europe*. Joint Nature Conservation Committee/European Union for Coastal Conservation, Peterborough, UK.

Edmondson, S.E., Gateley, P.S. & Nissenbaum, D. 1989. National Sand Dune Vegetation Survey: the Sefton Coast. NCC Report No. 917. Nature Conservancy Council, Peterborough, UK.

Edmondson, S.E., Gateley, P.S., Rooney, P.J. & Sturgess, P. 1993. Plant communities and succession. In: *The Sand Dunes of the Sefton Coast*. Eds: Atkinson, D. & Houston, J. National Museums & Galleries on Merseyside, Liverpool, UK. pp. 65-84.

Farrell, L. 1993. *English Nature Science No. 12 Lowland Heathland: The Extent of Habitat Change*. English Nature, Peterborough, UK.

Gimmingham, C.H. 1992. *English Nature Science No. 8 The Lowland Heath Management Handbook*. English Nature, Peterborough, UK.

Hill, M.O. 1979a. *TWINSPAN - a FORTRAN program for arranging multivariate data in an ordered two-way table by classification of the individuals and attributes*. Section of Ecology and Systematics, Cornell University, Ithaca, New York, USA.

Hill, M.O. 1979b. *DECORANA - a FORTRAN program for Detrended Correspondence Analysis and Reciprocal Averaging*. Section of Ecology and Systematics, Cornell University, Ithaca, New York, USA.

Innes, J.B. & Tooley, M.J. 1993. The age and vegetational history of the Sefton Coast dunes. In: *The Sand Dunes of the Sefton Coast*. Eds: Atkinson, D. & Houston, J. National Museums & Galleries on Merseyside, Liverpool, UK. pp. 35-40.

James, P.A. 1993. Soils and nutrient cycling. In: *The Sand Dunes of the Sefton Coast*. Eds: Atkinson, D. & Houston, J. National Museums & Galleries on Merseyside, Liverpool, UK. pp. 47-54.

Malloch, A.J.C. 1988. *VESPAN II: A computer package to handle and analyse multivariate species data and handle and display species distribution data*. Unit of Vegetation Science, University of Lancaster, UK.

Malloch, A.J.C. 1990. *Match: A Computer programme to aid the assignment of vegetation data to the communities and sub-communities of the National Vegetation Classification*. Unit of Vegetation Science, University of Lancaster, UK.

Plater, A.J., Huddart, D., Innes, J.B., Pye, K., Smith, A.J. & Tooley, M. 1993. Coastal and sea-level changes. In: *The Sand Dunes of the Sefton Coast*. Eds: Atkinson, D. & Houston, J. National Museums & Galleries on Merseyside, Liverpool, UK. pp. 23-34.

Radley, G.P. 1988. *Contract Surveys No. 24, National Sand Dune Vegetation Survey Site Report No. 7, North Walney*. English Nature, Peterborough, UK.

Radley, G.P. 1994. *Sand Dune Vegetation Survey of Great Britain: A National Inventory Part 1: England*. English Nature/Joint Nature Conservation Committee, Peterborough, UK. 126 pp.

Rodwell, J.S. (Ed.). 1991. *British Plant Communities Volume 2: Mires and Heaths*. Cambridge University Press, Cambridge, UK.

Salisbury, E.J. 1925. Note on the edaphic succession in sand dune soils with special reference to the time factor. *Journal of Ecology*, 13:322-328.

Salisbury, E.J. 1952. *Downs and Dunes: Their Plant Life and Its Environment*. Bell, London, UK.

Smith, A.J.E. 1980. *The Moss Flora of Britain and Ireland*. Cambridge University Press, Cambridge, UK.

Stace, C.A. 1991. *New Flora of the British Isles*. Cambridge University Press, Cambridge, UK.

Tansley, A.G. 1939. *The British Islands and Their Vegetation*. Cambridge University Press, Cambridge, UK.

Studies in European Coastal Management. Jones, Healy and Williams (eds)
1996, Samara Publishing Limited, Cardigan. ISBN 1 873692 07 2

The Effect of Trampling on the Microarthropod Fauna of Dune Sediments. A Case Study from Jutland, Denmark

H.H. Koehler, H. Harder, J. Meyerdirks & A. Voigt

Institute of Ecology and Evolutionary Biology, University of Bremen,
D 28334 Bremen, Germany

Abstract: In September 1994, two moderately frequented paths in the dunes of Houstrup Strand (West Jutland, Denmark) were selected to study the effects of trampling upon soil microarthropod communities. Analyses of vegetation, dune sediment parameters and Collembola and Acari communities revealed complex effects of trampling, including an increase in substrate temperature and shearing force and a decrease in water holding capacity, organic matter content and the number of predatory mites in trampled path-centre microhabitats. Other mites and Collembola were most abundant in the wayside and least abundant in the path-centre microhabitats. These effects may lead to a reduction in sand stabilisation, thus increasing the risk of erosion. Macroscale effects on the whole dune system may result where networks of paths are present. The negative effects of thatching as a means of path stabilisation are discussed and the strict channelling of users along a minimum of routes is recommended as a management measure.

Introduction

Coastal dunes are multifunctional landscapes; they provide unique habitats for plants and animals, they protect the hinterland from flooding by the sea and they are used for water processing and as military training areas. They are also a favourite destination for tourists. In this latter respect, the positive economic effects of mass tourism are countered by the negative effects on the ecology and stability of sand dune ecosystems, even when education and management are used to limit damage. One aspect of public pressure on dunes is the damage caused to vegetation by trampling; in extreme cases this may result in the uncontrolled development of blowouts.

The effects of trampling upon dune sediments and vegetation has been investigated by various authors (e.g. Liddle & Greig–Smith, 1975; Nordstrom *et al.*, 1991; Slatter, 1978), but no studies have investigated its effects upon soil microarthropod populations. The majority of soil microarthropods belongs to the springtails (Collembola, Insecta) and mites (Acari, Arachnida). The body size of these animals ranges from considerably less than 1 mm to 2 or 3 mm and they are well adapted to life in soil pores, which they cannot dig themselves. They can utilise a wide variety of food sources, including detritus, bacteria, fungi and other animals. By their feeding activity they exert an important controlling and regulating influence on their food populations and on ecosystem processes, including succession (ecosystem development), decomposition, nutrient cycling and soil biotic processes. Through their effect on these processes, soil microarthropods also contribute to dune longevity by sand stabilisation. Evidence for these processes is summarised in Koehler & Weidemann (1995).

Collembola and Acari communities are species rich and composed of many individuals. In dune sediments, the Collembola and Gamasina (a predatory group of mites) are each represented by approximately 20 species, and population densities of approximately 170,000 springtails/m^2 and up to 420,000 mites/m^2 have been documented (Koehler et al., 1995). Both the number of species and the abundance of individuals have been used as indicators of soil quality and environmental stress (Ghilarov, 1978; Karg, 1968; Koehler, 1992). Negative effects of trampling on the soil microarthropod fauna have been reported for forest soils and *Sphagnum* mosses (Garay & Nataf, 1982; Garay et al., 1981; Borcard & Matthey, 1995). Trampling causes soil compaction, reduction of plant cover and changes of microclimate, factors which are known to influence the species abundance and composition of soil microarthropod communities (Karg, 1967; Koehler & Born, 1989).

This study reports an investigation of trampling-induced changes in the soil microarthropod communities of two moderately frequented duneland footpaths in Denmark. The objective of the study described is to document impacts of trampling which go beyond vegetation change and to assess the consequences for dune stability.

Area of study

The large dune area near Houstrup Strand, Jutland, was selected for study. This site is subject to considerable visitor pressure as a result of people crossing the dune system from car-parks in order to gain access to the west-facing beach. Although most tourists are channelled along one major access path, uncontrolled access does occur elsewhere. For this investigation two c. 1 m wide paths of west to east orientation were selected for study. Both paths pass through yellow, grey and brown dune macrohabitats and both displayed a zonation of microhabitats from a central heavily trampled area with little vegetation through a marginal wayside band with damaged or ruderal vegetation and eventually to stands with an undisturbed composition and structure. Neither path was thatched or fenced and sampling took place within a two-week period in September 1994.

Methods

Vegetation

Vegetation was studied in representative areas of 2x2 m for the original vegetation and along strips for the wayside and path-centre microhabitats. The length of strip was adjusted to obtain an area approximately equal to 2x2 m. Dominant species were determined by recording cover abundance, and vegetation units have been named in accordance with Ellenberg (1986).

Sediment sampling

Four 100 cm³ replicate sediment samples were collected using a soil corer from each of the three microhabitats in yellow, grey and brown dune macrohabitats at both path sites. At each sampling point samples were divided at depths of 0-4, 4-8 and 8-12 cm, but for the sake of brevity these data have been used to derive mean values for the 0-12 cm depth range. Replicate samples from each of the three depth zones were bulked together by gentle mixing, a process which did not appear to harm the microarthropods. Data obtained from the two paths were sufficiently similar to permit the calculation of overall mean values. Measurements of bulk density, shearing strength, water capacity and water content were performed on unmixed, freshly collected samples.

Dune sediment physical properties

Temperature was recorded at the sediment surface and at depths of 2, 6 and 10 cm at all locations using an electronic thermometer. Readings were taken on a sunny day in the early afternoon, and values from different depths were used to calculate a mean temperature for the 0-10 cm depth range. Bulk density was determined by dividing the dry weight of sediment samples by their undisturbed volume (100 cm³) at the time of sampling. Estimates of porosity were derived from these data using the formula of Hartge & Horn (1992). Shearing strength was measured to give an estimate of the structural integrity of the sediment and was determined using a torque wrench. The readings have been transformed to kg/cm² (Schaffer, 1960). Water capacity was estimated crudely by calculating the difference between the weight of sample cores soaked carefully to field capacity and the dry weight of the same samples. Water content was determined volumetrically by subtracting the dry weight of samples from the fresh weight of undisturbed sample cores of known volume. Sediment particle size distribution was determined by dry sieving with mesh sizes of 0.63 mm (coarse), 0.2 mm (medium) and 0.063 mm (fine). The weight fractions are given here as percentages of the total sample weight. Organic matter content was determined gravimetrically by loss on ignition on subsamples passed through a 2 mm sieve.

Substrate chemistry

Material from the mixed sediment samples was used for chemical analysis following sieving (2 mm mesh size). pH (H_2O) and conductivity (as a measure of salinity) were measured with standard electrodes. Calcium carbonate content ($CaCO_3$) was determined semi-quantitatively by assessing the reaction of samples after treatment with a few drops of concentrated hydrochloric acid.

Microarthropods

Microarthropods were driven out of the dune sand samples using a Berlese-type extractor. Bulked samples of 250 cm³ were placed on a sieve over a funnel and heat from electric bulbs hanging over each sample expelled the microarthropods from the sand via the funnel directly into collecting vessels filled with 70% ethanol. Microarthropods were identified and counted using a binocular microscope. Two groups were differentiated within the Collembola (the Arthropleona and Sym-phypleona) and three groups within the Acari (the Gamasina, Acaridae from the group of astigmatic mites and other mites mainly referable to the Oribatei and Prostigmata).

Results

Vegetation

The three duneland macrohabitats were found to support vegetation units typical for the region where undisturbed by trampling (Table 1). However, a dramatic decrease in vegetation cover was observed towards the centre of each path, an effect which was most pronounced where the paths crossed through grey dune areas. Other obvious differences which were recorded on passing from undisturbed vegetation through the wayside zone to the centre of each path included the identity of the dominant species and the total number of species. For the yellow and brown dune macrohabitats the maximum number of vascular plant species was recorded in the wayside zones.

Table 1 **Principal characteristics of the vegetation of the trampled and untrampled study sites at Houstrup Strand (West Jutland, Denmark)**

Habitat		Veg. cover %	Vegetation	Dominant species	N
macro	micro				
Yellow dune	original vegetation	87.5	*Elymo- Ammophiletum*	AMMO, FEST	6
	wayside	70.0		AMMO, LATH, FEST	9
	centre	10.0		AMMO, LATH	5
Grey dune	original vegetation	97.5	*Corynephoretum maritimum festucetosum arenariae*	CORY, PILO, LI, BR	10
	wayside	55.0		CORY, PILO, BR	10
	centre	2.5		FEST, CORY	6
Brown dune	original vegetation	100.0	*Polypodio empetretum tortuletosum/ cladonietosum*	EMPE, BR	11
	wayside	92.5		EMPE	13
	centre	30.0		FEST, POAP	6

Key to abbreviations

AMMO	*Ammophila arenaria*	LATH	*Lathyrus japonicus*
CORY	*Corynephorus canescens*	POAP	*Poa pratensis*
EMPE	*Empetrum nigrum*	LI	Lichens
FEST	*Festuca rubra*	BR	Bryophytes
PILO	*Pilosella officinarum*	N	Number of vascular plant species

Sediment physics and chemistry

The results of the sediment physical and chemical analyses are summarised in Table 2. Sediments are almost entirely composed of pure medium sized sand with a negligible silt and clay content. The untrampled yellow and grey dune areas showed very little soil development, but the sediments of the brown dune macrohabitat had considerable accumulations of organic material. Shearing strength was found to increase steadily from the yellow to the brown dune macrohabitat, where roots contribute to the structural integrity of the sediment. All of the sediments assayed were weakly or moderately acidic, with pH varying from 6.3 in the yellow dunes to 5.7 in the landward brown dune macrohabitat. The calcium carbonate content showed a corresponding trend, and none was detected in the brown dune sediments. The total salinity of all of the sediments was also low, with the lowest readings being obtained for the brown dune macrohabitat.

The effect of trampling on the chemical and physical characteristics of the sediments of the three main vegetation types is shown graphically in Figure 1.

Table 2   **Summary of sediment physical and chemical data for the trampled and untrampled study sites for the 0-12 cm depth zone**

		Yellow dune			Grey dune			Brown dune		
		Centre	Wayside	Original vegetation	Centre	Wayside	Original vegetation	Centre	Wayside	Original vegetation
Temperature	°C	16.53	16.32	13.08	17.12	17.13	16.81	15.35	15.78	13.31
Bulk density	g/cm³	1.55	1.59	1.51	1.56	1.50	1.51	1.53	1.40	1.18
Shearing strength	kg/cm²	0.030	0.020	0.012	0.040	0.038	0.023	0.033	0.035	0.035
Porosity	% vol.	41.69	40.14	42.97	41.29	43.54	43.10	42.40	47.28	55.48
Water content	% dwt.	4.03	3.35	5.25	3.54	7.08	3.79	7.11	6.98	12.85
Water capacity	% dwt.	26.04	26.53	28.77	23.30	31.49	22.65	27.84	31.42	41.70
Coarse sand	%	1.39	0.35	0.79	2.48	2.47	2.36	1.65	2.15	3.99
Medium sand	%	93.73	93.53	92.78	90.47	90.98	89.08	90.56	87.90	83.84
Fine sand	%	4.46	5.74	6.05	6.87	6.21	8.04	7.58	9.02	10.67
Organic matter	% dwt.	0.14	0.15	0.20	0.31	0.55	0.75	0.80	2.21	2.68
pH		6.15	6.19	6.27	6.14	6.05	6.06	5.96	5.92	5.75
Salinity	mg/l	5.33	5.50	7.00	3.42	3.67	5.83	3.33	3.67	4.42

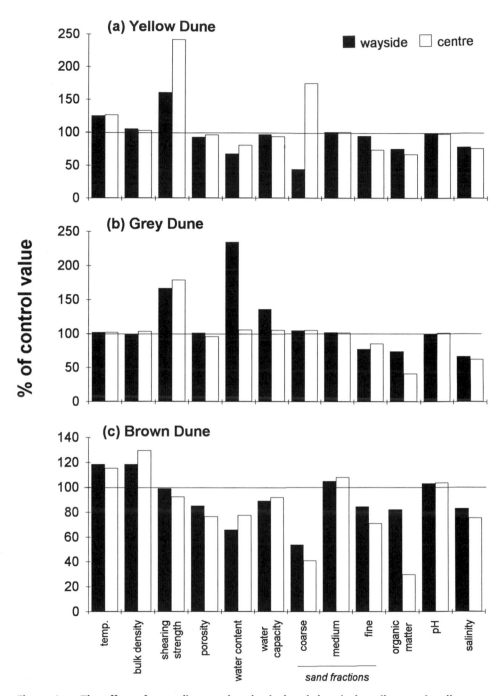

Figure 1 The effect of trampling on the physical and chemical attributes of sediments from (a) yellow, (b) grey and (c) brown dune macrohabitat types

Data for the wayside and path-centre microhabitats are shown as percentages of the control values (100%) obtained from comparable adjacent sediments which were unaffected by trampling

Plant shoot architecture is implicated for the differences in sediment temperature, reduced vegetation cover in the path–centre microhabitats of the yellow dune (*Ammophila arenaria*) and brown dune (*Empetrum nigrum*) communities resulting in a significant increase in sediment temperature (Figures 1a and c). This effect was hardly detectable in the grey dune sediments (Figure 1b) where the canopy architecture takes the form of a tightly knit, low growing lichen–rich cover. There is a slight trend towards higher values for bulk density in the sediments of the path–centre microhabitat. Shearing strength was also observed to increase towards the centre of paths, although this effect was less pronounced in the root–bound sediments of the brown dune macrohabitat (Figure 1c). A significant decrease in porosity for the path–centre and wayside zones was only recorded for the organic brown dune sediments. Sediment water content dropped towards the centre of the paths, although surprisingly the opposite trend was observed for the grey dune macrohabitat. Water capacity shows a similar trend and was most reduced in the compacted path–centre brown dune sediments. Trends for particle size distribution are for the most part unclear, but the reduced percentage of the fine sand fraction in the path–centre microhabitats could be explained by wind sorting of exposed sand. The organic matter content was found to decrease as the intensity of trampling increased from wayside to centre, a trend reflected by a slight increase in the pH of brown dune sediments (less acidic because of less humic acids). Salts are filtered from the atmosphere by a well developed vegetation, and this probably explains the lower salinity values which were recorded from all of the path–centre and wayside microhabitats when compared to sediments sampled from the original vegetation.

Table 3   **The number of individuals (thousands/m²) of soil microarthropods in the 0-12 cm depth zone of trampled and untrampled duneland sediments**

Habitat		Microarthropods			Collembola		Acari		
macro	micro	Total	Collembola	Acari	Arthropleona	Symphypleona	Gamasina	Astigmata	others *
Yellow dune	original vegetation	137.0	80.3	56.7	80.3	0.0	17.3	2.9	36.5
	wayside	252.1	172.2	79.9	172.1	0.1	6.3	4.8	68.8
	centre	84.1	64.3	19.8	64.3	0.0	0.8	3.1	15.9
Grey dune	original vegetation	139.6	71.4	68.2	68.7	2.7	14.6	1.4	52.2
	wayside	118.3	72.5	45.8	72.5	0.0	2.1	1.8	41.9
	centre	43.9	18.0	25.9	18.0	0.0	0.6	1.5	23.8
Brown dune	original vegetation	58.6	29.4	29.2	29.3	0.1	9.7	0.1	19.4
	wayside	100.6	42.5	58.1	42.4	0.1	3.4	0.4	54.3
	centre	25.4	6.2	19.2	6.2	0.0	0.2	0.0	19.0

* mites mostly referable to the Oribatei and Prostigmata (Acari)

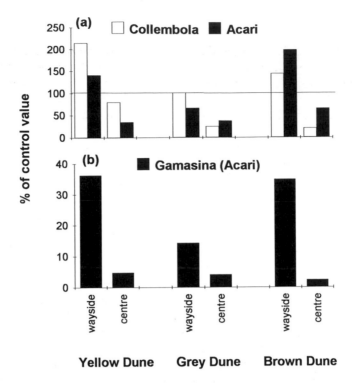

Figure 2   **The effect of trampling on the abundance of soil microarthropods (a) Collembola and Acari and (b) predatory mites (Gamasina, Acari)**

Data for the wayside and path-centre microhabitats are shown as percentages of the control values (100 %) obtained from comparable adjacent sediments which were unaffected by trampling

Microarthropods

The largest number of microarthropods was found in the yellow dune sediments, with progressively fewer animals being recorded in sediments of the grey and brown dunes (Table 3).

In the yellow dune sediments, Collembola were more frequent than Acari, but elsewhere the two groups were represented by similar numbers of individuals. Astigmatic mites and Symphypleona (Collembola) were rare at all sites. The number of Collembola was higher in the path wayside zones than in the original vegetation, and lowest in the centre of the paths at all sites (Figure 2a). The abundance of Acari exhibited the same trend with the exception of grey dune sediments, where more mites were found in samples from the original vegetation microhabitat. The predatory Gamasina (Acari) appeared to be very sensitive to trampling, with 10,000 or more individuals/m² being recorded in samples from the original vegetation, but only 1,000 or fewer individuals/m² in the centre of the paths (Figure 2b).

Discussion

The scope of this study was limited in space and time and it is acknowledged that other paths could yield different results. Nevertheless, the trend of the findings from the two paths were sufficiently similar to permit the calculation of single mean values. Seasonal variations could also alter the apparent effects of trampling which have been reported here, but September is generally considered to be an appropriate time for studies of soil fauna. Furthermore, the period of wet weather which preceded sampling created humid sediment conditions, a prerequisite for high extraction efficiency.

Although mixing of replicate sediment samples reduced the scope for statistical analysis, this was considered desirable because of large variations in microarthropod density between replicates. Similarly, the combination of data from different sedimentary horizons is believed to have yielded characteristic and representative trends, despite the presence of obvious soil horizons for the grey and brown dune macrohabitats.

One of the most obvious impacts of trampling was on the vegetation of the path–centre microhabitat; indeed this visible effect was the main factor leading to the selection of sampling sites. The number of vascular plant species reached a peak in the wayside zones, and this suggests that moderate trampling can have a positive effect on biodiversity by reducing the vigour of dominant species and by creating more open conditions. Soil microarthropods were also most numerous in the wayside zones, an observation which would be expected if these zones are serving as transitional habitats (Koehler, 1991). However, determination to species level would be required to test whether this trend is due to an increased representation of r–strategist species in the microarthropod community.

The dramatic decrease of Gamasina towards the path–centre may be caused by decreased plant cover which would result in a changed microclimate (Koehler & Born, 1989). Karg (1967) showed a decline in the abundance of Gamasina after removal of litter in a beech forest community, and Garay & Nataf (1982) observed that for forest paths the structure and abundance of soil microarthropod communities is correlated with edaphic perturbation and the amount of litter. In their studies, changes in the composition of the soil microarthropod community were found to serve as a more sensitive indicator of trampling damage than physical or chemical parameters.

Physical changes to the path sediments which could have affected the composition of the microarthropod community include the increase in bulk density of trampled sediments (also observed by Chappell et al., 1971) and the associated reduction of pore space. Liddle & Greig-Smith (1975) considered that this could lead to a decrease in the rate of gas exchange between the above ground atmosphere and the atmosphere within substrate pores, which would thus affect microbial and decomposition processes. Changes in the hydrology of sediments consequent upon trampling would also be expected to have an effect on these processes. Unfortunately, the scope of this paper does not allow a more thorough analysis of the nature of these biotic/abiotic interactions.

The findings of this study provide partial documentation of the complex effects which trampling can have on a broad spectrum of abiotic and biotic parameters. For dune stability, the reduction of plant cover may be the most important consequence, but this also has consequences for the dune sediment biota. Soil microarthropods may be protected to an extent by mimicking plant cover through thatching. This provides a nutritional base for decomposer organisms, and large numbers of microarthropods have been found in the straw mats used to stabilise the major access path to Houstrup beach (Koehler, unpublished data). However, thatching can result in the introduction of alien plant species, and may cause sediment eutrophication.

A complex network of footpaths can result in a sand dune ecosystem which is fragmented into numerous small to medium sized units. The effect of this upon macroscale variations in the composition of the microarthropod community deserves investigation.

Conclusion

In sand dunes, the effects of trampling by humans extends below ground level. In this study microarthropod numbers were found to vary in relation to trampling intensity, with the lowest numbers being recorded from path–centre sediments. Predatory mites (Gamasina) appear to be especially susceptible to trampling, with a ten fold reduction in animal density between the untrampled and path–centre microhabitats. Abiotic and other biotic parameters were also influenced and the effect upon sediment stability may mean that even moderately frequented paths become a potential erosion hazard. Macroscale effects for the dune system resulting from fragmentation of the landscape by footpaths need to be investigated. Management by thatching, a common practice, is undesirable as it may lead to eutrophication and the introduction of alien vascular plant species. The strict channelling of people seems to offer the best option for the preservation of the natural value of dunes and their structural integrity.

Acknowledgements

This study was carried out as part of the "dune ecology" curricular project within Professor Weidemann's working group at the University of Bremen.

References

Borcard, D. & Matthey W. 1995. Effect of controlled trampling of *Sphagnum* mosses on their Oribatid mite assemblages (Acari, Oribatei). *Pedobiologia*, 39:219-230.

Chappell, H.G., Ainsworth, J.F., Cameron, R.A.D. & Redfern, M. 1971. The effect of trampling on a chalk grassland ecosystem. *Journal of Applied Ecology*, 8:869-882.

Ellenberg, H. 1986. *Vegetation Mitteleuropas mit den Alpen in ökologischer Sicht.* 4th edition. Ulmer, Stuttgart, Germany.

Garay, I. & Nataf, L. 1982. Microarthropods as indicators of human trampling in suburban forests. In: *Urban Ecology.* Eds: Bornkamm, R., Lee, J.A. & Seaward, M.R.D. Blackwell Scientific Publications, Oxford, UK. pp. 201-208.

Garay, I., Cancela da Fonseca, J.P. & Blandin, P. 1981. The effects of trampling on the fauna of a forest floor. I. Microarthropods. In: *Soil Biology as related to Land Use Practices*. Ed.: Dindal, D.L. EPA, Washington, USA. pp. 200-212.

Ghilarov, M.S. 1978. Bodenwirbellose als Indikatoren des Bodenhaushaltes und von bodenbildenden Prozessen. *Pedobiologia*, 18:300-309.

Hartge, K.H. & Horn, R. 1992. *Die physikalische Untersuchung von Böden*. 3rd edition. Enke, Stuttgart, Germany.

Karg, W. 1967. Synökologische Untersuchungen von Bodenmilben aus forstwirt schaftlichen und landwirtschaftlichen Böden. *Pedobiologia*, 7:198-214.

Karg, W. 1968. Bodenbiologische Untersuchungen über die Eignung von Milben, insbesondere von parasitiformen Raubmilben, als Indikatoren. *Pedobiologia*, 8:30-39.

Koehler, H.H. 1991. A five year study on the secondary succession of Gamasina on a ruderal site: the influence of recultivation. In: *Modern Acarology*. Eds: Dusbabek, F. & Bukva, V. Academia, Prag, Czechoslovakia & SPB Acad. Publ. bv., The Hague, The Netherlands. pp. 373-383.

Koehler, H.H. 1992. The use of soil mesofauna for the judgement of a chemical impact on ecosystems. *Agriculture, Ecosystems & Environment*, 40:193-205.

Koehler, H.H. & Born, H. 1989. The influence of vegetation structure on the development of soil mesofauna. *Agriculture, Ecosystems & Environment*, 27:253-269.

Koehler, H.H. & Weidemann, G. 1995. Biogenic dune sand stabilisation. In: *Management of Polish Coastal Habitats*. Ed.: Dijk, H.W.J. van. EUCC, Leiden and Univ. Press, Gdansk. (in press).

Koehler, H.H., Munderloh, E. & Hofmann, S. 1995. Soil mesofauna (Acari, Collembola) from beach and dune: characteristics and ecosystem context. *Journal of Coastal Conservation*, 1:77-86.

Liddle, M.J. & Greig-Smith, P. 1975. A survey of tracks and paths in a sand dune ecosystem, I. Soils, II. Vegetation. *Journal of Applied Ecology*, 12:893-908 and 909-930.

Nordstrom, K., Psuty, N. & Carter, R.W.G. 1990. *Coastal Dunes: Form and Process*. John Willey & Sons, Chichester, UK.

Schaffer, G. 1960. Eine Methode der Abscherwiderstandsmessung bei Ackerböden zur Beurteilung ihrer Strukturfestigkeit im Felde. *Landwirtschaftliche Forschung*, 13:24-33.

Slatter, R.J. 1978. Ecological effects of trampling on sand dune vegetation. *Journal of Biological Education*, 12:89-96.

Studies in European Coastal Management. Jones, Healy and Williams (eds)
1996, Samara Publishing Limited, Cardigan. ISBN 1 873692 07 2

The Response of an Inter-tidal Algal Community to Persistent Trampling and the Implications for Rocky Shore Management

H. Fletcher & C.L.J. Frid

Dove Marine Laboratory, University of Newcastle-upon-Tyne, Tyne & Wear, UK

Abstract: The effect of human trampling upon two rocky shore ecosystems in the northeast of England has been examined experimentally. Marked plots in the inter-tidal zone were subjected to one of four treatments: 0 (control), 20, 80 and 160 footsteps per m^2, applied once in every set of spring tides. Levels of applied trampling were comparable to those observed during surveys of visitor activity at both sites. Percentage cover estimates of algae and bare substrate were made over a nine month period.

Sustained trampling caused changes in the species composition of the algal community in all trampled plots. The time taken for changes to become apparent varied between 1 and 4 months, depending on the intensity of the trampling regime. Trampling was found to significantly affect species richness and also resulted in an increase in the area of bare substrate.

'Recreational carrying capacity' at these two sites could be exceeded by only 20 footsteps per m^2 on a sustained basis. There were, however, differences between sites in the extent and timing of the response. The role of site-specific carrying capacity estimates in the management of rocky shores is discussed.

Introduction

Space is the major limiting resource for sessile organisms in rocky inter-tidal communities (Dayton, 1971; Paine, 1984). Consequently, processes which can create this valuable commodity are of considerable ecological importance. The processes whereby space is created, either directly or indirectly, are known as 'disturbances' and provide opportunities for new individuals to become established (Sousa, 1984).

For the marine rocky inter-tidal zone, disturbance has long been recognised as the major factor affecting community organisation (Sousa, 1985) and the effects of natural disturbance events, such as wave energy (e.g. Lubchenco & Menge, 1978; Paine & Levin, 1981), have been well-documented. Recently, man-made perturbations, such as the collection of inter-tidal organisms (e.g. Godoy & Moreno, 1989), have become more prevalent. Human trampling in the inter-tidal zone has also increased substantially due to many factors, such as improved coastal access (Brosnan & Crumrine, 1992). There is evidence that this additional use of the environment is adding to background levels of disturbance and may be causing irreversible changes in the composition of communities (e.g. Brosnan & Crumrine, 1994).

For example, Ghazanshahi *et al.* (1983) surveyed a number of Californian rocky shore locations which varied in terms of the intensity of public use and found that both the abundance of some species and species diversity decreased as the level of public use increased. In another Californian study, Beauchamp & Gowing (1982) recorded higher species densities and species diversity at less-trampled sites. In comparison, at sites subjected to a greater degree of trampling pressure, it was found that larger species of algae tended to be replaced by species with turf-like growth forms, e.g. *Endocladia* spp.

Other effects of human trampling pressure have also been reported. For example, Povey & Keough (1991) surveyed intensely trampled areas of the inter-tidal zone in Australia and found that there was almost no algal cover in areas which, before trampling, had been dominated by the brown alga *Hormosira banksii*. They suggested that this local increase in the area of bare substrate due to trampling disturbance might lead to a subsequent increase in the abundance of grazing molluscs, which preferentially graze on the microalgae. These microalgae contain spores of larger algal species, the consumption of which prevents their recolonisation and may result in persistent change to the species composition of the area.

The implication from previous studies is that inter-tidal environments with public access will be altered if human impacts continue unmanaged (Zedler, 1978). When levels of public use are sufficient to cause mortality and change in the ecosystem concerned, the 'recreational carrying capacity' of the shore is said to have been exceeded (Zedler, 1978). 'Recreational carrying capacity' in an ecological context is defined as the maximum intensity of use that an area can continue to support without there being a change in the biotic environment (Goldsmith, 1974; Miller, 1982) and its estimation has been used to devise management plans for both terrestrial and coastal areas (e.g. Yapp & Barrow, 1979; Carlson & Godfrey, 1989).

There are, however, problems with the carrying capacity concept. Its measurement involves extensive monitoring and detailed site evaluation which is time-consuming, difficult and expensive (Hayden, 1975; Yapp & Barrow, 1979) and, it has been suggested, subjective in approach (e.g. Lein, 1993). As a result, management plans have often been put into practice without first quantifying the carrying capacity of protected areas. Examples of such management techniques for the inter-tidal zone include access restrictions (e.g. Brosnan & Crumrine, 1992), the designation of footpaths (Clark, 1991), zoning (e.g. Kelleher & Kenchington, 1982; Salm & Clark, 1984), education and the provision of interpretative material (Chan, 1970; Salm & Clark, 1984).

Despite the limitations of the concept, Clark (1991) considered an estimation of carrying capacity to be an essential part of the management plan of any protected area. Similarly, Yapp & Barrow (1979) supported the use of this technique, concluding that if management regimes are applied without this kind of ecological evaluation, there is a risk that ecosystems will be insufficiently or incompletely protected. If an estimation of carrying capacity is made before the application of management techniques, and variables such as season and the activities of visitors are taken into account, the concept could be highly effective as an aid to the conservation of protected areas (Goldsmith, 1974).

The aim of this study was to subject experimental plots in the rocky inter-tidal zone to different sustained trampling intensities over a nine month period. It was hoped that this would allow an estimation of the amount of visitor use (the carrying capacity) that the study sites could continue to support, without there being associated adverse effects on the inter-tidal community (for example, changes in species composition).

Materials and methods

Study sites

Two moderately exposed sandstone shores on the northeast coast of England were chosen for study (Figure 1). Cullercoats Bay (NZ 365714) is subject to considerably less visitor pressure than St. Mary's Island (NZ 352753), a Local Nature Reserve which is very popular with both tourists and local residents.

Experimental design

Experimental plots (1 x 1 m) were arranged in blocks of four in areas of the mid–eulittoral zone. At both sites, areas of shore which were distant from the main sites of visitor activity were used. There were four replicate blocks, each containing

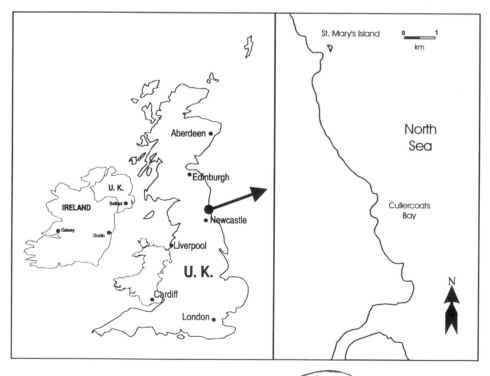

Figure 1   Location of study sites

235

four plots, and one of four trampling intensities was assigned to each plot in a random block design. Trampling intensities were designed to mimic normal and heavy usage of the shore and were determined by prior surveys of visitor pressure at both sites. The four treatments were 0 (control), 20, 80 and 160 footsteps per m^2, applied once in every set of spring tides (hereafter referred to as steps/m^2/st.).

The experimental plots were established in March 1994 and were monitored monthly for the first three months, and subsequently at two month intervals until November 1994, a total of six sampling events.

At each sampling instance, visual estimates were made of the percentage cover of algae and bare substrate. Estimates of ground cover were made by the same worker at all sampling times to ensure consistency. Plots were unmarked so as to reduce any possible trampling bias associated with people being attracted to marked areas of the shore, and were relocated by means of maps.

Data analysis

Values of percentage cover for algae and bare substrate were arc–sin transformed (Underwood, 1981) and were then tested for normality using Hartley's test statistic (Winer, 1971) prior to analysis.

Data collected prior to the onset of the trampling treatments were analysed to check for statistically significant differences both between treatments within a block (Friedman test) and between blocks (parametric Analysis of Variance [ANOVA]). Any blocks differing significantly from the remaining blocks at that site at time 0 were not included in subsequent analyses. One way ANOVA was also used to test for significant differences in the percentage cover of algal species and bare substrate between the two sites at time 0.

Principal Components Analysis (PCA) of the transformed data for the eleven most common algal species at each site was performed. Mean values of percentage algal cover for the blocks combined (one block omitted in the case of Cullercoats Bay) were used to form composite samples for analysis.

A Kruskall–Wallis test was used to assess whether there were significant differences in species richness between treatments at any sampling time, and ANOVA was carried out to assess whether there were significant differences in the extent of bare substrate present between treatments at any of the sampling times.

Data for species richness, bare substrate and a PCA of the algal species matrix are given here. Changes in the percentage cover of the most common species, for example fucoid algae, will be discussed elsewhere.

Results

A total of 28 species of algae was recorded (Table 1). The most abundant species at both sites were fucoid algae (*Fucus serratus, F. spiralis* and *F. vesiculosus*). Multivariate analyses were confined to an 11 species data set composed of the most consistently recorded taxa.

Table 1   **List of algal species recorded during the study at St. Mary's Island and Cullercoats Bay**

Chlorophyta	**Rhodophyta**
Cladophora rupestris Kuetz.	*Ahnfeltia plicata* Fries
Enteromorpha spp.	*Audouinella* spp.
Spongomorpha aeruginosa Hoek.	*Ceramium* spp.
Ulva lactuca L.	*Chondrus crispus* Stackh.
	Corallina officinalis L.
Phaeophyta	*Dumontia contorta* Rupr.
Ascophyllum nodosum Le Jolis.	*Hildenbrandia* spp.
Cladostephus spongiosus J. Agaidh.	*Laurencia pinnatifida* Lamouroux
Ectocarpus spp.	*Lithothamnium glaciale* Kjellman
Elachista fucicola Aresch.	*Lomentaria articulata* Lyngb.
Fucus serratus L.	*Mastocarpus stellatus* Stackh.
Fucus spiralis L.	*Palmaria palmata* O. Kuntze
Fucus vesiculosus L.	*Phymatolithon lenormandii* Adey
Ralfsia verrucosa J. Agaidh.	*Porphyra* spp.

Site differences

Although the abundance of fucoid species and the extent of bare substrate were not found to differ significantly between sites prior to trampling, there were significant site differences in the abundance of some of the understorey species. These species were *Lomentaria articulata* (ANOVA, $F = 11.56$, $p = 0.002$), *Ceramium* spp. (ANOVA, $F = 8.41$, $p = 0.007$), *Mastocarpus stellatus* (ANOVA, $F = 24.88, p = 0.000$) and *Palmaria palmata* (ANOVA, $F = 9.07, p = 0.005$). Given these between–site differences, further data analysis was carried out seperately for each site.

St. Mary's Island

The first three components extracted by PCA account for a total of 65% of the variation in this eleven species data set. The ordination of composite samples on the first two PCA axes, which account for 53% of the variation, is shown in Figure 2a. The pattern for composite samples derived from control plots through time differs from that of plots subjected to trampling. The dispersion of control plot samples reflects seasonally induced changes in community composition, and for each sampling event these remain distinct from composite samples derived from treatment plots.

(a) St. Mary's Island

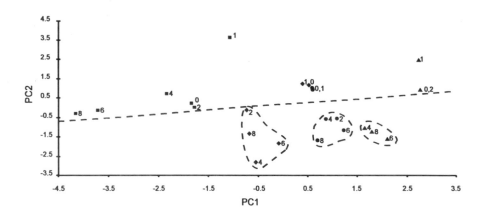

(b) Cullercoats Bay

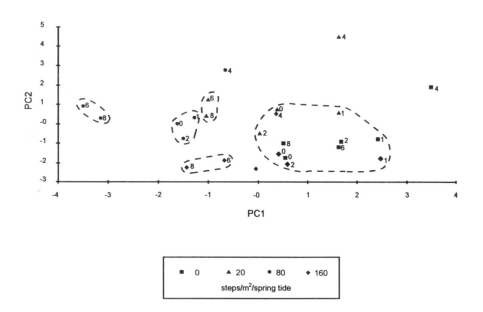

■ 0   ▲ 20   ● 80   ◆ 160

steps/m²/spring tide

Figure 2   Principal components analysis ordinations of composite samples from (a) St. Mary's Island and (b) Cullercoats Bay

The ordinations are based on percentage cover estimates for eleven algal species and summarise changes in species composition and abundance over time in relation to three trampling intensities and a control (0 trampling). Numbers adjacent to each data point refer to the time in months since the onset of trampling. Dashed lines have no statistical significance and are used to highlight distinguishable sample groups

In contrast, each of the three applied treatments are represented by two distinct composite sample groups according to time. Composite samples from plots receiving 20 steps/m²/st. are grouped together at time 0 and 1 and 2 months. Samples collected 4, 6 and 8 months after the onset of trampling are still tightly clustered, but are well separated from the earlier samples on PCA axes 1 and 2. This indicates that the composition of the community changed between 2 and 4 months after the onset of trampling.

The distribution of composite samples from the remaining two treatments (80 and 160 steps/m²/st.) is similar to that observed for the 20 steps/m²/st. treatment. Composite samples for times 0 and 1 (one month after the onset of trampling) are clumped together, while samples collected later occur in a seperate cluster. The time period for the change in community composition for these treatments thus lies between 1 and 2 months after the onset of trampling. The clusters of composite samples for the three treatment types are much less dispersed than for the control plots, indicating that these communities underwent less seasonal change than the untrampled areas.

Species richness at the St. Mary's Island site (Figure 3a) did not differ significantly between treatments at any sampling time.

The mean area of bare substrate per plot increased substantially two months after the onset of trampling under the most intensive treatment, but declined thereafter (Figure 4a). However, there were no significant differences in the extent of bare substrate between treatments at any sampling time (ANOVA, p >0.05).

Cullercoats Bay

The first three components extracted by PCA account for 67% of the variation in the data matrix, with components one and two accounting for 50% of the variation. As for the St Mary's Island data, the distribution of composite samples on PCA axes 1 and 2 can, to an extent, be resolved into groups on the basis of treatment type and sampling time (Figure 2b). Obvious composite sample clusters which can be detected on PCA axes 1 and 2 include those corresponding to the control treatment for all sampling dates (except at 4 months) and the 20 and 80 steps/m²/st. treatments at times 0, 1 and 2 and times 6 and 8 months respectively. Composite samples from the most intensely trampled plots form a more wide-spread, although still distinct, group. However, samples for all treatments at time 4 (4 months after the onset of trampling) are displaced towards the upper right quadrant of the ordination relative to the other sampling times.

The plot of species richness for the four treatments against time (Figure 3b), shows a downward trend for plots exposed to 160 steps/m²/st. There was a significant difference in species richness between treatments at time 8 (Kruskall–Wallis, H = 9.47, p = 0.024).

There was a great deal of variation in the area of bare substrate in the control and treatment plots through time (Figure 4b), with significant variations between treatments 2 months after the onset of trampling (ANOVA, F = 15.0, p = 0.001).

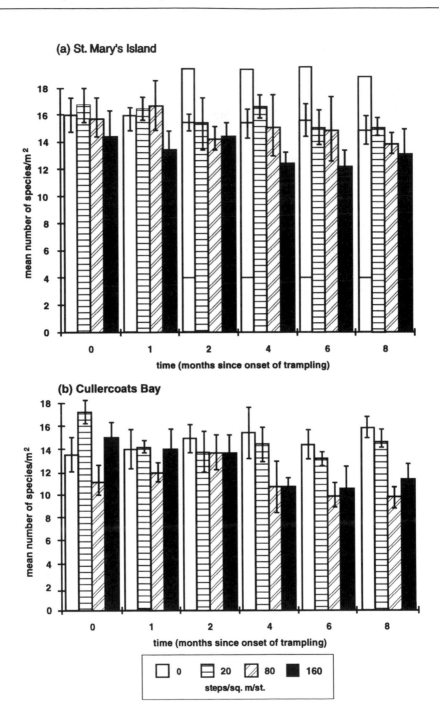

Figure 3 Mean number of species per 1 m² plot (±1 S.E.) for three trampling intensities and a control (0 trampling) over an eight month period at (a) St. Mary's Island and (b) Cullercoats Bay, northeast England

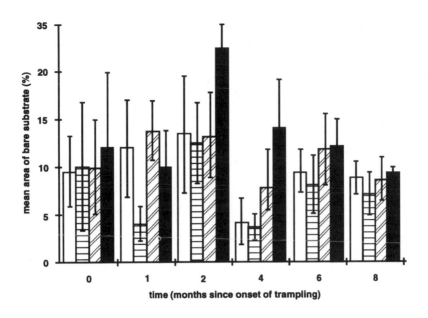

(a) St. Mary's Island

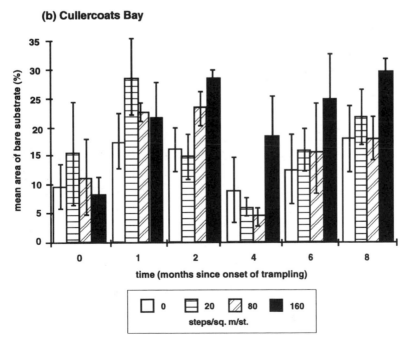

(b) Cullercoats Bay

Figure 4   Mean percentage area of bare substrate per plot (±1 S.E.) for three trampling intensities and a control (0 trampling) over an eight month period at (a) St. Mary's Island and (b) Cullercoats Bay, northeast England

Discussion

As far as we are aware, there has only been one other study where trampling intensity has been manipulated in the rocky inter-tidal zone. Povey & Keough (1991) observed that low intensity trampling caused considerable damage when sustained through time at an Australian inter-tidal zone site. They observed that as few as two visitors a day, walking across the inter-tidal zone in a strip measuring 0.5 m by 2 m, resulted in loss of algal cover and an increase in the area of bare substrate.

In this study, human trampling was found to change the species composition of the rocky inter-tidal algal community at both St. Mary's Island and Cullercoats Bay. The 'recreational carrying capacity' of the shore, defined as the "maximum intensity of use that an area can continue to support without there being a change in the biotic environment" (Goldsmith, 1974), was exceeded at both sites by all three of the applied trampling regimes. The species composition of the algal community was altered by as few as 20 steps/m²/st. If the average gait of a person is taken as less than a metre, this carrying capacity could be exceeded by only five people taking the same route out and back across the rocky shore during each spring tide period.

As well as changes in the composition of the species assemblage, the number of species declined at Cullercoats under the most intense trampling regime (160 steps/m²/st.). In support of this finding, observations of reduced species richness as a result of increasing levels of visitor pressure have been made on the west coast of the USA (e.g. Beauchamp & Gowing, 1982; Ghazanshahi et al., 1983), where use of the shoreline for tourism and education has increased rapidly (Brosnan & Crumrine, 1992).

Space is the major limiting resource for sessile organisms of hard-bottom inter-tidal communities (e.g. Dayton, 1971) and disturbances, such as trampling, provide opportunities for new individuals to become established, thus potentially altering the species composition of the community. After two months of sustained trampling, the area of bare substrate at both sites was consistently greatest in the most intensely trampled plots. This raises the possibility that the community may shift to one containing a higher proportion of opportunistic species, such as *Ulva* spp., which are able to thrive under highly disturbed conditions (Sousa, 1979). In this study, the community underwent changes in composition, but there were no gross changes in the abundance of any one species. This was probably due to the fact that these shores experience considerable disturbance from natural agents – particularly wave action. On sheltered shores, where the community is dominated by long-lived algae and bare substrate is rarely produced (e.g. Lewis, 1964), the generation of bare substrate by trampling would lead to more pronounced changes in species abundance as perennial species were replaced by 'opportunistic' taxa.

Although the two sites were geographically close and similar in terms geology, aspect and other physical factors such as wave exposure, there were biological differences between them. The foliose algal species *Palmaria palmata*, for example, was significantly more abundant at St. Mary's Island. These differences meant that communities differed in the timing of the response to trampling. Changes in the algal community at Cullercoats Bay in all trampled plots occurred after 2-4 months, while at St. Mary's Island, changes in the algal community occurred after only 1-2 months in the two most intensely trampled plots.

This study has shown that the onset of measurable change resulting from trampling varies not only between sites but also with respect to trampling intensity. Differences between sites may, in part, relate to interspecific differences in the susceptibility to trampling among those species present at the start of the study. For example, Povey & Keough (1991), working in the Australian inter-tidal zone, found that only 33 days of high intensity trampling (25 passages along a 0.5 m by 2 m strip) resulted in visible damage to the alga *Hormosira banksii,* whereas *Corallina* spp. only exhibited significant damage after exposure to a longer period of more intense trampling. Species such as *Corallina*, with a turf-like growth form, are more resistant to trampling and have been found to dominate heavily-trampled areas (e.g. Beauchamp & Gowing, 1982; Brosnan & Crumrine, 1993). In all cases (this study included) periods of between 1 and 4 months exposure to trampling have resulted in marked changes.

In the summer months both study sites are exposed to hundreds of visitors. This level of visitor pressure at both sites is exceeding the recreational carrying capacity of those areas of shore which are most accessible to visitors, for example the areas around the main access points. The result is ecological damage to the inter-tidal community. To prevent further change to the composition of the rocky shore community, and to preserve both its biodiversity and aesthetic appeal, it is therefore necessary to restrict this visitor activity, either in a spatial or temporal framework.

Spatially, damage at both study sites is generally confined to existing pathways, and is characterised by a reduced cover of fucoid algae and large areas of bare substrate. These features are persistent because trampling pressure is sustained throughout the year. Although pathways concentrate some of the visitor pressure within small 'sacrificial' areas of the shore, trampling on a lesser scale occurs over the whole inter-tidal zone. As estimations of the carrying capacity have shown, ecological damage can be brought about by the activities of as few as five visitors during each spring tide period.

The existence of a 'time threshold' before trampling impacts become apparent (Figures 2a and b) implies that effective management regimes, such as the rotation of closed access zones, could compensate for the loss of ecological value in sacrificial areas (e.g. around access points). Such measures have been taken at other inter-tidal sites. For example, Brosnan & Crumrine (1992), when developing a management plan for part of the Oregon coastline, suggested that small areas of shore should be closed to public access for a period of 3-4 months to allow recovery of the algal community. The fragility of the community in our study implies that closed seasons may need to be longer than this, but when combined with such measures as public education (e.g. Chan, 1970) will lead to the preservation of biodiversity and ecological value, while still maintaining public access.

Conclusions

The experimental application of human trampling has been shown to cause significant changes to two rocky shore algal communities in northeast England. Even the minimum applied trampling intensity (equivalent to five people taking the same route to low water and back in one set of spring tides) led to changes in species composition, a decrease in species richness and an increase in the area of bare substrate. These changes indicate that the 'recreational carrying capacity' of the ecosystem can be exceeded under a low intensity of trampling.

The extent and timing of the observed changes varied between sites and in relation to trampling intensity. The existence of a time lag between disturbance and response indicates that one effective way of minimising the impact of trampling would be to limit public access over time to certain parts of the shore. Access to the shore could still be mainatined through the rotation of 'closed access areas'.

Acknowledgements

This study was carried out as part of a research studentship granted to H.F. by the University of Newcastle-Upon-Tyne and this support is gratefully acknowledged.

We also wish to thank English Nature and North Tyneside Council for allowing us to use the study sites. We are grateful for the support of all those who helped with field work, particularly Chris Young.

References

Beauchamp, K.A. & Gowing, M.M. 1982. A quantitative assessment of human trampling effects on a rocky intertidal community. *Marine Environmental Research*, 7:279-293.

Brosnan, D.M. & Crumrine, L.L. 1992. *Human impact and a management strategy for Yaquina head Outstanding Natural Area*. A report to the Bureau of Land Management, Department of the Interior. Salem, Oregon. 105 pp.

Brosnan, D.M & Crumrine, L.L. 1993. The effect of human trampling on biodiversity of rocky shores: monitoring and management strategies. *Recent Advances in Marine Science and Technology*, 1992:333-341.

Brosnan, D.M. & Crumrine, L.L. 1994. Effects of human trampling on marine rocky shore communities. *Journal of Experimental Marine Biology and Ecology*, 177:79-97.

Carlson, L.H. & Godfrey, P.J. 1989. Human impact management in a coastal recreation and natural area. *Biological Conservation*, 49:141-156.

Chan, G.L. 1970. *Analysis of the effects of public and educational school field trips on a marine environment, Duxbury Reef*. PhD Thesis. University of California, Berkeley. 139 pp.

Clark, J.R. 1991. Carrying capacity: a status report on marine and coastal parks and reserves. Third International Seminar on Coastal and Marine Parks and Protected Areas. Miami, Florida, USA. May 11-June 5, 1991. Report for the US Department of the Interior.

Dayton, P.K. 1971. Competition, disturbance and community organistaion: the provision and subsequent utilisation of space in a rocky intertidal community. *Ecological Monographs*, 41:351-389.

Ghazanshahi, J., Huchel, T.D. & Devinny, J.S. 1983. Alteration of southern Californian rocky shore ecosystems by public recreational use. *Journal of Environmental Management*, 16:379-394.

Godoy, C & Moreno, C.A. 1989. Indirect effects of human exclusion from the rocky intertidal in southern Chile: a case of cross-linkage between herbivores. *Oikos,* 54:101-106

Goldmith, F.B. 1974. Ecological effects of visitors in the countryside. In: *Conservation in Practice.* Eds: Warren, A. & Goldsmith, F.B. John Wiley & Sons, London, UK. pp. 217-231.

Hayden, B. 1975. The carrying capacity dilemma: an alternate approach. *American Antiquity,* 40:11-21.

Kelleher, G. & Kenchington, R. 1982. Australia's Great Barrier Reef Marine Park: making development compatible with conservation. In: *Proceedings of the World Congress on National Parks.* Bali, Indonesia, 11-22 October, 1982.

Keough, M.J. & Quinn, G.P. 1991. Causality and the choice of measurements for detecting human impacts in marine environments. *Australian Journal of Marine and Freshwater Research,* 42:539-554.

Lein, J.K. 1993. Applying expert systems technology to carrying capacity assessment: a demonstration prototype. *Journal of Environmental Management,* 37:63-84.

Lewis, J.R. 1964. *The Ecology of Rocky Shores.* English Universities Press, London, UK. 323 pp.

Lubchenco, J. & Menge, B.A. 1978. Community development and persistence in a low rocky intertidal zone. *Ecological Monographs,* 48:67-94.

Miller, T.E. 1982. Community diversity and interactions between the size and frequency of disturbance. *American Naturalist,* 120:533-536.

Paine, R.T. 1984. Ecological determinism in the competition for space. *Ecology,* 65:1339-1348.

Paine, R.T. & Levin, S.A. 1981. Intertidal landscapes: disturbance and the dynamics of pattern. *Ecological Monographs,* 51:145-178.

Povey, A. & Keough, M.J. 1991. Effects of trampling on plant and animal populations on rocky shores. *Oikos,* 61:355-368.

Salm, R.V. & Clark, J.R. 1984. *Marine and Coastal Protected Areas: A Guide for Planners and Managers.* IUCN, Gland, Switzerland.

Souza, W.P. 1979. Experimental investigations of disturbance and ecological succession in a rocky intertidal algal community. *Ecological Monographs,* 49:227-254.

Souza, W.P. 1984. The role of disturbance in natural communities. *Annual Review of Ecology and Systematics,* 15:353-391.

Souza, W.P. 1985. Disturbance and patch dynamics on rocky intertidal shores. In: *The Ecology of Natural Disturbance and Patch Dynamics.* Eds: Pickett, S.T.A. & White, P.S. Academic Press, London, UK. pp. 101-124.

Underwood, A.J. 1981. Techniques of analysis of variance in experimental marine biology and ecology. *Oceanography and Marine Biology Annual Review,* 19:513-605.

Winer, B.J. 1971. *Statistical Principles in Experimental Design.* 2nd edition. McGraw-Hill Kogakusha, Tokyo. 907 pp.

Yapp, G.A. & Garrow, G.C. 1979. Zonation and carrying capacity estimates in Canadian Park planning. *Biological Conservation,* 15:191-206.

Zedler, J.B. 1978. *Public use effects in the Cabrillo National Monument intertidal zone.* Project Report for the US Department of the Interior National Park Service.

Coastal Management Studies
in South Wales, UK

Studies in European Coastal Management. Jones, Healy and Williams (eds)
1996, Samara Publishing Limited, Cardigan. ISBN 1 873692 07 2

An Introduction to the Coastline of South Wales

A.T. Williams

School of Applied Sciences, University of Glamorgan, Pontypridd, Wales, UK

Abstract: South Wales is fringed by an immensely varied coastline which ranges from high sea cliffs to low energy sedimentary embayments and estuaries. Although much of the natural resource has been significantly altered by the development of industry and the growth of population centres around the major ports of the region, large areas of unspoiled coastal landscape still survive. This background forms a classic recipe for conflict and the region is subject to many of the issues which currently affect the conservation of the European coastal resource.

Introduction

The popular image of South Wales seems to be one of pollution and coal tips – over 29 billion tonnes of coal have been extracted from the South Wales coalfield of which 12 billion tonnes came from the famed Rhondda valley. Some 50% of these totals remain as waste spoil heaps along hill slopes, but extensive land reclamation measures have done much to improve the industrially scarred landscape.

On the coast, the growth of coastal towns such as Barry, Cardiff and Port Talbot in the late nineteenth century was little short of astounding and occurred in response to the drive to export coal to all parts of the World. The 'glory days' of coal are now over and industry has largely deserted the Welsh valleys in favour of sites within easy reach of the coast and M4 motorway Euro-route. Here, development in the post World War II era has continued apace and industrial complexes in the coastal zone include those associated with steel production, power generation and petrochemical processing.

Tourism is perhaps the most recent industry to develop in South Wales. Wales as a whole is a significant UK tourist destination by virtue of its accessibility and distinct cultural, historical and scenic character. The three Welsh National Parks (the Pembrokeshire Coast and Brecon Beacons in the south and Snowdonia in the north) serve as popular destinations while other designated regions such as Heritage Coasts and Areas of Outstanding Natural Beauty also attract large numbers of visitors.

While industry, both past and present, has had a significant impact upon the coastline and coastal hinterland of South Wales, many unspoiled landscapes remain. These not only support numerous sites of outstanding importance for nature conservation, but also continue to provide an essential open space resource for the industrial communities of South Wales.

The purpose of this paper is to provide a brief introductory account to the varied geology, landscape, landuse and conservation interest of the South Wales coast. A more detailed account of the region is provided by Barne *et al.* (1995).

The coastline of South Wales

The varied character of the South Wales coastline is a product of many factors. As with any landscape, this region can be viewed as comprising a physical foundation upon which is superimposed a cultural environment moulded by past and present patterns of landuse. The physical component is probably the most important element of the South Wales coastal landscape and the geology of the region is very varied.

Geology

The county of Pembrokeshire in the west comprises a region of outstanding geological interest and natural beauty and some 21 rock types of coastal formations have been classified (Owen, 1974). The Precambrian outcrops in the St Bride's Bay area and is mainly igneous in origin; the Cambrian are represented in the Newgale-St David's area and consist of sedimentary muds and sands; volcanics comprise the Ordovician series (e.g. at Ramsey Island and Fishguard); the Silurian (e.g. in the Milford Haven region) consists of grits and shales; the Old Red Sandstone (e.g. Mill Bay) is a very thick series which in turn is followed by the Carboniferous consisting of coal, grits and limestone formations. Carboniferous Limestone also outcrops at Gower in the central region and to the east of Swansea at Southerndown and Porthcawl. Between Cardiff and Swansea, Jurassic Limestone and shales form the bulk of the Glamorgan Heritage Coast. The Jurassic rocks of the area between Ogmore and Lavernock in particular (Figure 1) represent some of the most underrated coastal scenery in the UK. "...the magnificent Liassic cliffs of Glamorgan are probably the most neglected of all the much studied Jurassic cliffs of Britain" (Agar, 1974).

In the Penarth area and at Ogmore, small exposures of Triassic rocks occur, which were laid down after the rapid erosion that occurred in the Variscan orogeny when the climate was hot and arid. Quaternary age sediments are ubiquitous in the region and are represented by silts, clays, sands and shingle.

Maritime influence

The sea exerts a strong influence across all parts of the South Wales coast. Wave climate is mainly influenced by the partially enclosed nature of the Irish Sea and the influence of the westerly air flows that predominate over the British Isles. It has been shown that a 50 year predicted wave height of 15 m can occur and storm wave energies of >40,000 j/m/s, with an average from thirty-three storm events of >16,000 j/m/s, commonly occur from the southwest quadrant (Jones & Williams, 1991).

Tidal influences due to the funnelling effect of the Bristol Channel start to become appreciable in the region of the Gower Peninsula. Further east, the tidal range in the Inner Bristol Channel and Severn Estuary reaches 16.4 m at Avonmouth and in global terms is second only to the Bay of Fundy in Canada.

Figure 1   The Jurassic limestone cliffs of the Glamorgan Heritage Coast

Summary of human landuse along the South Wales coast

The eastern edge of coastal South Wales is dominated by large scale urban sites, for example Cardiff, Penarth and Barry. The former serves as the capital of Wales and as such is the seat of many administrative, banking and legislative institutions. Its main growth can be traced to coal, although its history is long and varied. The declining output in the South Wales coal field has resulted in a much reduced volume of maritime trade at Cardiff. Nevertheless, a wide range of cargoes is still handled.

The other main city in the region is Swansea - the venue of the fifth congress of the EUCC in 1995. The port of Swansea also expanded greatly as a result of coal export but as with Cardiff, a general decline in maritime trade has occurred. An extensive marina complex now occupies a large area of dockland at Swansea, a trend which is repeated at many sites along the South Wales coast.

Large sections of the coast between these two main cities is urban fringe in character. To the west of Cardiff lies the seaside town of Penarth and the docks at Barry while the industrial coastline of Swansea Bay is described later in this section. To the west of Swansea the town of Llanelli, once the home of the tin plate industry, marks the western extent of industrialised coastline of southeast Wales. Recreation is the main 'industry' westwards along this coastal stretch until the oil port of Milford Haven is reached.

Agriculture forms the dominant pattern of landuse along much of the undeveloped South Wales coast and grazing plays a key role in maintaining the open, species-rich character of many cliff top grassland sites.

A review of important natural features along the South Wales coastline

Although the effect of man upon the landscape is all too obvious along large stretches of the South Wales coastline, many unspoiled areas still survive which are of considerable importance for nature conservation. To the east, extensive inter-tidal mudlflats fringe the northern shore of the Severn Estuary as far west as Cardiff Bay and much of this area has now been designated as a Special Protection Area under the Birds Directive (Council Directive 79/409/EEC for the conservation of wild birds). To the west of Cardiff Bay, Jurassic Limestone cliffs form the dominant coastal landform and a 22 km stretch has been incorporated within the Glamorgan Heritage Coast, one of the original Heritage Coast pilot schemes inaugurated in 1973/74 by the Countryside Commission.

The western end of the Glamorgan Heritage Coast marks the start of the predominantly dune backed coast of Swansea Bay. Kenfig National Nature Reserve is the largest surviving fragment of this dune coastline, much of which has been destroyed by industrial development. To the west of Swansea, Carboniferous Limestone cliffs form the southern shore of the Gower Peninsula, Britain's first Area of Outstanding Natural Beauty. These Limestone cliffs support an extremely rich limestone flora and much of the Peninsula is safeguarded through a range of statutory designations. The northern coastline of the Gower Peninsula is fringed by the largest saltmarsh in Wales which to the west is replaced by the dune backed coast of Carmarthen Bay. The two extensive dune systems of Pembrey and Pendine (Laugharne) support an exceptionally rich suite of sand dune habitats, although much of the Pembrey system is now afforested.

To the west of Pendine, the seaside resort towns of Saundersfoot and Tenby mark the start of the Pembrokeshire Coast National Park. Carboniferous Limestone cliffs dominate the coast of South Pembrokeshire before being succeeded to the west by the complex and rich geology of the west Pembrokeshire coast.

The famous bird colony islands of Skokholm, Skomer and Grassholm mark the western tip of the South Wales coast. The large breeding populations of gannet (*Morus bassanus*), and manx shearwater (*Puffinus puffinus*) are of international importance and all three islands are protected as SPAs in addition to being included within the Pembrokeshire Islands proposed Special Area of Conservation (EC Directive 92/43/EEC on the conservation of natural habitats and of wild fauna and flora).

Excursion accounts

As part of the fifth congress of the European Union for Coastal Conservation, simultaneous excursions to four separate regions of the South Wales coast were arranged to enable first hand examination of some of the issues raised by the main themes of the conference. The field trip to Cardiff Bay (Figure 2) was linked to the conference theme of Shoreline Management and focused on the controversial urban regeneration of this internationally important nature conservation resource. Kenfig National Nature Reserve, a 600 ha dune system and candidate Special Area of Conservation, provided the venue for an analysis of the impact of the Habitats Directive on the conservation of terrestrial coastal sites in the UK. The excursion to the Gower Peninsula enabled an examination of some of the issues raised by tourism and also illustrated the requirement for an integrated approach to coastal management where many agencies are involved. Milford Haven was the venue for the fourth excursion which focused on the issue of planning in the coastal zone.

Information in support of each of these excursions is provided in the following section in the form of four case studies.

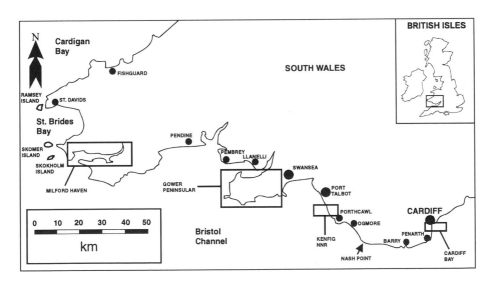

Figure 2   Location of the four coastal areas visited during the fifth congress of the European Union for Coastal Conservation, July 1995

References

Agar, D.V. 1974. The Jurassic Period in Wales. In: *The Upper Palaeozoic and post Palaeozoic rocks of Wales*. Ed.: Owen, T.R. University of Wales Press.

Barne, J.H., Robson, C.F., Kaznowska, S.S. & Doody, J.P. 1995. *Coasts and Seas of the United Kingdom. Region 12 Wales: Margam to Little Orme*. Joint Nature Conservation Committee, Peterborough, UK. 239 pp.

Owen T.R. (Ed.). 1974. *The Upper Palaeozoic and post Palaeozoic rocks of Wales*. University of Wales Press. 426 pp.

Jones, D.G. & Williams, A.T. 1991. Statistical analysis of factors influencing coastal erosion along a section of the west Wales coast, UK. *Earth Surface Processes and Landforms*, 16 (2), 95–112.

Studies in European Coastal Management. Jones, Healy and Williams (eds)
1996, Samara Publishing Limited, Cardigan. ISBN 1 873692 07 2

Kenfig National Nature Reserve: A Profile of a British West Coast Dune System

P.S. Jones

Kenfig National Nature Reserve, Bridgend, Wales, UK

Abstract: Kenfig National Nature Reserve comprises a 600 ha hindshore type dune system located on the southeastern shoreline of Swansea Bay. Kenfig is the largest dune system in South Wales to still bear an almost complete cover of semi-natural vegetation and an exceptional diversity of community types and species are present. The site has been subject to marginal habitat loss and intense recreational pressure for many years, but the surviving resource is now well protected by a range of designations. The most recent of these concerns the widely welcomed proposal to designate Kenfig National Nature Reserve as a Special Area of Conservation under the EC Habitats and Species Directive. Sediment starvation and undergrazing are now the major issues which affect ecological diversity at the site and much effort will be required in the coming decades to maintain the features of European Interest at a favourable conservation status.

Introduction

The coastline of South Wales supports in excess of twenty distinct sand dune systems amounting to a total dune area of approximately 4,760 ha (Dargie, 1995). This extremely rich nature conservation resource includes a variety of dune system types ranging from small (<10 ha) bay systems to large (>500 ha) hindshore complexes. These dunes also support a wide range of habitat types, ranging from mobile foredunes and dune blowouts to closed scrub woodland, and the majority of the UK dune vegetation types recognised by the National Vegetation Classification (NVC; Rodwell, in press) have been recorded in the region (Dargie, 1995). Taken together, these systems represent one of the most important dune regions on the Atlantic coast of Europe. Kenfig National Nature Reserve, the largest unafforested dune system in South Wales, presents an ideal site for a case study of some of the issues which currently affect the conservation of sand dune habitats.

Kenfig National Nature Reserve: regional context and designation

This 600 ha hindshore dune system is located on the southeastern shoreline of Swansea Bay and supports the largest area of semi-natural dune vegetation in South Wales (Figure 1). It is the largest surviving fragment of the virtually continuous 27 km arc of dunes which once fringed the eastern and northern

Figure 1   Aerial view of Kenfig National Nature Reserve from the northeast. Approximately two-thirds of the reserve is visible in this photograph which also shows numerous flooded slacks and the 28 ha Kenfig Pool

shorelines of the bay. The loss of much of the original dune habitat is primarily related to the location of this area within the industrial heartland of South Wales. A large available labour force, good sea and rail links, the early establishment of a metal smelting industry and the close proximity of large coal reserves are all factors which contributed to the local development of steel making on a large scale from 1903 onwards. Subsequent developments have included the construction of petro-chemical plants, housing estates, enhanced road, rail and harbour networks, landfill sites and industrial estates. It is fortunate that Kenfig, as the largest original component system of the Swansea Bay dune complex, has survived to the present day.

Past developments which directly affected the Kenfig dune system prior to its designation as a NNR, included the construction of a large railway yard to the northeast of the reserve, the installation of a pipe to remove water for industrial cooling from Kenfig Pool (a large dune lake), the construction of a 3 km long road through the foredune belt to aid the construction of a breakwater at Port Talbot and the extraction of sand from the beach and foredune areas. These past developments continue to influence the management of the reserve to the present day.

Kenfig National Nature Reserve is owned by the Kenfig Corporation Trustees and managed by Bridgend County Borough Council in consultation with a range of interested parties including the Countryside Council for Wales, the executive agency for nature conservation in Wales. The reserve is one of the very few NNRs in the UK under local authority management.

In spite of the importance of the Kenfig dune system not all of it has been designated as a Site of Special Scientific Interest or NNR. This is because some areas of the dune system are owned or leased by other parties and subject to long-established patterns of landuse (mainly golfing and agriculture). Despite this, many important areas for nature conservation still survive outside the boundary of the reserve and current policy is aimed at encouraging owners and occupiers to adopt management practices favourable to wildlife. The relationship between these peripheral areas and the core statutorily protected part of the system is summarised in Figure 2.

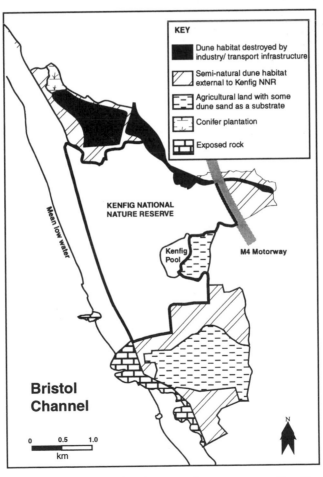

Figure 2   **Classification of landuse for the coastal zone surrounding Kenfig National Nature Reserve**

History and formation of the Kenfig dune system

Glacigenic sand supply, a large tidal range, predominantly onshore winds and a low–lying coastal hinterland has produced a classic hindshore dune system at Kenfig, which extends 3.2 km inland at its widest point. The formation of the current beach/dune system is thought to have commenced some 2,000-2,500 years before present (Carr & Blackley, 1977; Price & Brooks, 1980), the system probably succeeding an earlier suite of dunes to seaward which were mobilised by the postglacial rise in relative sealevel (Culver, 1977). After this very little is known about the evolution of the dune system until the period covered by the last 700 years or so. During this time the mediaeval township of Kenfig was inundated by sand drift and contemporary records indicate that *Ammophila arenaria* was planted extensively in an attempt to control sand movement.

Quite when the dune system reached its current landward boundary is uncertain, but the site was still comparatively mobile at the end of World War II. An early aerial photograph of the site taken in 1946 shows extensive mobile dune areas over the northern half of the reserve and many active blowouts. This contrasts sharply with recent aerial and ground based surveys which show that bare sand is now scarce, at *c.* 2.5% of the total area (Davies, 1995) with virtually no aeolian processes evident more than 100m landward of the shoreline. The negative sediment budget of Kenfig beach has resulted in the presence of a pronounced foredune cliff along much of the dune frontage.

Ecological evaluation

Plant communities

The Kenfig dune system is composed entirely of windblown beach sand. An appreciable marine and terrestrial mollusc shell component imparts a predominantly alkaline reaction to the sediments and pH within 5 cm of the surface only falls below 7.0 on some old inland dunes. The vegetation of much of the reserve therefore includes a significant calcicolous component, with *Hornungia petraea*, *Anthyllis vulneraria*, and *Iris foetidissima* common on the dry dunes and *Carex flacca* in all but the wettest of slacks. Many of the NVC communities defined for British sand dunes by Rodwell (in press) have been recorded at Kenfig, together with a small but significant number of as yet undescribed types (Jones, 1993). This account will include frequent references to the 18 major NVC sand dune types, all of which are prefixed with the abbreviation "SD".

The net negative sediment budget of the Kenfig foredune/beach system has resulted in the presence of a pronounced foredune cliff along much of the dune frontage. Tidal scour at the base of this cliff, coupled to the presence of a pronounced cobble storm beach, means that strandline plant communities are restricted in space and time.

Typical strandline species include *Honckenya peploides, Salsola kali, Cakile maritima, Euphorbia paralias* and *Elytrigia juncea,* whilst the rare alien *Corispermum leptopterum* has been recorded near the mouth of the River Kenfig.

The input of windblown sand from the beach to the foredune zone has now almost ceased and this, coupled to the net erosion regime, has resulted in the virtual absence of embryo dune communities. Whilst some small *Elytrigia juncea* dominated embryo dunes (SD 4) do occur at the northern end of the beach system, their total extent is limited to less than 1 ha.

Mobile dunes dominated by *Ammophila arenaria* (SD 6) are becoming increasingly scarce at Kenfig. Shifting dunes with vigorous flowering stands of *A. arenaria* are particularly rare and the most common mobile dune community is the relatively stable *Festuca rubra* sub-type.

Semi-fixed dune grasslands characterised by *Ammophila arenaria* and *Festuca rubra* (SD 7) still occur commonly at Kenfig, but many areas are developing a dominant grass component and stands with a complete vegetation cover now occur within a few metres of the foredune cliff. Lack of grazing by rabbits and agricultural stock and the virtual absence of a beach sand input are likely to be the primary causes for the apparently short-lived nature of these community types, which will presumably become rarer as the frequency of the precursor vegetation type (*Ammophila* dominated mobile dune) also declines. Nevertheless, species-rich examples still occur on many steep south facing solar slopes where the rich dune annual flora may include *Hornungia petraea*, *Cerastium diffusum*, *C. semidecandrum*, *Erophila verna*, *Saxifraga tridactylites*, *Valerianella locusta*, *Vulpia fasciculata* and *Phleum arenarium*.

Fixed dune grassland communities form the dominant vegetation of dry dunes at Kenfig, with a total area of *c.* 286 ha (Dargie, 1995). Dune grasslands in which *Festuca rubra* and *Galium verum* occur as the constant taxa (SD 8) are especially common and at a particular successional stage, or where grazed or mown, include some very species-rich examples. Nevertheless, there is a clear trend towards the development of more mesotrophic vegetation types in which coarse grasses such as *Arrhenatherum elatius* and *Dactylis glomerata* are frequent. These currently account for 30% of the fixed dune grassland resource and in the absence of grazing or mowing this proportion is likely to increase.

A range of leached dune communities occur towards the landward margin of the dune system, with bracken (*Pteridium aquilinum*) dominated mesotrophic grassland being the commonest and most species-poor type. Some small areas of short-sward acid grassland have also been recorded with *Anthoxanthum odoratum*, *Agrostis capillaris*, *Festuca ovina* and *Rumex acetosella* as characteristic components. Here again, mesotrophic elements are frequent and management will be required to maintain these important grasslands.

Primary dune heath (*sensu* Edmondson & Gateley, this volume) bearing an ericoid shrub cover is extremely rare and is represented by just a few mature stands of *Calluna vulgaris*. These areas shown little signs of young growth, occurring as 'islands' within a dense grassland sward. A programme of mowing with some limited surface scarification is planned as a means of encouraging the recruitment of young plants from the seedbank.

Dune scrub woodland is now commoner at Kenfig than at any other time in the recently documented past. Stand forming species on dry dunes include *Hippophae rhamnoides*, *Crataegus monogyna*, *Prunus spinosa*, *Populus candicans* and (unusually in

South Wales) *Populus tremula,* whereas in the wetter slacks and areas of flushed dune grassland *Betula pubescens, B. pendula, Salix cinerea* and *S. caprea* are common. Several mature (>40 years) stands of *Hippophae rhamnoides* and *Betula* spp. are now well established and as well as supporting a fairly rich dune woodland flora also provide a valuable habitat for nesting birds.

Kenfig displays the classical landform features of a large hindshore dune system with numerous parabolic dune slack systems extending from west to east along the line of the prevailing (westerly) wind direction. Each of these systems bear trailing dune arms with a mobile, or now more commonly stabilised, mass of sand at the head of the blowout. The associated dune slack flora is extremely rich with species composition and stand structure varying in accordance with hydrology and slack age (Jones & Etherington, 1989, 1992). It is only possible to summarise some of the key points of interest here.

In common with most other British west coast sites, *Salix repens* is the most common dominant dune slack species and is generally associated with a pleuro-carpous moss mat composed of pure or mixed communities of *Calliergon cuspidatum, Drepanocladus sendtneri, Campylium stellatum* and (rarely) *Drepanocladus lycopodioides.* Caespitose forms of *Equisetum variegatum* form the dominant cover in some wet slacks, while communities dominated or co-dominated by *Hydrocotyle vulgaris, Carex flacca, C. nigra* and *Festuca rubra* also occur. In stable areas with a restricted annual groundwater range, some rich fen-grassland communities occur. These are typified by the presence of *Gymnadenia conopsea, Epipactis palustris* and *Briza media.* Successionally young dune slack communities are still relatively frequent at Kenfig and the best examples support such notable species as *Littorella uniflora, Samolus valerandi, Carex viridula* ssp. *viridula, Baldellia ranunculoides, Liparis loeselii* var. *ovata* and *Petalophyllum ralfsii.* The Kenfig dune slacks constitute an UK stronghold for the latter two species and the site supports a larger area of young dune slack habitat than any other Welsh site (Dargie, 1995). Tall sedge and grass communities also occur fairly frequently and are variously dominated by *Cladium mariscus, Phragmites australis, Carex acutiformis, Typha latifolia* and *Calamagrostis epigejos.* Such areas con-tribute greatly to the structural diversity of dune slack vegetation at Kenfig.

A 28 ha freshwater dune lake (Kenfig Pool) occupies the southeastern quadrant of Kenfig NNR and displays both shallow marginal (*Littorellion uniflorae*) and permanent dune lake (*Potamogeton* and *Phragmites*) plant communities (as defined by Olson & van der Maarel, 1989). The pool has a rich flora including several Charophyte species and supports scarce aquatic plants such as *Potamogeton trichoides* and *P. perfoliatus.*

Recent surveys of macrofungi at Kenfig by the Cambrian Institute of Mycology have provided records of numerous scarce or rare species. The presence of a wide range of community types at different stages of succession is likely to be of key importance with respect to this group.

Invertebrate groups

Botanical diversity, habitat longevity and a wide range of vegetation/habitat types foster an expectedly high invertebrate diversity at Kenfig. Species numbers for the Araneae, Odonata, Hymenoptera, Mollusca, Lepidoptera, Orthoptera and

Coleoptera are high and Deeming (1995) has recorded more than 950 Diptera species. The invertebrate fauna of the site is known to include many scarce or rare components (Fowles, 1994) such as the strandline dwelling ground beetle *Nebria complanata*, the weevil *Tychius quinquepunctatus* and the medicinal leech (*Hirudo medicinalis*).

Vertebrate groups

Reptiles and amphibians are represented by three and four species respectively and the mammalian fauna of the site includes such notable species as the harvest mouse (*Micromys minutus*) as well as a relatively large hare (*Lepus capensis*) population. Rabbits (*Oryctolagus cuniculus*) have been present since at least 1314 AD and were once so abundant that culls were organised by the Ministry of Agriculture (HMSO, 1958). Myxomatosis resulted in the virtual eradication of the species after the late 1950s and numbers have failed to recover with a current population of just a few hundred animals. The rank nature of many grassland areas may be a factor preventing population expansion.

The number of breeding bird species is relatively low (*c.* 50) and yet reclusive ground nesting species such as the little tern (*Sterna albifrons*), shelduck (*Tadorna tadorna*), merlin (*Falco columbarius*), snipe (*Capella galinago*), and redshank (*Tringa totanus*) were all recorded as breeding during the first quarter of this century (Heathcote *et al.*, 1967). Human disturbance resulting from the increased recreational use of the dune system from as early as the First World War onwards was almost certainly the major reason for the loss of these species. Much contemporary interest is centred around Kenfig Pool which supports significant over-wintering duck populations. The reedbeds fringing the pool also provide an important habitat resource for breeding and passage migrant *Acrocephalus* warblers.

Ecological management

Two principal factors contribute to the need for extensive habitat management at Kenfig. Grazing by agricultural stock is limited to sheep at an approximate stocking density of 0.2/ha, a level which is too low for the effective management of well vegetated sand dunes (Oosterveld, 1985; Van Dijk, 1992). Unrestricted public access, coupled to other factors relating to the issue of enclosure, currently hinder the adoption of an appropriate stocking level across the whole site. Furthermore, the very small rabbit population removes another element of biomass control and the site is now grossly undergrazed.

The second major factor to influence habitat management concerns the negative sediment budget of the beach/foredune system. Several factors may be responsible for this including:

a) the extraction (prior to 1973) of 4.5×10^5 tonnes of sand from the foreshore and dune system (Carr & Blackley, 1977);

b) past and current dredging both from the nearshore and offshore zones;

c) the construction of an extensive breakwater 4.5 km to the north of Kenfig at Port Talbot in the late 1960s; and

d) a possible longer term 'natural' or cyclical reduction in sediment supply.

Of key importance is that aeolian processes which would be encouraged by sediment input have now all but ceased at Kenfig.

Of these two main factors undergrazing has perhaps the most obvious and immediate consequences, while the negative sediment regime has a more long term influence which will continue irrespective of the eventual establishment of a suitable grazing regime. Overall the consequences detected to-date can be summarised as follows:

a) the expansion of scrub woodland, both on dry dunes and in wet slacks;

b) an increase in the representation of mesotrophic elements such as *Arrhenatherum elatius* in species-rich *Festuca rubra-Galium verum* grasslands;

c) a general increase in the rate at which vegetation types pass onto later seral stages;

d) a reduction in the area of bare sand; and

e) the extinction of species restricted to either short sward or early successional stage communities. Prominent examples include *Coeloglossum viride, Herminium monorchis, Hypochaeris glabra, Radiola linoides, Rumex rupestris* and *Teesdalia nudicaulis*. Furthermore, two nationally rare plants listed in Annex II of the Habitats Directive, *Liparis loeselii* var. *ovata* and *Petalophyllum ralfsii*, have been displaced from many formerly suitable sites as a result of successional change (Jones *et al.*, 1995).

These trends are reflected in the key long term habitat management objectives for the site. Much effort is devoted to controlling the encroachment of scrub into rich slack and dune grassland areas and methods used include hand pulling, mechanical uprooting, felling, mowing and the treatment of cut stumps with herbicide ([(3, 5, 6 trichloro-2-pyridinyl) oxy] acetic acid; proprietal name Garlon). Nevertheless, the significance of dune woodland as a nature conservation resource is realised and many areas will be left to develop with little intervention.

In the absence of an appropriate grazing regime, mechanised mowing has to be used widely for the management of dune grasslands and slacks. This form of management is extremely labour intensive and requires a large capital outlay for equipment purchase. Furthermore, the harvesting and removal of cut biomass poses a formidable problem on such undulating terrain. Mowing cannot replace grazing at the level of the whole dune system (Van Dijk, 1992) but is regarded as a valuable localised method of biomass control (Figure 3). As an example, a regime of close-mowing has recently been used to remove most of the above ground biomass from five dune slacks as the first phase of a recovery programme for *Liparis loeselii* var. *ovata* in Wales. The project has been co-funded by the Countryside Council for Wales and British Steel and it is hoped that the resultant exposure of bare soil, coupled to the removal of the thick pleurocarpous moss mat, will create conditions suitable for the establishment of *Liparis* seedlings.

The reduction in the area of bare sand poses serious problems for the future, particularly in view of the virtual absence of habitat creation by aeolian processes. Current management reflects this, key elements of which are summarised below.

Figure 3   **A tractor mounted pick-up mower has recently been used to remove vegetation from a limited number of slacks as part of a recovery programme for *Liparis loeselii* var. *ovata* at Kenfig NNR**

a) Path erosion caused by visitors is tolerated; indeed uncompetitive plant taxa such as *Ornithopus perpusillus, Eleocharis quinqueflora, Baldellia ranunculoides, Isolepis cernua* and *Riccia fluitans* are now commoner on the margins of paths than anywhere else at Kenfig. Similarly, the value of erosion hollows created by sheep for shelter is considerable as these now provide important microhabitats for invertebrates and nationally scarce plants such as *Hornungia petraea* and *Vulpia fasciculata*.

b) In conjunction with the University of Wales, *Ammophila arenaria* shoots are being harvested from one large recently active parabolic blowout system to aid mobility. Uprooted material has been transplanted to the sand–capped surface of a nearby industrial tip to aid the development of a screening vegetation cover.

c) Foredune blowouts initiated by wave action are monitored, but are being left to develop unhindered.

d) An education programme has been initiated to inform the public and all relevant bodies of the value of mobility and destablilisation management. As part of this, the concept that geomorphological processes merit conservation in much the same way as biological systems is being actively promoted. This is an essential prerequisite when radical destabilisation management is being considered (e.g. Geelen *et al.*, 1995), especially at sites like Kenfig where sand blow has led historically to economic hardship.

In the future more radical measures are planned which may include soil stripping and the mechanical destabilisation of blowouts which have only recently become inactive. The value of such management has been amply demonstrated elsewhere (Grootjans *et al.*, 1988; Van Dijk & Grootjans, 1988; Jungerius *et al.*, 1995) and reflects the recent shift in emphasis away from stabilisation management to one where mobility is encouraged where appropriate (van der Meulen & van der Maarel, 1989; Doody, 1993).

Kenfig: A proposed Special Area of Conservation

The proposal to designate Kenfig as one of thirty-eight Special Areas of Conservation in Wales under the EU Habitats and Species Directive (Directive 92/43/EEC on the conservation of of natural habitats and of wild fauna and flora) was announced in March 1995. The area, which includes the nearby Merthyr Mawr dune system, has been proposed because of the presence of three habitats and two species of European interest, namely:

- Dune grasslands corresponding to CORINE type 16.22 – Fixed dunes with herbaceous vegetation (grey dunes);
- Dunes with *Salix arenaria*, CORINE type 16.26;
- Humid dune slacks (corresponding to CORINE types 16.31–35);
- *Liparis loeselii*; and
- *Petalophyllum ralfsii*.

The citation document (Anon., 1995) provides information which indicates the relative importance of Kenfig on a national scale with respect to each community type and species. For example, Kenfig supports more than 10% of the UK resource of the humid dune slacks habitat type for which it is considered to be one of the best areas in the country. Similarly, the site is known to support more than 40% of the total UK population of *Liparis loeselii*. Statements regarding the representation of different vegetation types on a comparative UK wide basis are greatly aided by the availability of a) an established nationally applicable vegetation classification, and b) site inventory data in mapped form for all (in this case dune) sites. In Britain these two vital data sets have been provided by the NVC and the National Sand Dune Survey of Great Britain (Radley, 1992). Similarly, statements concerning the national and local status of rare species can also only be made on the basis of prior survey data. In the case of *Liparis loeselii* var. *ovata*, surveys of all past duneland sites were carried out in the years following 1990 to establish its current status (Jones & Etherington, 1992; Jones *et al.*, 1994) while monitoring of all extant British sites has enabled accurate estimates of population size on a comparative basis.

It is too early to accurately assess what impact SAC status (if confirmed) will have at sites like Kenfig. Any additional tier of protection is obviously to be welcomed in an area which has already suffered extensive habitat loss. One immediate and highly beneficial consequence of the proposal has been to raise awareness of the site's importance in a European context amongst those local interest groups and authorities which are able to influence the scope of conservation management work at the site. Another beneficial aspect of the proposal is that reference to named habitats and species in the proposal citation focuses attention upon their conservation; this is especially important with respect to inconspicuous and declining species such as *Petalophyllum ralfsii*.

Future developments

Many valuable duneland habitats still survive outside the core statutorily protected part of the Kenfig dune system. These include leached dune grassland and semi-fixed dune communities, a species-rich sand dune-saltmarsh transition, mobile foredunes and extensive tracts of undulating dunes (*sensu* Olson & van der Maarel, 1989) which form a relatively thin sand sheet over boulder clay and bedrock to the southeast of the reserve. The extension of conservation management to some of these areas has begun and will hopefully be pursued through the implementation of a Coastal Zone Management strategy.

Another important recent development which will affect Kenfig has been the formation of a sand dune management group by the Countryside Council for Wales. This group will ultimately produce a framework for the management of the Welsh duneland resource as a whole, thus achieving better co-ordination of management effort between individual sites.

Conclusions

Kenfig NNR faces many of the problems which beset the conservation of the northwest European dune resource as a whole. Although habitat loss historically posed the greatest threat, sediment starvation and undergrazing are now identified as the key issues which affect biodiversity. In the future much effort will be required to ensure the favourable conservation status of target habitats and species. These aims will be furthered by viewing the management of Kenfig not only within the context of its neighbouring coastal zone but also the Welsh dune resource as a whole.

Acknowledgements

Numerous colleagues within the Planning Departments of Mid Glamorgan County Council (latterly Bridgend County Borough Council) provided help during the EUCC excursion to Kenfig and their support is gratefully acknowledged. Thanks are also due to British Steel Strip Products PLC for sponsoring the first stage of the excursion.

References

Anon. 1995. Countryside Council for Wales, Proposed Special Area of Conservation Citation Document for Kenfig National Nature Reserve, March 8th. 1995. pp. 3.

Carr, A.P. & Blackley, M.W.L. 1977. Swansea Bay (Sker) Project, Topic Report No. 1(a), *Introduction;* 1 (b), *Long Term Changes in the Coastline*. Institute of Oceanographic Sciences Report No. 42/77, Taunton, UK. pp. 63.

Culver, S.J. 1977. The development of the Swansea Bay area during the past 20,000 years. *Gower Journal*, 27:58-62.

Dargie, T.C.D. 1995. *Sand Dune Vegetation Survey of Great Britain - A National Inventory*. Part 3: Wales. Joint Nature Conservation Committee, Peterborough, UK. 153 pp.

Davies, A.J.D. 1995. The greening of Kenfig Burrows. BSc Thesis, University of Wales College, Swansea, UK. 105 pp.

Deeming, J.C. 1995. Diptera *(True Flies) from the Kenfig National Nature Reserve, Glamorgan*. National Museum of Wales Entomology Series No. 4. National Museum and Gallery of Wales, Cardiff, UK. 113 pp.

Dijk, H.W.J. van. 1992. Grazing domestic livestock in Dutch coastal dunes: Experiments, experiences and perspectives. In: *Coastal Dunes, Geomorphology, Ecology and Management for Conservation*. Eds: Carter, R.W.G., Curtis, T.G.F. & Sheehy-Skeffington, M. Balkema, Rotterdam, The Netherlands. pp. 235-250.

Dijk, H.W.J. van & Grootjans, A.P. 1988. Wet dune slacks: decline and new opportunities. *Hydrobiologia*, 265:281-304.

Doody, J.P. 1993. Changing attitudes to coastal conservation. *Enact*, 1(3):4-6. English Nature, Peterborough, UK.

Edmondson, S.E. & Gateley, P.S. 1996. Dune heath on the Sefton Coast sand dune system, Merseyside, UK. This volume.

Fowles, A.P. 1994. *Invertebrates of Wales: a review of important sites and species*. Joint Nature Conservation Committee, Peterborough, UK. pp. 157.

Geelen, L., Cousin, E. & Schoon, R. 1995. Restoration of dune slacks in the Amsterdam water works. *Coastline*, 4(3/4):12-14.

Grootjans, A.P., Hendriksma, P., Engelmoer, M. & Westhoff, V. 1988. Vegetation dynamics in a wet dune slack I: rare species decline on the Wadden Island of Schiermonnikoog in The Netherlands. *Acta Botanica Neerlandica*, 37:265-278.

Heathcote, A., Griffin, D. & Morrey Salmon, H. 1967. *The Birds of Glamorgan*. The Cardiff Naturalists' Society, Cardiff, UK. 143 pp.

HMSO. 1958. Report of the Royal Commission on Common Land, 1955-1958, Cmnd. 462, presented to Parliament July 1958. Her Majesty's Stationary Office, London, UK.

Jones, P.S. 1993. Ecological and hydrological studies of dune slack vegetation at Kenfig National Nature Reserve, Mid Glamorgan. PhD Thesis, University of Wales, Cardiff, UK.

Jones, P.S. & Etherington, J.R. 1989. Ecological and physiological studies of dune slack vegetation at Kenfig Pool & Dunes Local Nature Reserve, Mid Glamorgan, Wales, UK. In: *Perspectives in Coastal Dune Management*. Eds: Meulen, F. van der, Jungerius, P.D. & Visser, J.H. SPB Academic Publishing, The Hague, The Netherlands. pp. 297-303.

Jones, P.S. & Etherington, J.R. 1992. Autecological studies on the rare orchid *Liparis loeselii* and their application to the management of dune slack ecosystems in South Wales. In: *Coastal Dunes, Geomorphology, Ecology and Management for Conservation*. Eds: Carter, R.W.G., Curtis, T.W.G. & Sheehy-Skeffington, M. Balkema, Rotterdam, The Netherlands. pp. 299-312.

Jones, P.S., Hurford, C. & Jones, A. 1994. The Fen Orchid – A Candidate for Species Recovery in Wales. Unpublished report to the Countryside Council for Wales, Bangor, UK. 9 pp.

Jones, P.S., Kay, Q.O.N. & Jones, A. 1995. The decline of rare plant species and community types in the sand dune systems of South Wales. In: *Directions in European Coastal Management*. Eds: Healy, M.G. & Doody, J.P. Samara Publishing Limited, Cardigan, Wales, UK. pp. 547-555.

Jungerius, P.D., Koehler, H.H., Kooijman, A.M., Mücher, H.J. & Graefe, U. 1995. Response of vegetation and soil ecosystem to mowing and sod removal in the coastal dunes 'Zwanenwater', The Netherlands. *Journal of Coastal Conservation*, 1:3-16.

Meulen, F. van der & Maarel, E. van der. 1989. Coastal defence alternatives and nature development perspectives. In: *Perspectives in Coastal Dune Management*. Eds: Meulen, F. van der, Jungerius, P.D. & Visser, J.H. SPB Academic Publishing, The Hague, The Netherlands. pp. 183-195.

Olson, J.S & Maarel, E. van der. 1989. Coastal dunes in Europe: A global view. In: *Perspectives in Coastal Dune Management*. Eds: Meulen, F. van der, Jungerius, P.D. & Visser, J.H. SPB Academic Publishing, The Hague, The Netherlands. pp. 3-32.

Oosterveld, P. 1985. Grazing in dune areas: the objectives of nature conservation and the aims of research for nature conservation management. In: *Focus on Nature Conservation No. 13: Sand Dunes and their Management*. Ed: Doody, J.P. Nature Conservancy Council, Peterborough, UK. pp. 187-203.

Price, C.R. & Brooks, M. 1980. Swansea Bay, bedrock geology and its influence over geomorphological development. In: *Industrialised Embayments and Their Environmental Problems, A Case Study of Swansea Bay*. Eds: Collins, M.B., Banner, F.T., Tyler, P.A., Wakefield, S.J. & James, A.E. Pergamon Press, Oxford, UK. pp. 23-38.

Radley, G.P. 1992. The dunes of England, an example of a national inventory. In: *Coastal Dunes, Geomorphology, Ecology and Management for Conservation*. Eds: Carter, R.W.G., Curtis, T.G.F. & Sheehy-Skeffington, M. Balkema, Rotterdam, The Netherlands. pp. 439-454.

Rodwell, J. In press. *British Plant Communities Volume V, Maritime and Ruderal Communities*. Cambridge University Press, Cambridge, UK.

Studies in European Coastal Management. Jones, Healy and Williams (eds)
1996, Samara Publishing Limited, Cardigan. ISBN 1 873692 07 2

The Gower Peninsula, Wales, UK

J. Mullard [a], J. Atkins[a], M.R. Hughes[b], S. Sell[c] & M. Winder[d]

a) *Planning Department, City and County of Swansea, Wales, UK*
b) *Countryside Council for Wales, Swansea, Wales, UK*
c) *Glamorgan-Gwent Archaeological Trust, Swansea, Wales, UK*
d) *The National Trust, Reynoldston, Gower, Wales, UK*

Abstract: The Gower Peninsula is fringed by a coastal landscape of outstanding natural beauty and ecological importance. The peninsula coastline supports many different landscape elements which are subject to varying degrees and forms of human pressure, particularly tourism and informal recreation. Examination of some of these elements provides useful insights into the role of different organisations on Gower and highlights the need for improved inter-agency co-operation, especially where large and complex ecosystems are involved.

Introduction

The Gower Peninsula was the first area in Britain to be designated as an Area of Outstanding Natural Beauty (AONB). The region includes many different geological and landscape elements and supports a high diversity of coastal habitats and species. The southern coastline of the Gower Peninsula is chiefly composed of Carboniferous Limestone cliffs which support one of the richest calcicolous maritime floras' in the United Kingdom. This high wave energy southern coast contrasts sharply with the low energy estuarine environment of the north Gower coast where the largest saltmarsh system in Wales forms the southern shoreline of the Burry Inlet and Loughor Estuary (Figure 1).

The importance of the Gower Peninsula as a landscape and ecological resource is reflected by the large number of organisations involved in its conservation and management and also by the many, often overlapping, designations which have evolved for its protection. Overall protection for the area is aided by its designation as an Area of Outstanding Natural Beauty and 95% of the 58 km coastline of Gower is designated as a Heritage Coast. Three discrete areas are scheduled as National Nature Reserves and two large areas of coastline have been proposed for designation as Special Areas of Conservation under the Habitats Directive (Council Directive 92/43/EEC on the conservation of natural habitats and of wild fauna and flora). The importance of the Burry Estuary is underlined by its designation as both a Ramsar Site and Special Protection Area under the Birds Directive (Council Directive 79/409/EEC on the conservation of wild birds).

With its extensive sand beaches, the Gower Peninsula is also a much favoured destination for recreation and tourism, attracting approximately 2 million visitors per annum (Mullard, 1995). Good road links, coupled to the close proximity of the large population centres of South Wales, place the area under particular pressure from day visitors, many of whom travel by car.

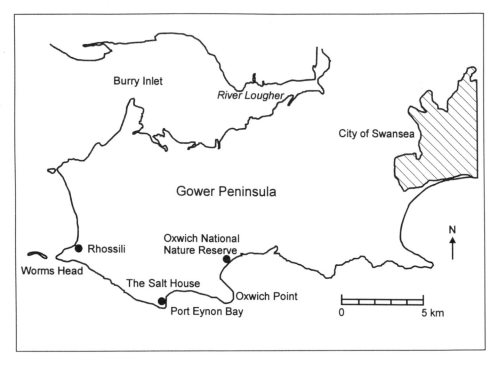

Figure 1 **Map of the Gower Peninsula showing the location of sites referred to in the text**

Four case studies – Oxwich National Nature Reserve, Port Eynon, Rhossili and the Burry Inlet/Loughor Estuary, will be discussed in the context of reviewing some of the tourist and recreational impacts on the coast.

Oxwich National Nature Reserve

Oxwich National Nature Reserve is located on the south coast of Gower and occupies a large embayment in the Carboniferous Limestone coastline (Figure 1). The reserve, which is managed by the Countryside Council for Wales, extends over an area of 289 ha and supports a wide range of coastal habitats. These include an extensive sand foreshore, calcareous dunes and slacks, ungrazed saltmarsh, freshwater marsh with *Phragmites australis* reedbeds, nutrient poor fen, freshwater ponds and alder (*Alnus glutinosa*) carr woodland. These habitats are flanked by wooded limestone cliffs. This mosaic of habitats results in many interesting ecotones, particularly between sand dune and freshwater marshland habitats. The diversity of habitat types also results in large species number totals for many plant and animal groups; for example 500 vascular plants, 162 breeding birds, 75 land snails, 272 Coleoptera and 530 Lepidoptera. A general account of the reserve has been provided by Hughes (1983).

Up to 300,000 people visit the reserve each year, including 10,000 school children and students engaged in field studies. The public also utilise the reserve and associated inter-tidal and marine nearshore zones for a range of recreational activities including walking, sunbathing, swimming, jet-skiing, camping and surfing. Increased leisure time and car ownership throughout the 1970s placed vulnerable components of the reserve, such as the foredune habitats, under particular pressure from visitors. In response, during the 1970s management effort was primarily targeted at mobile dune stabilisation through the use of sand traps, fencing and the planting of marram grass (*Ammophila arenaria*).

By 1981 most of the mobile frontal dune areas had become stabilised and for the rest of that decade the system was judged as reflecting a satisfactory equilibrium between the three management objectives of maintaining stability, encouraging diversity and allowing access for recreation and education (Hughes, 1993). During the early 1990s however, the frontal dunes began to exhibit symptoms of diversity decline through overstabilisation. Elsewhere on the reserve, lack of grazing has resulted in the development of coarse vegetation dominated by *Festuca rubra* and *Pteridium aquilinum*. Current management now consists of repeated mowing to eradicate stands of Pteridium aquilinum, grazing to prevent or retard the development of coarse grassland, control of scrub by cutting and goat browsing and re-creating early successional stages by turf stripping and excavation.

The management of duneland habitats at Oxwich National Nature Reserve has passed from an era of stabilisation management to one where much effort has to be devoted to the control of vegetation growth on stabilised dunes. Visitor pressure no longer constitutes a serious threat to biodiversity or dune system stability.

Port Eynon Bay

Port Eynon Bay is also located on the south coast of the Gower Peninsula (Figure 1) and comprises a large embayment flanked to the east and west by massive Carboniferous Limestone headlands. A large part of the coast is owned by Swansea City Council which co-ordinates management of the area through its Gower Countryside Service. Parts of the embayment are fringed by dunes and these are subject to intense visitor pressure. The limited width of the dune band contrasts with the more extensive Oxwich system, and stabilisation measures have been required to promote revegetation. Furthermore, fencing and surfaced paths serve to control visitor access and limit trampling damage.

Features of human heritage interest also occur in Port Eynon Bay. An old Salt House dating from the 16th century is one of the most significant of these and has recently been the subject of an excavation and restoration programme undertaken by the Glamorgan-Gwent Archaeological Trust in conjunction with the Manpower Services Commission and Swansea City Council. The impetus for this work arose from sea erosion of the site and a permanent protective seawall has now been constructed. Excavations have revealed a seawater reservoir and two smaller chambers, one of which contained the remains of a wooden pump. This was probably used to pump seawater to an upper chamber which was heated to drive off water as steam. The use of such technology as a means of procuring salt, an important commodity at the time, is of great historical interest. Furthermore, the Port Eynon Salt House may represent the earliest surviving example of what was, by then, a declining practice in the face of cheaper alternative sources of salt. Further excavation and restoration works will result in the removal of intrusive features and expose levels for consolidation leading to eventual public display. The Salt House project provides a good example of where multi-agency co-operation has led to the conservation of an outstanding historical feature of the coastal zone.

Rhossili

The village of Rhossili is located at the southwestern tip of the Gower Peninsula and overlooks a spectacular sand beach to the north and the elongated limestone headland of Worms Head to the south (Figure 1). The National Trust, as the owner of 2,226 ha of land on the Gower Peninsula, has a major presence at Rhossili where it operates a visitor centre and shop. Visitor activities on land owned by the Trust at Rhossili are diverse and include fishing, rock climbing, hang gliding, surfing, walking and beach recreation. A former cliff-top Coastguard lookout at the site has been converted to a visitor centre and the presence of Iron Age earth works, traditional dry-stone walls and mediaeval field systems, all within the context of a spectacular coastal landscape, offer many opportunities for visitor interpretation.

Elsewhere on the Gower Peninsula, land owned by the National Trust includes saltmarsh and sand dune habitats on the northern coastline, extensive sections of limestone cliff coastline and large areas of lowland heath. This land-holding constitutes a largely undeveloped natural/cultural landscape of great scenic beauty and value for nature conservation. Numerous overlapping designations serve to emphasise the importance of the Trust's land holding in the area and these include nine Scheduled Ancient Monuments, seven Sites of Special Scientific Interest, two National Nature Reserves, one Ramsar site and one Special Protection Area. Furthermore, much of the land owned by the Trust is registered as Common Land.

The Burry Inlet and Loughor Estuary

The Burry Inlet and Loughor Estuary define the northern coast of the Gower Peninsula and provide an internationally important habitat for wading birds and waterfowl (Pritchard et al., 1992). In 1992 the area was designated both as a Ramsar Site under the 1971 Ramsar Convention on the conservation of important wetlands and as a Special Protection Area under the EC Birds Directive. More recently, the inlet and estuary have been identified as a candidate Special Area of Conservation (SAC) under the EC Habitats Directive. Other designations which affect part or all of the area include Site of Special Scientific Interest, National Nature Reserve, Area of Outstanding Natural Beauty and Heritage Coast.

Human impacts in the inlet and estuary include the harvesting of shellfish (cockles) on a commercial basis, sewage discharge, sand winning, shooting and the urban and industrial development of much of the northern shoreline. Furthermore, the area is likely to come under increasing pressure from recreation in the future

(Stevens, 1995). These factors impact upon the natural features of the area in a variety of ways and conflicts of interest are inevitable. The management of the area is complicated further by the wide range of organisations with an interest in the inlet and estuary. It is against this complex background that the Burry Inlet and Loughor Estuary Liaison Group was formed in 1992. This brought together officers from relevant local authorities, statutory bodies, and organisations with the aim of resolving the various needs of conservation, enjoyment, and commercial interests through:

a)   an increased understanding of the area;

b)   information sharing; and

c)   liaison and consultation.

The group is independent from government and relies on the public for support and funding. The impetus for the formation of the group came from the publication, in 1990, of Turning the Tide: A Future for Estuaries by the Royal Society for the Protection of Birds (Rothwell & Housden, 1990). Following initial discussions, it soon became clear that the inlet and estuary would benefit from some form of management/liaison group to deal with emerging issues. Support for the idea of an officer-level liaison group representing local authorities was sought and an initial meeting was held on 5 September 1991, following which Terms of Reference and the Statement of Intent were drafted and refined.

The group was officially launched on 5 November 1992 and since then has encouraged discussion and liaison over issues affecting the inlet and estuary, particularly fisheries-related issues. However, it soon became clear that the group's existing knowledge base about the area was both incomplete and out of date. It was therefore decided that a conference was needed to discuss issues and pool information. This conference was held over 29-30 March 1995 and was marked by the publication of the first part of a report (Atkins, 1995). The conference was attended by a wide range of organisations and private individuals and proved to be an effective forum for debate and discussion.

The organisations involved in the group have pledged support to a Statement of Intent which recognises the international significance of the Burry Inlet and Loughor Estuary as an ecological resource, place of beauty, and important natural and cultural asset. The group meets quarterly to discuss and evaluate the effects of current issues, development proposals and policies affecting the estuary. Where necessary, the group makes collective representations and recommendations regarding new initiatives and research.

The group is fortunate in that it was founded at a time when pressures on the natural resources of the area were relatively light. However, these pressures are getting stronger. The economic climate and food hygiene legislation are creating pressures for the local cockle industry; redevelopment of the northern shore is renewing the demand for an urban, attractive and economically viable coastline; recent European legislation is requiring improvements in water quality; and increasing visitor pressure and agricul-tural restructuring are affecting the management of the southern shoreline and tidal marshes. Allied to these pressures is the increasing protection of the environmental wealth of the area through international nature conservation designations.

The Burry Inlet and Loughor Estuary is gradually being constricted between environmental designation and regulation on the one hand, and desires for its increased use and utilisation on the other. The response of local government and other statutory agencies has been an increase in planning activity for the area. For example, the National Rivers Authority are preparing a Catchment Management Plan, a Shoreline Management Plan dealing with sustainable coastal defences is being prepared for Carmarthen Bay, the Gower Management Plan is due for review and most of the Local Plans and Structure Plans affecting the area have been or are in the process of being reviewed. Furthermore, the imminent re-organisation of local government in Wales (April 1996) will affect the administration of the inlet and estuary and there is a clear need for all of these plans and projects to be co-ordinated and harmonised. The Liaison Group is ideally placed to undertake this role and would also provide an excellent foundation for any future Special Area of Conservation Committee. The group hopes to progress these aims over the next few years.

Conclusions

The Gower Peninsula is subject to many of the pressures and demands which influence the European coastal zone in the late 20th century. Tourism and recreation constitute the main sources of pressure at many sites and while highly effective mechanisms for visitor management have evolved, the long term sustainable use of the area will necessitate better integration between agencies. The development of networks to link different sectoral interests, such as the Burry Inlet and Loughor Estuary Liaison Group, is proving to be an extremely effective means by which issues can be identified and conflicts resolved.

References

Atkins, J. (Ed). 1995. *The Burry Inlet and Loughor Estuary Symposium: State of the Estuary Report Part 1.* Burry Inlet & Loughor Estuary Liaison Group, Swansea, UK. 116 pp.

Hughes, M.R. 1983. National Nature Reserves in Wales: a systematic survey. 3. Oxwich National Nature Reserve, West Glamorgan. *Nature in Wales* (new series), 1:27-33.

Hughes, M.R. 1993. Life after the sand trap. *Enact*, 1(3):12-14. English Nature, Peterborough, UK.

Mullard, J. 1995. Gower: A case study in integrated coastal management initiatives in the UK. In: *Directions in European Coastal Management.* Eds: Healy, M.G. & Doody, J.P. Samara Publishing Limited, Cardigan, UK. pp. 471-476.

Pritchard, D.E., Housden, S.E., Mudge, G.P., Galbraith, C.A. & Pienkowski, M.W. (Eds). 1992. *Important Bird Areas in the UK Including the Channel Islands and Isle of Man.* Royal Society for the Protection of Birds, Bedfordshire, UK. 540 pp.

Rothwell, P. & Housden, S.E. 1990. *Turning the Tide - A Future for Estuaries.* Royal Society for the Protection of Birds, Bedfordshire, UK.

Stevens, T. 1995. Sustainable approaches to recreational planning and management in estuaries: a model for the Loughor (Llwchwr) Estuary, South Wales. In: *Directions in European Coastal Management.* Eds: Healy, M.G. & Doody, J.P. Samara Publishing Limited, Cardigan, UK. pp. 97-102.

Studies in European Coastal Management. Jones, Healy and Williams (eds)
1996, Samara Publishing Limited, Cardigan. ISBN 1 873692 07 2

The Destruction of the Taff/Ely Estuary: A Conservationist Viewpoint

S.J. Tyler

Royal Society for the Protection of Birds, Newtown, Wales, UK[1]

Abstract: The inter-tidal mudflats of the combined estuary of the Rivers Taff and Ely (Cardiff Bay, Wales, UK) represent an important nature conservation resource for wintering water-fowl. The bay borders the southern margin of the expanding city of Cardiff and forms the gateway to its once thriving port. The decline in maritime trade, coupled to the perceived role of waterfront developments as a component in the economic rejuvenation of the city, led to the proposal to construct a barrage across the mouth of the estuary, thereby creating a large area of open water. Against much opposition from the statutory and non-statu-tory/voluntary conservation sectors, this proposal has become reality and a barrage is now under construction. Measures proposed to mitigate against the effects of habitat loss include the recently announced construction of a new 375 ha wetland reserve on the nearby Gwent Levels. The case of the Taff/Ely Estuary provides a classic example of the frequent conflict which exists between economic development and nature conservation in the coastal environment.

Introduction - The Taff/Ely Estuary

The combined estuary of the Rivers Taff and Ely (Cardiff Bay, Figure 1) is an important and integral part of the larger Severn Estuary complex, an area of international importance for wintering waterfowl (Pritchard *et al.*, 1992). The Severn Estuary has been scheduled as a Special Protection Area (SPA) under the Birds Directive (Council Directive 79/409/EEC on the conservation of wild birds) and as a Ramsar site and is also a possible Special Area of Conservation (SAC) under the Habitats Directive (Council Directive 92/43/EEC on the conservation of natural habitats and of wild fauna and flora). The Taff/Ely Estuary is a Site of Special Scientific Interest (SSSI) in its own right (named the Taf/Ely Estuary SSSI) and provides sheltered and productive feeding areas and roost sites for 7,000 to 9,000 wintering waterfowl. The site is especially significant because waders and wildfowl, notably redshank (*Tringa totanus*), dunlin (*Calidris alpina*) and shelduck (*Tadorna tadorna*) are able to spend more time feeding as its high level mudflats remain exposed when other areas in the Severn Estuary are submerged. The importance of the Taff/Ely Estuary is evident from the fact that it occupies only about 1% of the total Severn Estuary complex but supports some 10% of its birds. The estuary flanks the southern margin of the city of Cardiff and has

---

1   Present address: Yew Tree Cottage, Lone Lane, Penallt, Monmouth, NP5 4AJ, Wales, UK.

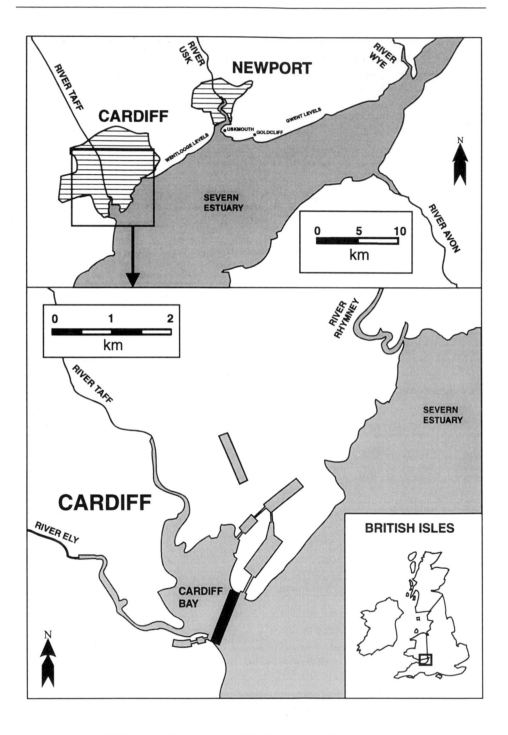

Figure 1   Cardiff Bay and its location within the Severn Estuary

historically been subject to land claim for dock developments (Countryside Council for Wales, 1993; Davidson *et al.*, 1991). The once thriving port of Cardiff has now declined in importance and Cardiff Bay is perceived as playing a key role in the urban regeneration of the southern part of the city.

The Taff Crossing Bill

In 1986, South Glamorgan County Council introduced the Taff Crossing Bill to enable the construction of a barrage across the uppermost part of the Taff/Ely Estuary. The aim was to make a new roadway, the Peripheral Distributor Road, to run west to east across the southern margin of the city of Cardiff. Despite petitions against this Bill by the former Nature Conservancy Council (NCC) and voluntary conservation bodies led by the Royal Society for the Protection of Birds (RSPB), the Bill was finally approved. However, a major concession was achieved by gaining agreement for the roadway to be routed across a bridge supported by piers rather than a barrage. The Bill was soon withdrawn because plans were already crystallising for a barrage across the mouth of the whole estuary.

The Cardiff Bay Barrage Bill No. 1

The Taff Crossing Bill was superseded by the Cardiff Bay Barrage Bill, a private Bill deposited in Parliament in November 1987 and promoted by South Glamorgan County Council with the support of the Cardiff Bay Development Corporation (CBDC). It sought authorisation for a barrage to impound estuarine waters to provide a permanent lake. The promoters argued that the mudflats were aesthetically unpleasant and that re-development of the derelict dockland area depended on the inter-tidal areas being permanently covered in water.

The NCC and a consortium of non-governmental organisations (NGOs) petitioned against the Bill and gave evidence to Select Committees in the House of Lords and House of Commons. The conservation bodies argued that developers would be attracted to the dockland and bay areas without the barrage and lake. Additional comments were made to the effect that the estuary would be a wonderful asset in a maritime city once anthropogenic dereliction around the periphery had been cleared. It was argued that a major nature reserve with public viewing and interpretative facilities could be developed which would make Cardiff a unique city.

Concerns which included water quality (e.g. eutrophication and algal growth), a probable mosquito problem in an impounded lake and the possible effects of rising ground water levels on adjacent property, were voiced strongly by the National Rivers Authority and local residents. NGOs fighting the Barrage Bill also commissioned consultants to look at alternatives which would achieve the same aims as the promoters of the Bill, but without destroying the whole estuary. One such proposal provided for a smaller area of permanent water in the northeastern part of the estuary.

As the Bill was *en route* through Parliament, many discussions took place about the need for compensation or mitigation should the estuary be destroyed. Statutory and voluntary conservation bodies participated in these discussions and it was accepted by the Bill's promoters that a sum of £5.7 million would be made available for mitigation. Initially there was a proposal to create new inter-tidal habitats by moving to landward a section of seawall fronting the Wentlooge Levels (an area of wet, low–lying coastal alluvial grassland) to the northeast of Cardiff. However, it was felt that this measure might not be successful as the additional area of inter-tidal habitat would be less than 30 ha (given the limited budget and high costs of relocating the seawall) compared to the 165 ha of the Taff/Ely Estuary SSSI. Furthermore, it was considered that continual management would be required to combat silting. This proposal was finally rejected during the Bill's passage on the grounds of expense and because it would have led to the total extinguishment of a farm business.

After lengthy hearings and debates, elected members of parliament (MPs) opposed to the barrage used parliamentary procedures to effectively prevent any further progress with the passage of the Bill. Conservation bodies, both statutory and voluntary, believed that they had won their case but the Government responded with the rapid introduction of a new Bill.

Cardiff Bay Barrage Bill No. 2

This new Bill was a hybrid Government Bill. Barrage opponents were technically unable to pursue their opposition to the principle of the barrage under parliamentary rules affecting Government bills. They could only argue, for example, to secure:

a) adequate mitigation for habitat loss;

b) compensation for householders affected by rising groundwater levels; and

c) responsibility for removing algae and rubbish from the impounded lake.

Opposition to the barrage was, however, pursued outside Parliament by challenging the economics of the scheme and by helping the European Commission with their enquiries over complaints made by NGOs. The debate intensified following the announcement that the Taff/Ely Estuary was to be excluded from the proposed Severn Estuary SPA. Nevertheless, the Barrage Bill received Royal Assent in December 1993. Discussions between the UK Government and the European Union eventually resulted in a ruling that the barrage could proceed provided that mitigation for habitat loss went ahead and that the Government:

a) confirmed the designation of the Severn as a SPA;

b) produced management plans for the conservation of the wildlife interests of the Severn Estuary; and

c) prepared action plans and monitoring programmes for dunlin and redshank throughout the UK.

Infilling of saltmarsh within the Taff/Ely Estuary SSSI

During the passage of the Barrage Bills, the CBDC sought planning permission from Cardiff City Council for infilling of a saltmarsh area within the Taff/Ely Estuary in order to create a Community Park with playing fields. In February, 1992 planning permission was given for silt disposal on the saltmarsh; this material resulting from the excavation of a tunnel as a component part of the Peripheral Distributor Road. Phase 1 of this saltmarsh reclamation was duly completed. As mitigation for the loss of an important area of saltmarsh used by roosting waders, a floating platform was provided and a small section of saltmarsh was cut off from the mainland to form an island. The platform has since been vandalised and removed but the island is being used by waders. Phase 2 reclamation soon followed and together with Phase 1 has resulted in the loss of a total area of over 7 ha of saltmarsh. In May, 1994, CBDC sought further permission for saltmarsh reclamation, this time allowing the disposal of silt excavated from the nearby Mount Stuart Graving Docks. This has destroyed an important creek within the saltmarsh that was used particularly by feeding redshank.

Future developments and conclusion

In January 1996 the Secretary of State for Wales announced plans to provide a bird reserve in compensation for the loss of the Taff/Ely Estuary. The new reserve will be located on the Gwent Levels between Goldcliff and Uskmouth and will comprise a 375 ha wetland complex of reedbeds, saline pools, wet pastures and possibly some arable land.

Negotiations over the purchase of approximately 80 ha of land at Goldcliff are currently underway, while redundant ash lagoons at the Uskmouth power station have already been purchased. The intention is to purchase the intervening land but it may be necessary to negotiate management agreements with farmers and landowners.

Whilst realising that this area has great potential for wetland development and nature conservation, the Wildlife Coalition Group (composed of those local and national voluntary conservation bodies that petitioned against the Cardiff Bay barrage) has a number of concerns. These relate to the uncertainty of management agreements, their costs and the length of time over which it is suggested that agreements may operate. Additionally, most of the compensation area is already designated as a SSSI which could thus theoretically be enhanced by existing mechanisms. The Countryside Council for Wales will be responsible for negotiating and paying the agreements, but the Coalition fears that unless dedicated money is made available by the Welsh Office, then the costs might erode the CCW budget and adversely affect nature conservation elsewhere in Wales.

Acknowledgements

My thanks to Brian Cleary of RSPB for his helpful comments on a draft of this paper.

References

Countryside Council for Wales. 1993. *Welsh Estuaries Review*. Countryside Council for Wales, Bangor, UK. 128 pp.

Davidson, N.C., Laffoley, D. d'A., Doody, J.P., Way, L.S., Gordon, J., Key, R., Pienkowski, M.W., Mitchell, R. & Duff, K.L. 1991. *Nature Conservation and Estuaries in Great Britain*. Nature Conservancy Council, Peterborough, UK. 422 pp.

Pritchard, D.E., Housden, S.E., Mudge, G.P., Galbraith, C.A & Pienkowski, M.W. (Eds). 1992. *Important Bird Areas in the UK Including the Channel Islands and the Isle of Man*. Royal Society for the Protection of Birds, Bedfordshire, UK. 540 pp.

Studies in European Coastal Management. Jones, Healy and Williams (eds)
1996, Samara Publishing Limited, Cardigan. ISBN 1 873692 07 2

Environmental Management in Milford Haven: An Integrated Approach

C.I. Morgan[a], G.A.D. King[b] & S.B. Evans[c]

a) *Ridgeway Environmental Management, Pembroke, Wales, UK*
b) *National Coasts & Estuaries Advisory Group, Swansea, Wales, UK*
c) *Countryside Council for Wales, Fishguard, Pembrokeshire, UK*

Abstract: Milford Haven comprises a 36 km long natural inlet of the sea on the southwestern tip of Wales. Its geographical location and hydrographic features have led to the development of the Haven as a harbour of international economic importance. The area is also under intense pressure from tourism and recreation. Nevertheless, the waterway is still of very high quality as a landscape and ecological resource and numerous conservation designations are in place to aid its protection.

A wide range of agencies have a role in the management of the waterway. These include local authorities with statutory planning powers, large multinational industrial corporations with a long established presence in the area, national agencies with executive control over issues such as water quality and nature conservation and local non-governmental agencies concerned with conservation and public education. Well established links between many of these bodies are of critical importance in this multi-user environment and one important aspect of this co-operation has been the formation of the Milford Haven Waterway Environmental Monitoring Steering Group. By identifying gaps in knowledge and priorities for future monitoring, the group has played a key role in establishing a baseline of data against which future trends, either natural or anthropogenic, may be judged. This data is likely to prove especially valuable in the aftermath of the recent oil pollution disaster which followed the stranding of the tanker MV *Sea Empress* in February 1996. The work of the monitoring group provides a useful model for adoption at locations where many competing demands influence the quality of the coastal environment.

Introduction

The Milford Haven waterway is an extensive natural inlet of the sea situated on the southwestern tip of Wales at the junction of the Bristol Channel and St. George's Channel. The Haven is approximately 36 km in length and is one of the biggest and best examples of a ria (drowned river valley) in the British Isles. Its deep, land locked waters provide one of the finest natural harbours in the World and the area has a long and distinguished maritime history.

Milford Haven is of considerable importance as a nature conservation, landscape and economic resource. This paper will review some of the essential features and issues which affect the Haven and will discuss the role of some of the many organisations which are responsible for its management and protection. The paper includes a detailed analysis of the history and need for environmental monitoring within the waterway and concludes with a discussion of how the lessons learnt from this can be applied to other British estuaries and inlets.

Physical description

Milford Haven forms the seaward extremity of the Daugleddau, the joint estuary of the Eastern and Western Cleddau Rivers (Figure 1). These two rivers, whose confluence is about 27 km from the mouth of the Haven, drain a catchment which covers most of the County of Pembrokeshire. The whole of Milford Haven and the Daugleddau is tidal, together with a considerable length of each of the two Cleddau rivers above their confluence, and the tidal range at the mouth of the Haven is approximately 6.3 m. Numerous creeks and pills feed into the Haven and the dendritic shape of the waterway results in a coastline of *c.* 110 km. Despite this, the entrance to the Haven is less than 3.0 km wide.

Another key feature of the Haven is that deep water (in excess of 10 m below chart datum) extends for 20 km upstream of its mouth. The presence of such an extensive, sheltered and navigable waterway has been the key feature leading to the development of the Haven as a major port which currently handles approximately 30 million tonnes of cargo each year.

The Environmental impact of man's use of the Haven

Industry has a major presence within the Haven. Three oil refineries are located within the harbour and have a combined crude oil handling capacity of 20 million tonnes/year. Extensive jetty complexes serve each of the refineries and the largest is capable of handling supertankers of up to 275,000 dead-weight tonnage.

The heavy concentration of oil-related industries in Milford Haven means that it is more at risk from oil pollution than any other Welsh estuary (Countryside Council for Wales [CCW], 1993). Furthermore, the long residence time of water within the waterway means that oil, once spilt, is likely to linger for some time. An estimated total of 621 oil pollution incidents occurred in Milford Haven between 1969 and 1990 (Welsh Office, 1991; cited in CCW, 1993), although many of these involved only relatively small volumes of oil.

At the time of writing (March 1996), Milford Haven and large parts of the coastline of southwest Wales have been severely affected by oil pollution resulting from the stranding of the tanker MV *Sea Empress* off St. Ann's Head on 15 February 1996. In the days that followed, 75,000 tonnes of light (Forties) crude oil escaped from the vessel, affecting many important nature conservation sites including two statutorily designated marine nature re-serves (surrounding the islands of Lundy and Skomer). The incident has been hailed as the worst British marine oil pollution incident since the *Torrey Canyon* spill in the English Channel in 1967 (Pearce, 1996). The *Sea Empress* disaster will doubtless attract much attention from environmentalists in the coming years and follows just two years on from the 85,000 tonne oil spill which resulted from the loss of the MV *Braer* off Shetland in 1993 (described further by Ritchie, 1995).

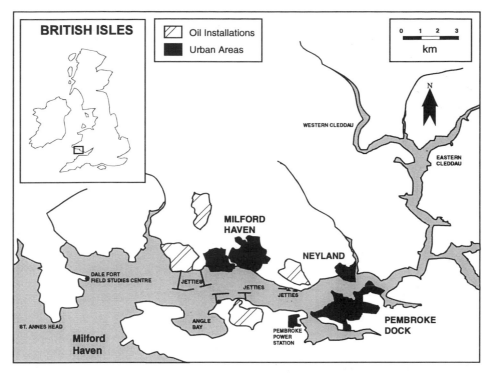

Figure 1   **Map of the Milford Haven waterway showing the location of major sites referred to in the text**

The ports of Milford Haven and Pembroke Dock are located on opposite shores of the Haven and are key components of the maritime transport infrastructure of the waterway. The two ports support a diverse maritime industry which includes a trawler fleet, trans-Irish sea passenger and vehicle ferry service and berthing and handling facilities for a range of cargoes. This intensive maritime transport role necessitates periodic dredging at a number of sites in order to maintain minimum depths of navigable water.

The power station at Pembroke constitutes another major industrial presence in the Haven. Although it will cease operating in April 1996, it is currently the subject of controversy as a result of the proposal to use Orimulsion (an emulsion of water and bitumen developed by the Venezuelan oil industry) as a fuel source. Although this would provide much needed employment, the issues of potential pollution of atmosphere and water, and the construction of a new jetty, have generated considerable local debate.

In recent years the largely unstructured and un-coordinated development of the recreation and tourism industry has also had a major impact upon the area with the growth in popularity of a wide range of watersports. These include fishing, sailing, windsurfing, power boating, jet-skiing and water-skiing. Hundreds of moorings for pleasure craft are available within the Haven and recent developments have included the provision of comprehensive marina facilities at a number of sites. The favourable water quality of the Haven is clearly important in regard to watersports but has also aided the development of a modest fish (including shellfish) farming industry.

Both these sets of activities have implications for the environment. The rise in the recreational use of the waterway has led to its being dubbed as a potential International Maritime Park and the general lack of regulation for activities taking place below low water is an important issue. Fish farming may also have a direct impact upon the composition of benthic communities as there is evidence that organic wastes from fish cages can accumulate in sea-bed sinks, some of which may lie at some distance from the point of origin (Frid & Mercer, 1989).

Many other occupation and recreation based activities take place in and around the Haven and each has an impact upon the environment. One of the most important of these is agriculture. Much of the waterway is surrounded by good quality agricultural land and the runoff of agrochemicals from the land is a matter for concern. Significant areas of saltmarsh are also utilised for grazing.

The 300 km long Pembrokeshire Coast path (a national trail for walkers) passes along both the northern and southern shorelines of the Haven and provides spectacular views across the waterway. The maintenance of the trail forms an important part of the countryside management remit of the Pembrokeshire Coast National Park Authority.

Features of nature conservation interest

The wide range of physical conditions within the Milford Haven waterway result in an exceptional diversity of ecosystem types. The relatively small input of freshwater and long residence time of water within the Haven results in well developed salinity gradients. This factor, coupled to the abundance of rocky shores and the presence of deep water, makes the Haven one of the most outstanding marine biological sites in the United Kingdom. The depth of water is notable in the national context and results in the presence of a range of rocky inter-tidal and sub-tidal habitats which are absent from virtually all other Welsh estuaries (Little & Hiscock, 1987). The species richness of sediment communities throughout the Haven is particularly high. Shallow, sandy/muddy substrates support extensive beds of the notable eelgrass (*Zostera angustifolia*), while wide inter-tidal mudflats with rich and productive annelid and mollusc communities fringe the upper reaches of the Haven as well as the embayments. Other important sub-littoral habitats and species have been identified and mapped by the Field Studies Council.

Saltmarsh habitats form an important part of the coastal zone with a total area of 385 ha being recorded during a survey in 1983. A wide diversity of communities are present, although 198 ha was recorded as being dominated by the invasive cord grass (*Spartina anglica*) in 1983. The extent of *Phragmites australis* dominated marsh (30 ha) is notable as it represents almost 25% of the total Welsh resource of this community type.

The saltmarsh and mudflat habitats support nationally significant wildfowl and wader populations. Synchronised waterfowl counts undertaken by volunteers from the Dyfed Wildlife Trust, in collaboration with staff from the Countryside Council for Wales, National Trust and Pembrokeshire Coast National Park, have provided invaluable data and average peak counts for the five year period preceding the winter of 1988/89 revealed an overwintering population of 20,000 waterfowl. Populations of shelduck (*Tadorna tadorna*) and teal (*Anas crecca*) were registered as being of international significance at that time, whilst nationally important populations of widgeon (*Anas penelope*), curlew (*Numenius arquata*) and redshank (*Tringa totanus*) were also noted. The relatively sheltered feeding grounds of the Haven are of greatest importance during hard winters on the east coast of Britain and counts since 1989 have revealed reduced numbers of wintering birds, perhaps due to milder conditions.

The ecological value of the Haven extends far above high water. For example, ancient woodland borders at least 25% of the sheltered low cliff coastline of the Haven and supports notable species such as *Sorbus torminalis* as well as important old-forest lichen and invertebrate communities.

Summary of conservation designations in Milford Haven

The ecological importance of the Haven is reflected by a plethora of statutory and non-statutory designations (Barne *et al.*, 1995). The Government's statutory advisor on wildlife, countryside and maritime conservation matters in Wales, the Countryside Council for Wales, plays a key role in this respect and no fewer than 17 Sites of Special Scientific Interest (SSSI) have been designated on or bordering the waterway. These include all of the major shallow embayments within the Haven, designated for the marine biological features of their shores and for their feeding waders and waterfowl. Despite this site specific approach, it is important to consider the waterway and its adjacent habitats as a single interdependent system, especially as the SSSI designation cannot extend below low water. The proposal to include a large part of the Haven within the proposed Pembrokeshire Islands Special Area of Conservation under EC Directive 92/43/EEC (The Habitats & Species Directive) has been the subject of consultation, although concerns about the socio-economic implications of such a label have yet to be fully resolved.

Landscape conservation has been aided greatly by the inclusion of much of the Haven and Daugleddau Estuary within the Pembrokeshire Coast National Park. Additional areas are also designated as Heritage Coast whilst conservation through ownership has been pursued by the National Trust, as well as other organisations. Furthermore, the Dyfed Wildlife Trust manages a number of reserves located on the shores of the Daugleddau Estuary.

Despite the wide range of designations affecting different parts of the Haven, the overall level of protection for this nationally important area is still regarded as inadequate (CCW, 1993).

Planning for environmental conservation and management in Milford Haven

Numerous mechanisms under the control of a range of authorities are used to control development and aid environmental management within the Milford Haven waterway. The Pembrokeshire Coast National Park Authority administers strategic planning control for the area in the context of the Dyfed County Structure Plan. This has identified the upper estuary as a special protection area due to its scenic quality. Local plans for the area which includes the Haven are also well advanced. These plans seek to conserve the natural beauty of the area but also have a duty in regard to the social and economic well being of local communities. The local planning authorities aim to achieve a fair balance between these two (sometimes conflicting) demands and are aided in this by consultations with other relevant agencies such as the CCW and the Milford Haven Port Authority.

The regulation of development below low water is currently achieved through sectoral controls for particular categories of development. Many important water-based issues are dealt with by the River Cleddau Catchment Management Plan which was produced by the National Rivers Authority (NRA) in 1995. This plan seeks to conserve and enhance the total river environment through effective land and resource management. The plan includes statutory Water Quality Objectives (WQOs) as laid down in the UK Water Resources Act (1991) and a phased programme of measures are planned to improve water quality. These include improved sewage treatment facilities; the protection of river corridors and floodplains, the development of a policy concerning water abstraction; and the development of mechanisms to reduce conflicts between different user groups.

Other recent environmental management initiatives in the Haven have included the production of a Recreational Plan and the development of the Pembrokeshire Marine Protocol. Industry has also taken a leading role in the establishment of environmental liaison fora. Such groups have considerable value as they provide early and informal opportunities to discuss difficult issues, of which the disposal of spoil arising from dredging is a recent example.

Numerous non-governmental organisations also have an interest in the management of the Haven, although only two will be mentioned here. The Dyfed Wildlife Trust, founded in 1938, was the first nature conservation body to work in the area. The Trust is a charitable organisation concerned with all aspects of Wildlife protection in southwest Wales and in addition to managing a number of nature reserves on the shores of the waterway, also runs a local emergency centre for the treatment and care of oiled birds. Volunteers and staff from the Trust play a valuable role in monitoring potential dangers to wildlife and because of its non-governmental status the organisation provides an effective independent lobby for many environmental issues.

The Field Studies Council (FSC) is an independent environmental education charity which exists to promote environmental understanding for all. The organisation has a strong presence at Milford Haven with field studies centres located on opposite coasts of the waterway. Until recently the organisation also ran a research centre, but this has now been sold to a private consultancy. The field studies centre at Dale Fort is located on the northern shore of the Haven near its mouth (Figure 1) and offers a year-round comprehensive programme of environmental education courses. The centre has undertaken extensive research on the animal and plant communities of rocky shores in the area (e.g. Ballentine, 1961). The former FSC Research Centre is located at Fort Popton on the southern shore of the Haven (Figure 1). The institution originated in 1967 as the Oil Pollution Research Unit and typical research projects have included the following: the production of beach clean-up guidelines for the Haven in the event of an oil spill; studies to assess the effectiveness of oil spill clean-up techniques on shorelines; and the production of coastal sensitivity maps for Milford Haven (as well as other sites in the UK). The research centre has played a major role in acquiring knowledge and expertise in these areas and has also encouraged the development of best practice in environmental management on the part of industry.

Environmental research and monitoring in Milford Haven

During the 1960s and 70s concern over the possible impacts of industry, especially oil pollution, on the environment stimulated a growth of academic interest in the Haven. As a result, many environmentally orientated studies of Milford Haven and the Daugleddau Estuary have been carried out. Routine monitoring and collection of data in fulfilment of statutory obligations has added further to the mass of environmental information available for the waterway. However, most of this information has resulted from a selection of independent and disparate projects with widely differing aims and objectives. Although much necessary information has been collected, it was never part of a co-ordinated research and monitoring programme covering the waterway. Consequently there is the very real possibility that vital components of the waterway system have been overlooked. In recognition of this the main parties with interests in the waterway have come together to form the Milford Haven Waterway Environmental Monitoring Steering Group (MHWEMSG). This composition of this group is listed in Table 1.

Table 1   Component organisations of the Milford Haven Waterway Environmental Monitoring Steering Group

Countryside Council for Wales	National Power
Dyfed County Council[1]	National Rivers Authority[2]
Elf Oil Limited	Pembrokeshire Coast National Park
Field Studies Council	Preseli Pembrokeshire District Council[1]
Gulf Oil	South Pembrokeshire District Council[1]
Milford Haven Port Authority	Texaco Limited
Milford Port Health Authority	Welsh Water/Dŵr Cymru

1   As a result of local government reorganisation in Wales these organisations have now been replaced by a single tier of local government (Pembrokeshire County Council) within the boundary of the study area

2   The National Rivers Authority will join with Her Majesty's Inspectorate of Pollution to become the Environment Agency after 1 April 1996

The original terms of reference of the group were to establish:

a) the extent of existing environmental knowledge and the need for additional monitoring;

b) arrangements for the collation and presentation of data to allow agencies with statutory responsibilities within the waterway to produce co-ordinated plans for its management;

c) investigate the cost and funding of any monitoring programmes; and

d) produce recommendations for future ongoing monitoring.

The first task of this group was to review the current state of knowledge concerning the environment of the Milford Haven waterway. This included collating and analysing information, and identifying gaps in knowledge and deficiencies in current research and monitoring programmes. The findings have been published in a comprehensive report (Hobbs & Morgan, 1992) which covers the whole of the Milford Haven waterway up to high spring tide level. Terrestrial ecosystems were not included in this review which is biased towards the marine and maritime environment.

The review identified the existence of 268 published sources of information relating to the waterway, although the overall data archive included over 450 items. Most projects have been of a self-contained nature and whilst drawing upon previous studies for background information, have not intentionally contributed to a co-ordinated research and monitoring strategy.

The review identified that by early 1992 monitoring activity in Milford Haven had become extremely limited and was mostly related to ensuring that industrial emissions were within permitted limits. For example, monitoring of consented discharge points by the NRA had been undertaken on a regular basis, whilst the refineries and power station undertook chemical monitoring of their main effluent discharge points. Selected waters within the Haven used for bathing were monitored throughout the summer months by the NRA in conjunction with local authorities. Furthermore the Milford Port Health Authority monitored the coliform content of shellfish. The report also noted that surveys of selected inter-tidal areas within the Haven were carried out regularly as part of student field courses held at the Orielton and Dale Fort Field Centres. While this material might be considered to be less reliable than published scientific work, it is clearly of great value as a long term biological data set. A similar set of data has been provided by the monthly counts of wildfowl and wading birds conducted throughout the waterway by volunteers and co-ordinated by the Dyfed Wildlife Trust for the British Trust for Ornithology and the Wildfowl and Wetlands Trust.

Gaps in knowledge

The review of existing information has allowed gaps in knowledge to be identified. For example, the major hydrological and hydrographic studies appeared to present conflicting information. Many of these conflicts relate to differences in the prevailing weather conditions, and hence differences in water flow. While these differences are alluded to in several studies, no attempt had been made to reconcile hydrographic and meteorological data – thus imposing a major restriction upon the interpretation of both physical and biological information. Similarly, while several of these studies took place under different seasonal conditions, they were all of relatively short duration with no attempt to investigate seasonal variation in the variables measured.

Somewhat surprisingly, given the industrialised nature of the waterway, the review revealed a notable lack of routine general monitoring of water chemistry. While various estimates had been made of oil and metal contaminant inputs, accurate information was available only for those industrial discharges monitored for the purposes of consent compliance. Inputs from, for example, atmospheric sources (by direct precipitation), road run-off, sewage, marinas and recreational boating activity remained unquantified. Yet these are thought to make a significant contribution to the contaminant budget of the waterway.

The fate of contaminants once they enter the water body had also received scant attention and there was no data to form a baseline against which the effects of a specific incident could be measured. Similarly, pollutants from historical uses of the estuary which remain locked in sediments could be released by dredging and other forms of physical disturbance (not necessarily anthropogenic). Little is known about the distribution of these contaminants or the potential effects of their release into the environment. While limited information about pesticides is held in raw data form, there appears to have been no analysis or interpretation of this information.

Information concerning the composition and distribution of sediments within certain parts of the waterway was available from historical surveys. However, the active sediment transport within the waterway would be expected to lead to changes in the distribution of sediment types. Unfortunately a comprehensive programme to map the sediments of Milford Haven ceased in 1984 when funding was withdrawn, although a limited number of sites were sampled in 1988.

In the biological environment, the main problem appeared to be the historical nature of most of the information available. Biological monitoring in Milford Haven had concentrated largely upon rocky inter-tidal areas and sublittoral sediments, with baseline data available for both those habitats (although only those for rocky shores pre-date the advent of the oil industry). However, all marine biological monitoring in the waterway had lapsed: the last full survey of rocky shores was conducted in 1982 and the last sublittoral survey took place in 1984. Thus, a considerable gap was present in the run of data during which natural and anthropogenic changes were likely to have occurred. This caused many problems when attempting to separate the effects of pollution incidents from general background changes. Indeed, Little et al. (1989) reported just such a problem in the aftermath of the oil spill from the tanker MV El Omar in 1988.

Autecological studies of selected rocky shore animals which were carried out up until the 1980s had also lapsed. Again this had implications when attempting to link apparent environmental damage to specific pollution incidents. Extensions to these studies could provide particularly useful data if linked with the ongoing programme to monitor tri-butyl tin concentrations within the waterway.

The flora and fauna of the water column had also received scant attention in recent years. There was little available information concerning non-commercially exploited fish species and most studies of plankton in the lower Haven dated from the 1970s. Phytoplankton productivity was studied as part of a project on hypernutrification in Milford Haven, while parts of the Daugleddau had been subject to investigations as part of a study of the commercial oyster fishery.

Conclusions and advantages of the monitoring review approach

The review was intended to be as exhaustive as possible. On the basis of the information available it was concluded that the environmental quality of Milford Haven, the Daugleddau Estuary and the tidal reaches of the Eastern and Western Cleddau Rivers appeared to be good at the time of the review. However, this conclusion was based on published sources which were often incomplete in terms of coverage. Furthermore some of the studies were conducted many years ago.

The information incorporated into the review represented thirty years of *ad hoc* un-coordinated monitoring; yet its systematic collation and analysis has proved to be an invaluable aid to industry, local authorities and other agencies.

Since completion, information from the review has been incorporated into Integrated Pollution Control (IPC) applications and Control of Industrial Major Accident Hazards (CIMAH) submissions and has assisted the local development control process. Furthermore, information from the review has featured in the recreation plan for the waterway and has been incorporated into environmental assessments produced for dredging, seashore reclamation and sewage treatment facilities.

The review identified several area of potential environmental concern, some relating to issues where previous studies were inadequate or lacking. These include:

a) contribution of run-off from within what remains a largely agricultural catchment;

b) organic enrichment through agricultural, domestic and industrial inputs;

c) sediment contaminant loadings, particularly in sump areas; and

d) the effects of the above on the benthic fauna.

Subsequently, it has been possible to obtain a consensus among the funding parties on the priorities for continuing existing projects and implementing new studies. Indeed, over the four years since the completion of the review enormous progress has been made towards achieving a comprehensive monitoring baseline, with £140,000 worth of work commissioned or committed to-date. This is being done with the objective of assisting all parties to understand and manage those of their activities which might have an impact in the context of a multi-user waterway.

Priorities for monitoring which have been identified for the year 1995/6 include:

a) inter-tidal rocky shore biology;

b) seabed rocky shore biology;

c) water quality monitoring (ongoing);

d) ornithological studies (ongoing); and

e) contaminant sourcing studies.

At the time of writing (March 1996) the data gathered to-date as a result of this major collaborative programme is proving invaluable in assessing the impact of the MV *Sea Empress* oil spill.

While establishing and maintaining the Milford Haven monitoring programme would be expensive for a single operator, sharing the cost through participation is highly cost effective for the partners. The level of funding available means that the range and scope of projects to be undertaken is greater than might otherwise have been possible.

Transferring the experience

Several other major industrialised estuaries in Britain have also been the focus for intensive research and monitoring studies (Davidson *et al.*, 1991). As in Milford Haven they may have been carried out over a long time frame, but elsewhere many remain un-coordinated and not part of a strategic environmental management plan. The diverse commercial, local authority and statutory interests who fund them may fail to share results or disseminate them widely. Such *ad hoc* arrangements represent a lost opportunity. Monitoring is a crucial element of the environmental management process, but it can also be expensive if carried out rigorously. While often there will be sound commercial reasons for a company not to collaborate with others in developing and implementing joint monitoring programmes, for studies of impact in the wider environment there are considerable cost benefits and the potential for more meaningful reporting.

Ideally, an environmental monitoring programme should be initiated at the pre-development stage of a project, continuing through development and post-development phases as appropriate. In multi-user waterways, obtaining the commitment to this process may be easier if established programmes exist which potential developers can buy into. Environmental assessments undertaken for new developments will benefit greatly from the existence of long term data sets, suggesting that where such data sets exist they are precious assets and that the monitoring programmes which generate them should not be abandoned at whim. Collaboration is one way of ensuring that long term programmes continue even if some funding parties withdraw.

Conclusions

The management of complex marine and coastal systems such as the Milford Haven waterway presents many challenges for the future. Communication between agencies with widely differing aims and objectives for the waterway is essential as a means of achieving long term sustainable use. The formation of the Milford Haven Waterway Environmental Monitoring Steering Group has been an important aspect of this; although the group itself does not make management decisions concerning the waterway, its component organisations are committed to a comprehensive programme of environmental monitoring. The information produced by the group helps those organisations with statutory responsibilities to manage the waterway in a more integrated way, thus indicating a model for adoption elsewhere.

Acknowledgements

Many people helped to make the EUCC congress excursion to Milford Haven a success. We wish to thank Mrs Linda Bridge in particular for her meticulous organisation of the excursion. The Milford Haven Port Authority sponsored the excursion and their financial and logistical help is gratefully acknowledged. Representatives from numerous agencies also gave presentations and the contributions made by the following individuals is acknowledged: J.H. Ambrey, M.C. Andrews, D. Astins, P.H. Begbie, J. Everett, B. Haycock, J. Hodges, M.J. Hyslop, I. Jones, D. Levell, D.R. Saunders and M. Williams.

References

Ballantine, W.J. 1961. A biologically defined exposure scale for the comparative description of rocky shores. *Field Studies*, 2:1-19.

Barne, J.H., Robson, C.F., Kaznowska, S.S. & Doody, J.P. (Eds). 1995. *Coasts and seas of the United Kingdom. Region 12 Wales: Margam to Little Orme.* Joint Nature Conservation Committee, Peterborough, UK. 239 pp.

Countryside Council for Wales. 1993. *Welsh Estuaries Review.* Countryside Council for Wales, Bangor, UK. 128 pp.

Davidson, N.C., Laffoley, D. d'A., Doody, J.P., Way, L.S., Gordon, J., Key, R., Pienkowski, M.W., Mitchell, R. & Duff, K.L. 1991. *Nature Conservation and Estuaries in Great Britain.* Nature Conservancy Council, Peterborough, UK. 422 pp.

Frid, C.L. & Mercer, T.S. 1989. Environmental monitoring of caged fish farming in macrotidal environments. *Marine Pollution Bulletin*, 20:379-383.

Hobbs, G. & Morgan, C.I. 1992. A review of the current state of environmental knowledge of the Milford Haven Waterway. A report to the Milford Haven Waterway Environmental Monitoring Steering Group from the Field Studies Council Research Centre, Pembroke, UK. 140 pp.

Little, A.E. & Hiscock, K. 1987. Survey of harbours, rias and estuaries in southern Britain. Milford Haven and the estuary of the River Cleddau, Volume 1. Nature Conservancy Council, Chief Scientists Directorate Report No. 735. NCC, Peterborough, UK.

Little, A.E., Little, D.I. & Morgan, C.I. 1989. Ecological impact of the 'El Omar' oil spill, Milford Haven, December 1988. Report to the West of England Shipowners Insurance Services Ltd from the Field Studies Council Oil Pollution Research Unit, Pembroke, UK.

Pearce, F. 1996. Black tide engulfs marine reserves. *New Scientist*, 2019:5.

Ritchie, W. 1995. Maritime oil spills – Environmental lessons and experiences with special reference to low risk coastlines. *Journal of Coastal Conservation*, 1:63-76.